September 2010

To Daphne with appreciation of your friendship and guidance through the National Trust 'mysteries'.

Best wishes for the future

Love

Margaret.

(The Dame!)

Open Wide

Open Wide

Memoir of the Dental Dame

by

Margaret Seward

The Memoir Club

First published in 2009 by
The Memoir Club
Arya House
Langley Park
Durham
DH7 9XE

British Library Cataloguing in
Publication Data.
A catalogue record for this book
is available from the
British Library

ISBN: 978-1-84104-107-0

Typeset by TW Typesetting, Plymouth, Devon
Printed by J F Print, Sparkford, Somerset

Contents

List of Illustrations

Preface

If you are expecting a 'kiss and tell' tale then you will be disappointed. However, if you are looking for my life story interspersed with unexpected twists and turns, coupled with my reflections on these events, then I am sure you will find this memoir interesting and even intriguing.

I am the first to accept that I have been fortunate to be in the right place at the right time. There was no grand plan but I was driven by sound advice which I try to pass on to anyone who cares to listen: take risks and cherish challenges. Throughout my life's journey I have been blessed with good health, a sense of humour, the loving companionship of my husband Gordon for nearly fifty years, a supportive family and fantastic friends.

Collectively they have urged me, 'Margaret, you have had an amazing life; you should write a book.' It has taken time for me to warm to this idea and even longer to write it all down, for I was determined to consult minutes, documents and speeches so that the description of events is as accurate as possible, but if there are errors, especially in interpretation, I take full responsibility. I would also have loved the luxury of unlimited space so that I could mention all the exceptional people who have influenced me on my journey but this has not been possible, so I apologise to anyone to whom by omission or commission I may have caused offence.

With the luxury of the retroscope I might have done things differently but I harbour no regrets, only gratitude for a life I consider well spent. Now I sincerely hope you will 'Open Wide' and enjoy sharing my memories.

Acknowledgements

Many of the people who have assisted me in various ways are acknowledged in the book. However, I do wish to record my special thanks to those who willingly satisfied my requests for factual information: Sue Lawn at The Latymer Foundation, Sylvia Medland at the General Dental Council and Roger Farbey, Head of Library and Knowledge Services at the British Dental Association. I also wish to recognise the artistic skill of Paul Raymonde whose caricature of me graces the cover.

I am particularly grateful to my husband Gordon who diligently read every chapter and through his continual and firm encouragement ensured I completed the project. My daughter Pamela Lisseter was most helpful with her comments on the early chapters, as was Geoffrey Mills, former headmaster, on the chapter 'Latymer; a continuing thread?'

I am indebted to the staff of The Memoir Club who have been a delight to work with since the time they approached me to write this book. My thanks go to Vi Todd for her typing skills, Eileen Finlayson for her sympathetic editorial attention and to Lynn Davidson, managing director, for her meticulous care and guidance throughout the publication process.

Foreword

Dame Margaret Seward is clearly one of those fortunate people who were born to succeed in their chosen career; what makes her case special is that she has done so in such spectacular style, rising to become chief dental officer for England. En route, and fittingly for one who so vigorously championed the role of women in dentistry, she became 'the first woman to . . .' countless times. Her exceptional talents were quickly recognised and she has been in great demand in many influential circles both at home and abroad ever since – everyone it seems wants a part of Margaret!

For her services to dentistry, she was appointed CBE in 1994 and made a Dame in 1999. Other landmarks include presidency of the BDA and a place among the upper echelons of the FDI.

Those privileged to have had Margaret as a champion of their cause will testify to the enthusiasm and energy she devotes to achieving her aims and among those who have reason to be grateful for her support are women dentists, and dental technicians and ancillaries, later known as professionals complementary to dentistry.

We first met – and a bond was forged – in 1973 at a Bickiepegs press launch previewing *Nothing but the Tooth*, a film based on her research into teething that was to win international acclaim. The next time our paths crossed she had become the doyen of the press corps as the highly esteemed editor of the *British Dental Journal*, which she revamped and turned into the thriving publication it is today. I saw her often during this period and although she used to tease me about my 'throw-away rag' (*Dental Practice*) it was done affectionately and without a shred of malice.

A few years on and she was meeting a new challenge as president of the General Dental Council – another establishment on which she was to make her mark. I will never forget her retirement party at the Lansdowne Club during which all the guests were given Salsa lessons and then encouraged – nay, instructed – to perform. Even Lord Colwyn with his neck in a brace at the time had to take to the floor.

Retirement, however, was not for Margaret; in 2000 she joined the Department of Health as chief dental officer and proved a breath of fresh air to the civil servants as she led the implementation of the government's dental strategy.

Throughout these memoirs, readers get to meet a veritable who's who (and who was) in dentistry, but anyone who thinks this may make for a less than enthralling read should fear not. This is a story that will grip you from beginning to end as fascinating anecdotes behind the eminent dental and political names emerge. And her encounters are not confined to the dental world; she once crossed the Atlantic in Concorde seated next to that idol of the screen Robert Redford – what woman wouldn't relish an experience like that!

Romance is in the story, too, as houseman Margaret is wooed and won by Gordon Seward, her senior registrar at The London Hospital. Grandparents now, they remain an utterly devoted couple living contentedly in a flat in Bournemouth that affords them a glorious view of the sea.

Retirement for real? I wouldn't bet on it!

Mary Newing, MBE

Chapter 1

Growing up

'THAT'S NOT YOUR REAL MOTHER' was the taunting jibe from a seven-year-old boy who lived round the corner from our family home, which was a smart, half pebble-dashed, semi-detached house in Uvedale Road, Enfield, the terminus for the number 629 trolley bus as it completed its hour long journey from Tottenham Court Road in London. In the 1940s, it was commonplace for children to play together in the streets, that is, those children left in the London suburbs, because many were evacuated to schools in the country, especially when the intensity of the bombing during the Second World War increased. Naturally, when I returned home for supper that evening, I told my mother what the little boy had said. Immediately she said that it was a nasty story to make up and I should forget all about it – which is precisely what I did. Mum was always right.

I was born on 5 August 1935 and most probably my childhood mirrored that of many of my generation. New toys were in scarce supply and we either played with the home-made variety or acquired second-hand games, although the Mickey Mouse gas mask was at times treated as a favourite possession. Certainly I was lucky to come by a fascinating Meccano seaplane construction set from an older child and so began my preference for nuts and bolts and all things mechanical as opposed to dolls and their clothes.

Occasionally, our parents would be tipped off as to when a delivery of new toys was expected at Howards, the local family radio and electrical shop in Enfield Town. Then, when children were hard at work at school, a queue of mums, dads or other dragooned family members would be observed snaking round the shop waiting for the doors to open so that their offspring's desires could be satisfied. I treasured for many years my mum's purchase, on one of these forays, of a beautiful Dinky Toy of a United Dairies delivery milk float, complete with a brown horse which slipped into the float's shafts, and individual little pint bottles of milk which filled the half-dozen or so crates, which were repeatedly loaded on and off the float.

However, the real version was even more exciting when, on a Saturday morning, I was allowed to help the milkman deliver the milk bottles to the door, collect the money owing for the week's milk and in return, if the books balanced, sit up high on the driver's bench and, with reins in hands, gently coax the good steed on its way up the street to the next delivery stop. However enjoyable the experience, it did convince me that I did not want to be a milkman when I grew up. The fact that the job, like many other exciting occupations, was not open to women to apply did not even cross my mind.

I was brought up in a caring, loving and Christian home and even in wartime, although I was an only child, there were plenty of youth activities on offer at our local church, St Paul's Presbyterian Church in Old Park Avenue. Most social events were arranged by the older members of the congregation who had not been called up to serve in the armed forces or drafted away to work on the land or in munition factories. There was an active Brownie Pack and I enjoyed being a member of the Kelpie six and rose to assume responsibility as a sixer – my first taste of power and experience of badge mania, as there seemed to be a 'sewing-on' ritual after each Friday evening as I completed the test for 'cooking', 'animal lover' and so on. The only drawback was that most uniforms were 'hand-me-downs' as clothing coupons were often too precious to spend on such purchases, but if you were lucky enough, as I was, to have a new one, then the size of the hem was almost the length of the skirt because it had to last a full five years from age six to eleven.

Junior Choir and Sunday School on Sunday afternoons at 3 p.m. flourished and, like the multiplication tables, we learnt Bible passages by heart. Then we regurgitated them in Scripture Union exams also, with high marks all round, and were given another Bible to mark the achievement. The one dampener in the afternoon was that it always seemed that the choice for the closing hymn was given to the youngest child, Elizabeth Shearman, whose repertoire did not stretch beyond 'Jesus bids us shine'. It is true that hymns and music generally are associated with memories and certainly I never fail to smile when this hymn is announced in church or on the radio and I still try to sing it with some enjoyment. More to the point Elizabeth – now Elizabeth Macleod – and I still remain firm friends.

My memory of school days is that they were continually interrupted with sirens demanding immediate evacuation from the classroom in order to find safe refuge in the air-raid shelter which was often located, and partially buried, in the school playground, so robbing us of our much-enjoyed outside playing area.

At home people used varying types of protection. It could be a steel Morrison shelter which doubled up as a dining-room table. Alternatively it could be an Anderson shelter dug out in the garden which could get notoriously damp as it was covered over with garden turf as camouflage. For the lucky few like ourselves, there was an above-ground shelter built outside the back door from thick concrete blocks. It housed four bunk beds and, at the height of the Blitz, when the silent V-2 bombs replaced the doodle-bug, which at least had a warning drone until it cut out, I went to bed each night in the shelter, snugly clothed in a brown zip-up siren suit, a miniature version of the attire made famous in the war by Sir Winston Churchill.

But sometimes the interruptions had a more profound effect. One day in 1942 I arrived at my school, the Enfield Collegiate School, housed in a double-fronted Victorian building in London Road, to discover that it had been completely demolished in the night by a rocket. As only a crater remained, lessons were obviously suspended until further notice, which as children we thought was great fun.

This did, however, mean a frantic search by my parents for a new seat of learning for me, and as many schools had already been evacuated, they fortunately alighted upon Palmers Green High School and Kindergarten in Hoppers Road, some three miles away. This was an independent girls' school, established in 1905, catering for infants, juniors and seniors and encompassing an age range of four to sixteen years of age. Thus I swapped my mundane navy blue blazer of the Collegiate School for an instantly recognisable strong bottle-green serge tunic, green heavy linen blouse and green and pink striped tie, topped with a dark blue velour hat made distinctive with a green band and badge.

In the summer term, irrespective of the English weather, it was a light dress, coloured again green, and this time completed with a panama hat with elastic under the chin to try to ensure its safe transport. I have to confess that more often than not, once out of sight of school, it doubled up as a shopping basket or boat to float on the nearby Broomfield Park boating pond! I am sure that now, in later life, when I should be viewing lawn bowls as a favourite leisure pastime enjoyed by many of my friends, it is the thought of being required to wear 'whites' and a panama hat which fills me with horror. What untold damage can be done in the name of uniform to the young and impressionable mind. As the war progressed, the bombing over London intensified, blackouts were frequent and windows on buses and shops were taped up to stop the glass splintering from stray shrapnel. There was a hole in the covering so adults could see where they were but it was far above the eye-level of a child and I felt very insecure worrying that I would miss my bus stop. Food was also in scarce supply; we had coupons for meat, bread and clothing, and bananas were a luxury fruit not seen until after the war. As a result, at home we tried to produce basic items and the allotment between our house and the New River, at that time devoid of houses, was a treasure trove of the best of potatoes, onions, peas and marrows, to name a few delicious and nutritious home-grown vegetables. We kept chickens (six Rhode Island Reds) at the top of our small garden and they became pets with individual names as I fed them daily and, with great delight, collected the eggs for tea.

No wonder I was excited when Bill Duncan, my teenage American cousin, arrived at Uvedale Road in his army uniform for an overnight stop on his way to take part in the 1944 American assault on the area known as Omaha, the beach just to the west of Port-en-Bessin in Normandy. The excitement was compounded because Bill was laden with candies and other goodies for us and soon we were receiving, on a regular basis, food parcels from his parents in the USA: the contents of the packet of chocolate powder are still a delicious memory.

Houses and other buildings were being consistently bombed or requisitioned by the army for military use. This was the fate of Keeble local preparatory school for boys in nearby Winchmore Hill and so suddenly some of the classrooms at Palmers Green High School were commandeered by little boys in short grey flannel trousers, yellow blazers and caps – an exciting and less traumatic invasion, although we were carefully segregated and supervised in the playground. In more recent times I have discovered that a local friend of ours, John Flashman, was one of the 'invaders' and he recounts his time at a girls' school in a somewhat different light.

Our teachers at PGHS, as the school was colloquially referred to, were all women who seemed to us to be between elderly and ancient. We must have been grossly mistaken as Miss Godfray, who taught us nature, has just celebrated her eighty-third birthday, so simple arithmetic will quickly confirm that this 'elderly' lady was in her early twenties.

The school was run strictly to rules by the two headmistresses. Miss Levesley was in charge of the Senior School, and always appeared to me a serious and forbidding lady, especially as she was prevailed upon to deal with any miscreant Junior pupil – so I got to know her quite well. Otherwise the younger children came within the domain of a kindly, white-haired and bespectacled lady, Miss Elvidge. The standard of teaching, especially in the three Rs, as well as in biology, history and geography, was generally acknowledged to be good. Any weakness was in the range of science subjects but this shortcoming could be and often was rectified later for many pupils who transferred to other institutions for their sixth form studies. Such observations on the quality of education were made long before the invention of government league tables, and the criteria for a school's performance were left to the judgement of parents and youngsters to decide if the skills, knowledge and competence acquired made their future career aspirations possible.

To this day I am forever grateful for the early elocution training and encouragement I received at PGHS to study for and sit the examination of the Poetry Society, because it has paid dividends throughout my life, ensuring that I know how to project my voice (and use clear diction) when speaking in public, although the underlying cockney twang has never completely deserted me. Certainly it still confuses even the most experienced interviewer on TV or radio who observes 'Margaret, I can't quite place your accent – are you from Australia?'

However, the elocution lessons did lead me into a serious brush with authority. My renowned energetic approach to life manifested itself early on and, according to school reports, my teachers classed me as 'highly spirited and at times headstrong'! My daily school routine was to catch a 629 trolley bus from the top of Uvedale Road in Enfield to the bottom of Hoppers Road in Palmers Green, a distance of some three miles. The choice seat was normally on the top deck and topics were freely discussed and at a noise level which would probably contravene the Noise Abatement Act of today!

Little was I to know that a passenger on the bus on a certain day was a very close friend of one of the principals, until I was summoned to Miss Levesley's study and told how I had let the school down as I was wearing the distinctive PGHS bottle-green uniform. My punishment was to be banned from travelling by trolley bus to and from school for the remaining five weeks of term. So, with no private cars in those days, I pedalled on my bike there and back and not all on flat terrain which, although it took longer, no doubt was healthier and prevented me from becoming obese (fat in those days), which we are now told is the twenty-first century childhood disease. Despite the inconvenience, it taught me an invaluable lesson that, when talking about confidential matters, never do so in public places as you just never know who may be listening.

In my bookcase is a book entitled *Children of the Green Earth* by Ellice Benton, which has miraculously survived the many enforced book culls when moving house, for the simple reason that it was the first school prize I ever won. Receiving it at the first Speech Day after the war in front of parents was a bonus. The label inside the front cover states 'Upper I Form Prize – awarded July 1945'. To win a prize at this stage meant that I was encouraged to sit the eleven-plus examination which, if passed, would propel me to a grammar school where I would be given education beyond sixteen years of age which would provide access to the necessary subjects and examinations for future entry to university, an ideal cherished by my parents.

With some apprehension the day arrived for me to take the eleven-plus test at the school but disaster struck because I appeared at breakfast covered in spots from head to toe and it was quickly diagnosed as a violent attack of measles. That was the end of the chance to sit the exam at school that day. I was given, along with the other pupils who had missed the test for various reasons, the opportunity to take the exam, although it was on a date after the allocation of places had been made on the results of the original test – the practicality and fairness of such a procedure still mystifies me.

This time I did not have the luxury of taking it in familiar surroundings but in the Minchenden Grammar School in Southgate. I thought I had done well enough on the various questions but the examiner did not share my optimism and in a stroke I became labelled as an eleven-plus failure. My parents were mortified because my scholastic fate, as for many unsuccessful children, had been sealed. Instead of progress in the state system to a grammar school overflowing with opportunities I would be consigned to, in their eyes, the second-best, a secondary modern or technical school to major on non-academic and business studies. To remain at Palmers Green High School was not an option, because my place had already been allocated to a new entrant. How much this act was the result of the confidence held by the staff in my ability to pass the eleven-plus, or their belief that life could be smoother without my tomboy tendencies in the school, I will never know. Suffice to say my parents agreed to take me away and hunt for pastures new. I felt many years later that I had redeemed myself in the eyes of the school when I was invited back by the headmistress, Mrs Grant, to present the prizes and give the talk at Speech Day, an occasion which I thoroughly enjoyed and revelled in seeing happy smiling faces in the familiar green attire.

But the untold trauma inflicted on children and their families and friends by this iniquitous exam which segregated, with an impermeable barrier, children into academic and non-academic at an early stage in their formative impressionable years, filled me with a great sense of injustice. I did not enjoy being labelled a failure – in truth who does? Later on, when I held the position of School Governor, I was able to speak out from first-hand experience about the effects of this exam and I became a staunch advocate for its abolition, which eventually did happen and not before time.

I was fortunate to be given a lifeline by a state school in the Borough of Edmonton – Raglan Junior School in Bury Street, which conveniently was within walking distance of my home and I entered in 1946 its Scholarship Class along with twenty-eight other pupils, all focused on gaining entry to a neighbouring Grammar School through passing the eleven-plus exam. I settled in quickly to the new regime, where teaching was aimed at the essential subjects needed to pass the eleven-plus, with plenty of practice at completing examination questions posed in previous years' papers.

Seating was in double wooden desks with flap-up lids revealing a cavernous space inside for writing implements and books and other goodies – and the tallest girls were allocated to the desk at the back of the classroom. I was placed next to Brenda Glashier, who today, as Brenda Hipkin, remains one of my dearest and most loyal friends. Her kindness to me was immediate, because when she realised I had difficulty reading the questions carefully chalked up on the blackboard she let me copy them from her exercise book. Unfortunately, the teacher was not so understanding and reprimanded us both for cheating – not an auspicious start for me in a new school. However, it ensured an urgent trip to the opticians and I have worn glasses ever since. Thank goodness today there are eye tests for young infants and it is not left to chance to discover the true beauties of the world.

With great jubilation, and thanks to dedicated and experienced teaching, I passed the eleven-plus, albeit now designated as 'over-age' – yet another label with more consequences to unfold later. The real bonus was that many other friends in my class, including Brenda, gained entry to the school of our first choice – The Latymer School in Edmonton, which was to play an important part throughout my life.

Chapter 2

My roots

I have lived and breathed dentistry from my earliest years. My father, John Hutton Mitchell, ran a single-handed dental practice from our four-bedroom semi-detached house in Enfield. As my parents were the first occupants of Uvedale Road in 1931 they were able to make the necessary modifications for it to function as a dental surgery. The largest bedroom upstairs at the rear of the house was fitted uniquely with a large bay window and this room housed the dental chair and spittoon, the dental engines, both electric-driven and foot pedal variety, and cylinders of oxygen and nitrous oxide for general anaesthetics. In addition there was a beautiful mahogany cabinet with drawer upon drawer of dental instruments marshalled in their appropriate place, and cupboards crammed with dental materials.

Today, many of these materials are obsolete but the zinc oxide powder when mixed with eugenol was used as a temporary filling material. The eugenol, commonly known as oil of cloves, had a pungent and penetrating odour, so much so that my friends whom I brought proudly home for tea would say bluntly, 'Your house stinks – what is that terrible smell?' and frankly were not keen for a return invitation. In one of the corners of the surgery there was a plumbed-in sink and, along another wall, a writing desk and, unusually for a general practice, an X-ray machine as soon as it became available – a Philips Oralex. Today no self-respecting practice would be without an X-ray machine, albeit of a more sophisticated and a safer version.

At the front of the house upstairs, the smallest bedroom was furnished as the waiting room for patients, with a well-thumbed supply of magazines including the favourites *Reader's Digest* and *The Scots Magazine*. Along most of the length of one wall was a divan which was multi-purpose – for patients awaiting treatment, for those who needed to recover, for example after a general anaesthetic, and as a bed for me when I had to vacate my bedroom when my parents' family or friends came to stay. The reception area was squeezed into the stair landing well, a space between the surgery and waiting room, and was completely occupied by a tall and functional chest of drawers which was the official resting place for the appointment book, telephone, and practice stationery.

As a young child I was thrilled by the stream of people coming in and out of the house – fifty or sixty a day was not uncommon – and I enjoyed helping when at home on school holidays or weekends when a prospective patient would arrive with a 'fat face' and obviously in a great deal of pain and distress. There were also the drawbacks of living in 'the shop', and I recall one Christmas Day just as we were sitting down to a mouth-watering lunch of roast turkey so lovingly cooked by my mother and ready on the table to carve. Swiftly it had to go back in the oven, as an 'emergency' came to the door, for my father never turned anyone away and his profound sense of service and care for people in need was always in evidence. I have always tried to follow his incredible example of selflessness, although I know at times not with the same degree of accomplishment.

However, I am told by former patients of lighter interludes. After I was given a bus conductor's outfit one Christmas, I became a force to reckon with! I had rigged up, out of string, a simulated bell-pull along the banisters and this was not activated by me and permission granted to climb the stairs up to the waiting room until a ticket to ride had been purchased from me – I fear this activity would hardly be considered a practice builder today.

My father was a most popular local dental surgeon who had received his training at the Glasgow Dental Hospital and School after his demobilisation in 1918 from the Royal Army Medical Corps at the end of the First World War. He had served in Ypres and in Egypt as a medical orderly and his field logbook recorded that he had extracted many thousands of teeth from the troops and had received a special commendation from his superiors for his skill and devotion to duty.

After qualification in 1923 with the Licence in Dental Surgery from the Royal College of Surgeons and Physicians of Glasgow, he was entitled to call himself dental surgeon, to be distinctive from those who qualified before 1921 and were called dentists. In those days there was tremendous antagonism between the two groups, each with their own professional associations. To refer, as one does today, to dentist or dental practitioner would have been anathema to my father, who took me to task when I returned home from school one day and said that all of us had been asked by the teacher to tell her about our fathers' jobs. I related that I had said my father was a dentist. 'Most definitely not,' my mother intervened. 'He is a dental surgeon and don't ever call him a dentist again.'

Like so many of his contemporaries in Scotland, father moved south over the border into England to find employment. By then he had married my mother, a tall and elegant lady who was born Marion Findlay Duncan in Ayrshire within a year of my father and who also went to Kilmarnock Academy. She trained as a junior school teacher and was to be my father's soulmate for over forty years, although she never worked in her chosen profession after marriage, which was the norm for her contemporaries.

My father's first post was as a salaried dental officer to the railway staff employed by the Great Western Railway and was based in Swindon, the hub of works of GWR in those days. Eight years later in 1931, he moved to Enfield in Middlesex some eleven miles from the centre of London and surrounded by rural areas such as Forty Hill, Botany Bay and on the edge of the Hertfordshire boundary and accompanying rolling farming countryside.

Because he was starting a 'cold squat' practice and was building up his patient list, my father worked morning sessions at the Royal Free Hospital in Gray's Inn Road, London, where he was appointed chief of staff at a time when Mr Endicott was director. This hospital was adjacent to the Eastman Dental Hospital which enjoyed international fame through its USA connections and was, and still is, the Mecca for serious students of dental postgraduate courses and degrees. One young man who came to study at the Eastman in 1946 was a distant relative of the Mitchells called Alex Rennie. He tells me that Uncle Jack, as my father was known within the family, encouraged him to change his university course from agriculture to dentistry at Glasgow and then suggested he came to the Eastman for further studies. Alex Rennie received the not so handsome salary of £7 a week, out of which he had to fund lodgings and travel as well as save to make a trip back to Scotland to see his folks. Uncle Jack came to the rescue, as he did for many postgraduate students, and helped him to supplement his meagre income by allowing him to work in the Uvedale Road surgery after he had finished for the day, that is from 6 to 9 p.m. Alex recalls coming downstairs to the dining room for supper with the family and, as I had dubbed him a favourite 'Uncle', I would sit on his knee. The enjoyment was mutual, especially if he also took time to help with my homework.

Alex further writes: 'I am convinced that my professional success, culminating as a Regional Dental Officer in Manchester, was due to your father, who was a kind, patient and talented teacher.' By way of compensation he recalls that when Uncle Jack bought a second-hand black Standard 10 saloon car after the war, he helped him to pass the driving test. With a car this meant holidays in the country so Thaxted in Essex was chosen, where I sampled for the first time Miss Muffett Junket and have detested it ever since! A more pleasant memory is that I was encouraged to learn to ride and thought I was the 'bees knees', kitted out in my riding gear and completely in charge, with my riding crop, received as a present, in hand. Such faith was shortly to be unceremoniously dispelled. One day, I was asked to ride along the country lanes and bring a pony back from a local gymkhana. This great treat began well enough until a motorcyclist throttled his engine as he passed. The horse bolted and decided to find his own way home across the fields, with yours truly hanging on for dear life, completely out of control – not a situation I relished then or now.

By the end of 1942, as travel into London at the height of the Blitz became increasingly difficult, my father relinquished his appointment at the Royal Free Hospital to concentrate on his practice in Enfield. A skilled operator, and with his valuable hospital experience, he was soon recruited to the staff of the local Enfield War Memorial Hospital in Chase Side, where he removed wisdom teeth and undertook other minor oral surgery procedures for his own patients as well as those of other local practitioners.

Another modification which had been made to the family home was the installation of a functional room in the roof space which was accessed from the landing by climbing up a pull-down Slingsby ladder. The floor in the loft area was boarded and benches were fitted around the sloping eaves. The bench under the skylight had good lighting, although it was supplemented by electric lights. In this self-contained dental laboratory my father, in the early days of his practice, would work late into the night constructing the various stages involved in making dentures for his patients. Like many of his generation he had learnt the craft of dental mechanics under the supervision and in the workshop of a private practitioner. Two years later in 1923, the General Medical Council, which at that time was responsible for the dental curriculum, introduced requirements that future instruction should take place in dental schools. Many, then and since, have felt this was a short-sighted approach, as the skills inherited from early masters of the profession were discarded, and may well have had some bearing on technical shortcomings witnessed in future generations.

The installation of a laboratory in a dwelling place was well before the days of the Health and Safety Executive and regulations regarding the use of hazardous substances in commercial premises, let alone in homes. Fortunately no mishaps occurred, although many materials used in denture construction were inflammable and a gas blow-torch was routinely used in a confined space. The loft for me was a coveted play area. I learned how to use a fretsaw, to cut basic wood joints, to mix plaster of Paris, to build planes out of balsa wood, and to assemble model kits. I was particularly proud when my painstakingly constructed and painted destroyer – HMS *Cossack* – won first prize at the St Paul's Church annual arts and crafts exhibition – although it was deemed a little strange that a girl had won a prize for making a ship!

There were other compensations for living in the 'shop'. It meant that I believed I had built-in playmates, for my father's dental nurse and receptionist, Gwen and Maureen, would appear in the kitchen to take their coffee or tea breaks at staggered intervals.

During the war there was little domestic help available as the younger women had joined the armed forces or gone to work on the farms as land-girls. Thus my mother had her work cut out to keep the house clean, tidy up after the surgery each evening, and undertake the ritual of boiling individual patients' bibs, made out of white towelling, and hanging them to dry either outside in the garden in the summer months or, when the weather was inclement, hoisting them up on a wooden bar pulley in the kitchen above the Ideal boiler. I can recall the great excitement when this drudgery was removed in a stroke with the arrival of an electric washing machine.

Callers to the house were not just patients. There were the salesmen from the dental supply companies, many of whom, unlike today, were UK based and family-owned. Cottrell's was a firm favourite with my father. Another regular caller was Bill Coxshall, the dental mechanic who had been encouraged by my father to follow this craft as a career when he had failed to achieve academic qualifications. Bill, who lived nearby, would collect on his bicycle, en route for the laboratory in Wood Green some four miles away where he worked, a box tightly packed with prostheses in varying stages of construction for patients and then return the completed items on his homeward journey.

However, in January 1945, one caller to the house was destined to shatter the cosy existence of the close-knit Mitchell family of three. The caller, a youth with curly auburn hair, announced bluntly to the dental receptionist who opened the door, 'I thought you would like to know that Margaret's mother has died' and then promptly departed down the path. The receptionist, Maureen, was shocked, especially as she had been speaking to Mrs Mitchell in the kitchen a few minutes beforehand. Nevertheless, she thought she should report this strange caller and his even stranger remark.

That afternoon, on returning from school, I was ushered quickly into the drawing room without my customary piece of cake or delicious pancake cooked on my mother's Scotch cast-iron girdle of which she was justly proud, as her pancakes won many compliments among Scottish friends. But there was no time for the niceties and the silence was broken by my mother asking me, 'Do you remember the little boy who told you that I was not your real mother?' I nodded, so she continued, 'He was telling you the truth – I am not your real mother – we adopted you.'

There were tears and hugs and a great deal of confusion filled my nine-year old head. This meant my mother had lied to me – but mothers always tell the truth. Why had I not been told before? Why now, and where and who are my real mother and father? Gently, and taking time, she explained that while I was at school a young man had come to the door with some news and, as it was thought probable that he could come back and want to see me, it was decided that it was now time to tell all. The young man of sixteen was in fact my brother Derek and so, piece by piece, my family history was unravelled and put together again.

I had been born on 5 August 1935 and christened Felicity Bridget Oldershaw. For the first fifteen months of my life I had lived with the Oldershaws – my mother and father, and two brothers, Leslie, ten years, and Derek, seven years, older than me. When I arrived I was the much wanted little girl, so happily the family was complete. We lived, I was told, in a three-storey Victorian semi-detached house with a very large garden, at 35 Melcombe Avenue in Weymouth, Dorset, which is the town that appears on my passport. My birth father was Dr Eric Oldershaw, the much-loved medical officer of health for the town. He had gained experience in other posts around the country – Nottingham, Colne – and was a deputy medical officer at Swindon for eighteen months from 1928 to 1929 where he had worked alongside Mr Mitchell as a colleague.

My birth mother, Gwen Oldershaw, had trained at Guy's Hospital as a nurse and had passed her State Registered Nurse examination. She then became a registered member of the Chartered Society of Massage and Medical Gymnastics, which was later incorporated into the Society of Physiotherapists. As already mentioned, and in common with many women, she did not work after she married and certainly there was no need to do so in Weymouth where there was plenty of help available, a cook/maid, a nanny for me, and a part-time gardener, allowing mother plenty of time to enjoy her children and entertain, especially holding popular bridge parties in the afternoons.

Slowly, I learned that I had a blood cousin, Gill Oldershaw, a couple of years younger than me, the daughter of my father's brother, Leslie Oldershaw, who was also a doctor and medical officer of health in Paddington, London. Each year on my birthday and at Christmas I wrote to two people who lived in Lincoln and whom I called Grandma and Grandad because they were elderly. Now I was told they were my real grandparents, the father and mother of my own father, Eric Oldershaw, and Grandad had been a distinguished headmaster of the Monks Road Junior School and a leading figure in the Co-op. In due course as I grew older I spent holidays with them in their home at 31 Greetwell Gate just outside the boundary wall, although the sound of the Lincoln Cathedral clock chime at each quarter of an hour and the full strike on each hour throughout the night was the least attractive aspect of my visit, as sleep deprivation soon set in. I gather today it is more civilised and the clock is silent during normal sleeping hours. As befits a Yorkshire household, Grandma made the most sumptuous Yorkshire pudding served as a separate course before any main roast dinner and covered in steaming gravy from the joint to follow. The real treat came after lunch when I was allowed in the scullery to restore the shine and sharpness to the knives in a wonderful circular drum cleaner; the faster you could spin the drum the brighter the knives became.

Over the years, Grandad wrote many letters to me in his strong bold handwriting and using a Waterman ink pen. These I have kept and I also wear Grandma's engagement ring which Grandad gave to me on my twenty-first birthday to accompany the beautiful zip-up Bible and Concordance which was his present to mark the occasion.

Many of my visits to Greetwell Gate coincided with the visit of my eldest brother, Leslie, who by then was a medical student at the London Hospital following in his father's footsteps. Derek was already in the regular army serving in the Royal Artillery in Hong Kong and Malaya but made great efforts to take me out to the theatre when he was home on leave. On one occasion I asked to see *The Reluctant Heroes*, a farce, at the Whitehall Theatre. My sister-in-law, Nan, who was requested by Derek to get the tickets, thought this was a strange choice for a young lady and promptly purchased tickets for *The Reluctant Debutante* which was running in the West End Theatre at the same time. Suffice to say that these encounters were very special to me and helped me to bond with another family as, bit by bit, like introducing characters in a play, the major players and landmark events were unveiled to me.

My birth father, Frederick William Oldershaw, though known as Eric, was born on 6 August 1895. He was a gifted scholar and was due to sit the Indian Civil Service examination in January 1915. Earlier he had volunteered for service in the First World War and so instead of sitting the exam he was sent to the Royal Military College at Camberley and by the end of August he was on his way to Gallipoli as a second lieutenant with the Sherwood Foresters, later serving with the 6th Lincolnshire Regiment in Sulva, from where he was sent home to recover from typhoid. As soon as practicable he was back in France where he attained rapid promotion to captain and temporary adjutant. There he remained for three years, was recommended for the Military Cross and awarded the Croix de Guerre for meritorious service.

There were two major long-term effects of the war on my father. Firstly, the 'gassing' in the trenches on the Somme left him with damaged heart and lungs. Second, the impact of witnessing the severe loss of life and bloodshed decided him to turn his back on pursuing what was hailed as a promising career in the Civil Service and study medicine. He entered the London Hospital Medical College, later to become the Alma Mater for my brother Leslie to study medicine and for me to follow the dental course. On graduation in 1925, as Dr Oldershaw, he entered the public health service and was appointed in 1931 to the prestigious post of medical officer of health in Weymouth, where sadly he was to die after five years in office at the early age of 41. The tragedy shook the town and the Weymouth *Daily News*, reporting the death, wrote, 'He has won the highest regard and indeed affection of many people. The sick children whom he tended, the duties of the health centres, the general contact with people needing his skill all appealed to him and his cheerful disposition made him immensely popular.'

Because of his chronic medical problems as a result of the war he had been unable to obtain a life insurance and as a result my mother was left with three young children and no pension. With assistance from the Weymouth County Council and in recognition of his outstanding service, my mother was able to acquire suitable premises from which she could run a boarding house in the town but it did not prove to be a successful venture.

The traumatic effects of these events pushed Gwen Oldershaw into depression and so it was considered to split up the family on a temporary basis. The eldest son, Leslie, now aged 11, was sent to live with his grandparents in Lincoln. After attending Lincoln Grammar School he passed the entrance exam for Epsom College where bursaries were available to help children of medical practitioners. Derek, aged 8, was sent to live with Uncle Leslie, his father's younger brother. I was just fifteen months old and was sent to an orphanage, the exact location of which is unknown.

Derek did not remain long with his uncle because their family had been enlarged with the birth of a daughter and so Derek was then sent to an orphanage in the Midlands. My mother eventually regained better health and sought employment as a physiotherapist, first working at the Royal Northern Hospital in Holloway and subsequently at the South Lodge Hospital in World's End Lane in Enfield, where by strange coincidence many years later I was responsible for the dental well-being of the patients.

My mother found lodgings near the hospital and renewed her acquaintance with the Mitchells whom she had met socially when her husband was medical officer of health to the Great Western Railway and Mr Mitchell was the dental officer to the staff. Aware that Mrs Mitchell was unable to have the children she much wanted, Gwen asked if she could help to look after me. It was agreed that the best future would be for the Mitchells to adopt me and so, on 1 November 1937, an adoption order was made at the Enfield Juvenile Court. At the cost of 7s 0d and the transaction sealed with a one penny stamp, I changed my name at the age of two years and three months from Felicity Bridget Oldershaw to Margaret Helen Elizabeth Mitchell and went to live permanently at 85 Uvedale Road.

Before taking this final step there had been trial days and weekends out of the orphanage and Betty Pollock, ten years older than me and niece of Mr Mitchell, was recruited to help me settle in, because each visit was accompanied by tremors, screaming and sobbing, and coaxing me into a bath was nearly impossible. Betty also recounts my near hysteria when I was presented with a 'golliwog'. She believes these episodes acted as triggers for unhappy associations with the orphanage, but this can only remain as one person's conjectures.

Gradually, the Oldershaws' way of life improved. Gwen purchased a house in Enfield in 1941 and Derek bade farewell to his orphanage and went to live with his mother and to attend Enfield Grammar School. Because the Mitchells and Oldershaws were friends, my birth mother came regularly to visit me with Derek and on one occasion brought the much loved and previously mentioned bus conductor's outfit. However, it became increasingly upsetting for her to visit me and to be called 'Auntie Gwen' and so the visits and contact ceased. However, she did encourage Derek to sign up for a paper round in Uvedale and adjoining roads so that he could report back on my progress: learning to ride a bike, going to Brownies, or starting a new school.

Following an abdominal operation at the age of 49, Gwen Oldershaw suddenly died of a pulmonary embolism on 29 December 1944. By then Derek and Leslie were living with their mother in Glenloch Road in Belsize Park but Derek felt that he should let the Mitchells know of her death. It had been many years since he had visited the Mitchells with his mother and so he just assumed that the lady who opened the door was Mrs Mitchell. He departed without realising the tremendous consequences his unannounced visit and brief message would have.

It does raise the question which I have pondered many times from this personal experience – just when do you tell children about their past? In the 1940s, adoption was something not talked about. There was a veil of secrecy. Many adopted children grow up oblivious of their past, only to stumble on different beginnings when researching their roots, and then yearning to trace their birth mothers. There can be no ideal time to tell all. For me I believe it was a character-strengthening life event once I had worked through my identity crisis. However, I do still ponder the after-life. We are told that we will be reunited with our loved ones. Can I have two fathers and two mothers in Heaven? I do hope so.

Chapter 3

The Latymer family

It is commendable to be punctual when arriving at your new school, but to arrive twenty-four hours early is ridiculous. However, in September 1947 that is exactly what I did, although fortunately with another over-eager pupil, Rhoda Morris, which did give us a head start in finding our way round Latymer, the largest voluntary co-educational grammar school in North London, with some 1,200 pupils aged between eleven and eighteen. When Rhoda, who later married the Latin Master, Ernest Cox, and I meet, albeit a good half-century later, we still reminisce about this foolish mistake and still wonder how we got it so wrong when the other 178 first form entrants got it so right.

Nevertheless, it did not take me long to discover that I had become a member of a worldwide family soaked in tradition dating back to its illustrious founder Edward Latymer. In 1624 as a wealthy City merchant, he made a bequest in his will, transferring property to trustees on condition that they were to clothe and educate 'eight poor bois of Edmonton' while at the same time, through his beneficence, funding the establishment of the Latymer Upper School for boys in Hammersmith.

Nearly two hundred years later the then trustees received another substantial bequest from an East End of London widow, Ann Wyatt, which enabled a new school to be built in Church Street, Edmonton, next to the All Saints' Church. Honour is given annually to the benefactors in May when the Foundation Day Service is held in the church attended by civic dignitaries, governors past and present, the staff and pupils. After the service while governors and staff prepare for lunch, the pupils are rewarded with the remainder of the day off school, which encourages a respectful reverence and gratitude to the benefactors.

By the time I entered Latymer, new school premises had been built in Hazelbury Road in 1910, which was initially surrounded by fields but now encircled by houses. During the past years there have been numerous major building programmes as the pupil numbers increased and the demands of the curriculum required modern or specialised facilities.

The first extension in 1926, known as the North Block, was the designated home for me as a lowly first former. Progress through the school was matched by one's advancement to the Middle Block, and on reaching the sixth form the South Block became the venue for classrooms and common rooms for senior pupils and prefects. The centrepiece of the building programme in 1928 was the Great Hall, opened by the Duke and Duchess of York, later King George VI and Queen

Elizabeth which, with its balconies, was able to seat over 1,000 pupils. This became the focal point throughout our school life for the morning assembly, the twenty-minute daily act of worship attended by all pupils filling the rows of seats with juniors at the front, seniors in the balconies and prefects around the sides to ensure we were on our best behaviour. Apart from singing, the only time the silence was broken was from the long and sustained applause, which greeted the announcement of the school match or house competition results or individual achievements. An additional assembly was held to mark the end of each term, concluding with a rousing rendition of Latymer's own school song written by the English teacher, Alice Lindford, with music by the School's first music master, Ronald Cunliffe, to celebrate the tercentenary of Latymer. Due to frequent repetition throughout one's school years, there are few Latymerians who are not word-perfect when, on Old Students' Day, they assemble at 4 p.m. in the Great Hall to the strains of the organ to sing the school song with gusto and emotion, especially as with the passage of the years the depth of feeling and the perception conveyed through the words are fully understood:

Sing it, Latymer, loud and long,
Song of Latymer's deathless throng;
Past and present and those to be,
Steadfast sons in loyalty.
Here or there or seas asunder
One great name we shelter under,
Sing it, Latymer, loud and long,
Fifty, hundred, a thousand strong.
Clear before us, the task heroic;
High endeavour, lasting fame
Glorious end from small beginning,
Priceless worth of honoured name,
Sing again the song courageous,
Glad and gay from the distant past;
'Ye who endure while strife engages
Strong in soul shall win at last.'

The hall in the original building, referred to as the Old Hall, was put to a less glamorous use when filled with row upon row of tables and benches, as here took place the daily ritual of providing school dinners (but served at lunch-time!). For the first two terms I elected to go home for lunch but when regaled by the delectables that I was missing, but even more importantly the chance to forge playground friendships during lunch breaks, I opted to stay for school dinners, although I never did become an ardent fan of the sago (frogspawn) pudding.

On our official first day at school we were allocated to one of six forms from A to F, each with thirty pupils, evenly mixed with boys and girls. I found myself in form D, separated from most of my Raglan friends, who languished in forms A and B. My placement was also a surprise to my junior school teachers but the assignment was based on the results of the eleven-plus examination and as I had taken this, classed as an above average-age pupil, my mark was adjusted downwards to compensate for any advantage gained by my advanced years.

In all other aspects life at Latymer got off to a good start and I quickly shone at science and history. The love of these subjects has remained with me and I am convinced that the outstanding teachers contributed much to that success. In history, I was privileged to be taught by Miss Dorothy Warne, who spent her entire teaching career of forty years at Latymer and was also our form teacher throughout our school journey. In her obituary in the Latymer magazine of 1979, a former pupil records: 'Her pupils will remember her for her example of humanity. Her conscientiousness, her meticulous attention to detail, and the quality of her preparation and presentation were all civilising influences that remain with us far more than the historical facts that fade with declining memory.' I endorse those observations wholeheartedly and would add that her immaculate dress and modesty lace were much admired, as were the punnets of soft fruits gathered from her garden and handed out to the winners of the weekly history test, a treat that rarely made it home.

Music and drama have always been important and acclaimed activities at Latymer, taking full advantage of the magnificent stage facilities in the Great Hall to put on concerts and school plays, in which I usually took part in a minor way as a member of the choir or with not much more than a walk-on part in a play. However, to mark the coronation of Queen Elizabeth II, a pageant was the crowning glory and Ruth Medus (Churchill) as Queen Elizabeth I, and Sheila Matheson (MacLeod) as Lady Courtier possess the photographic proof of myself, disguised in a doublet and hose and with a sizeable beard, cast as the male music director conducting the madrigal group who were called to sing Summer is a coming in – sing cuckoo – fortunately there is no tape recording!

At Latymer there were many more talented people around and I recall, from two years above me, Eileen Atkins playing The Light in Maeterlinck's famous play *The Bluebird*, a humble beginning for someone who brilliantly portrayed Queen Elizabeth I in the 1970s' award-winning TV series. Eileen, now Dame Eileen, when interviewed a couple or so years ago for Radio 4's *Desert Island Discs*, talked about the influence of a Latymer teacher, Revd E. Burton, on her future career, which has been meteoric, as she is surely one of our greatest character actresses of this century. I was also fortunate to be taught English Literature by this inspirational teacher who unconventionally dramatised in the classroom the readings from our set books for the O Level GCE course, with the result that the form's marks for exams on H. G. Wells's *The History of Mr Polly* and Shakespeare's *Julius Caesar*, outshone all the others.

In the year of the production of *The Bluebird*, the staff chose to adapt the title to *The Blue Pencil* for their charity concert, performed traditionally to the whole school on the penultimate day of the Christmas Term. Our respect and admiration for our teachers increased by leaps and bounds when we witnessed the most staid teachers cavort on the stage as fairies in the flimsiest of garbs, dance routines to nearly modern music, and crack jokes which were verging on funny. The tall and kindly woodwork master, Tom Spurgeon, with his dark bushy eyebrows and a melodious deep singing voice, which was always put to good effect in these productions, also turned his brilliance to construct imaginative screen sets which would challenge the best to be found in any London West End production. The entire event, in retrospect, was a subtle lesson in encouraging us to understand that teachers were human after all, as well as raising funds for deserving charities.

However, there was no sense of humour in a situation that was developing at the end of the second year. The pupils in forms A, B and C who had learned French as their foreign language were given the opportunity to specialise when they entered the third year. On offer was the coveted chance to enter a science form and to be taught physics, chemistry and biology as separate subjects, with additional mathematics. For those with a preference towards languages there was the alternative to enter the modern form and learn French, German and Latin. Even as a thirteen-year-old, dentistry was well within my sights as a career, and so with my interest in science truly kindled I wanted to enter the science form and be with like-motivated people. I was not best pleased when I was told bluntly that this option was only for pupils from the forms A to C and, as I had studied German and not French as my foreign language, it would be an impossible task for teachers to adjust the complicated timetable to suit one pupil – me.

My parents were fiercely supportive of my wishes, believing this intransigence to be an ongoing injustice as a result of the eleven-plus exam. So they went to see the headmaster, Mr V. S. E. Davis, a modest kindly man who after twenty-five years as headmaster had earned a reputation for caution and of being an advocate of the status quo. Hope did not abound following the visit, so my father approached one of his patients, the headmaster of Tottenham Grammar School, who offered a place for me to transfer to his school and to follow the science course. Whether the knowledge of this exit strategy influenced Mr Davis we will never know but, on arriving on the first day of the Autumn term, I found myself allocated to Form 3 Science, along with two other boys, Richard Wakefield and Don Everton from my form 2D, to keep me company. Staff were amazed to discover we had surmounted the impenetrable timetabling barrier and so set a precedent, which was followed in subsequent years.

It is certainly worth noting that when the next headmaster, Dr Trefor Jones, was appointed to Latymer in 1957, he set about with reforming zeal to change certain aspects of the school, including the strangling timetable. He felt passionately that all new pupils should start from the same baseline and so he abandoned the old system, which befell myself, in placing new entrants in six streams in order of merit according to their performance in the eleven-plus test and instead arranged his new pupils in six parallel forms according to alphabetical order of names. I like also to believe the gamble taken by Mr Davis was seen in his eyes as a success because, during my final term at school, he invited my mother to present the prizes at the school sports day, a duty which she discharged with great aplomb, splendidly dressed in her Sunday best. However, no budding Latymerian stepped on to the podium to eclipse the world-breaking record set by Roger Bannister two months before, through running the mile in under four minutes. My mother too believed the invitation had vindicated her action those years previously when she stood her ground, as she could as a former teacher herself, to ensure the best for her offspring.

Some may wonder why my father had not considered another option of transferring me to the private secondary educational sector. There was an overwhelming reason for not doing so because in 1948 my father's dental practice was in considerable financial difficulties following the introduction on 5 July of Aneurin Bevan's National Health Service. The dentists' professional organisation, the British Dental Association, in company with the doctors' body, the British Medical Association, detested the scheme. Both organisations strongly advised their members not to join and my father, along with the vast majority of staunch BDA supporters, stayed out of the NHS, only to watch with heartbreak their patients leave and go to those who provided free NHS dental care which included many newly arrived Australian dentists intent, as reported, to 'Bash the Nash'. Long-standing and loyal patients with tears in their eyes bade farewell to my father and the future he faced trying to earn a living outside the state system was looking grim, and certainly not conducive to taking on the commitment of private education for me. The final straw for my father came when the senior negotiators at the BDA capitulated and its Secretary changed sides and took the top job at the Department of Health. The offensive crumbled and most dentists signed up to the NHS system, only to be rewarded with the slashing of the generous fees for dental treatment and, after three years, Hugh Gaitskell in his budget introduced the first of many subsequent patients' charges for dentures, followed by other treatments.

This brief résumé of an innovation that has had the deepest effects on lives and attitudes in Britain ever since is of profound importance because forty years later I was able to empathise with the feeling of anger and betrayal experienced by thousands of NHS dentists when the new 1990 dental contract was imposed, followed by the fee cut in 1992, leaving a deep scar which has its repercussions today, as frustrations have surfaced during attempts to modernise the dental service – a topic I will return to later.

Once embarked on my third year at Latymer in the science specialist form, my coterie of friends changed as the gender balance was skewed markedly towards more boys in the class, and friendships were formed with Maurice Levitt, Tony Cudworth and Roger Pearce, to name but a few. I was incredibly fortunate to continue to enjoy being taught by enthusiastic and dedicated teachers who brought the subjects alive and by example imbued us with the renowned Latymer spirit of selfless service and search for excellence to succeed. The Latymer ethos was encapsulated in our school motto, embroidered on our blazer badge, and for boys it also appeared on the cap badge, *Qui Patitur Vincit* – 'He who endures conquers', or as now translated into a modern idiom, 'Keep at it and you will succeed'.

Chemistry was taught in laboratory 48 by Percy Blackwell, who was generally known under the not very original nickname of Inke. He was a strikingly handsome man, whether in his black gown or brown lab coat, and, as a firm disciplinarian and head of senior school, invoked a degree of respect, if not terror, in those wasting their opportunity to learn. As girls were sparse in number in the science form, he arranged for us to sit on the stools along the front bench in the laboratory so that we could view at close hand the results of his experiments. When exquisite colours were conceived from colourless liquids he would then set about convincing us that we would look first class in a hat of that colour although, alas, we were too young to appreciate such fashion accessories. I emerged from his tutelage with A grades, both at Ordinary and Advanced level, undoubtedly a tribute to his brilliance as a teacher. Extracurricular activities undertaken by Inke also raised his popularity stakes with pupils as he exhibited a prowess at all sports, especially cricket and soccer following the Tottenham (Spurs) football team which eventually had as a player a Latymerian in the year above me, Johnny Haynes, who rose to captain England. Inke ran the Senior Science Society of which we were all keen members and later I was to serve as a committee member. The highlight of the year's programme was his lecture on pyrotechnics given on 5 November, followed by a fireworks display in the school playground, which must have been one of the first corporately organised fireworks events, let alone on school premises.

One day he stopped me in the corridor and said quizzically, 'Tell me – why do you always seem to be smiling?' I then realised that the value of a smile was imparted to me at an early age by a treasured friend of my mother, Miss Molyneux, who lived just two doors up from our house in Uvedale Road. Known as 'Auntie Mollie' and an elder in St George's Presbyterian Church in Palmers Green, she would take me when I was quite small to her church for special Sunday School events. The long pull up Fox Lane to her church at the top of the hill was a challenge to my small legs and to encourage me on my way I was asked to count the 'cherries' and 'plums' that passed by. Then on the return journey I was asked to smile at both the cherries and plums and count how many smiled back. It was remarkable how many surprised plums smiled, as well as all the cherries. A smile is to be treasured and is the most effective tool in my communicative armamentarium: uniquely it is the same in all languages and so rarely fails as an icebreaker when conversations can and do falter.

Today, science is taught by discovery but to be a budding Einstein was not the method used by our Zoology teacher, Miss Satterly. She dictated the most comprehensive notes and made the simplest hydra appear a complex and captivating animal. To excel in exams depended solely on one's ability to memorise and regurgitate the written facts at the appropriate time. Fortunately I have been blessed with a good and photographic memory and so exams were no hardship and, with monotonous regularity and to the annoyance of fellow classmates, I received the subject prize.

Gym classes on the other hand for me were not far short of purgatory, despite the best efforts of our young gym teacher, Miss Munns, herself a former Latymerian. I was tall for my years and my performance in executing handstands or vaulting over the leather horse were by any standard dismal. The comments in the end of term reports by the gym teacher were predictable and confirmed what I already knew, and marred otherwise good to glowing reports on other subjects. I felt the urge to put my time to better use and so sought out safe havens for refuge during gym lessons. A whole term passed without discovery and May Munns in my end of term report observed 'Margaret has shown great improvement this term.' Some years later when I shared my secret with her she took it in good part, explaining that as I had not drawn attention to myself in the gym classes that term she had assumed I had improved.

On the other hand I loved and excelled at ball sports and was chosen to be in the school team in most activities. In hockey in my position as goalie, well clad in pads and with arms and stick waving, I used to enjoy running out to deflect the approaching ball and earned the nickname 'Barge' which I was delighted to shed after leaving school. Sadly, my legendary right hook at hockey became my downfall in later years when I tried to take up golf.

Tennis, however, did lead me into playing competitively after leaving school, joining Enfield Chace Tennis Club, and enjoying the social activities and American Tournaments run at weekends. At school I played in the 1st tennis team with a superb partner, Ann Holman, who was a dab hand at the net leaving me to patrol the baseline. Mixed doubles was also pursued energetically with Bill Willbraham although we did not play many fixtures as there were few co-educational secondary schools in the area.

Time out from school often found Brenda Glashier and myself cycling to the nearby Enfield town park to picnic, play tennis or cricket. From a grateful patient of my father's, I had acquired a beautiful and almost new full-sized cricket bat. This was eagerly eyed by the local boys who, sensing the opportunity to hold this in their hands, offered to play cricket with us, except we grew tired of always being banished to field on the boundary. As often as not we would drift away, returning in time to reclaim my bat and go home for supper which, if prepared by Brenda's mother, was the most delicious fry-up of sausage, egg and chips – havoc to the waistline but it still remains a firm favourite meal of mine.

But Brenda and I got up to more daring escapades together. Going to the Capitol cinema in Winchmore Hill was a popular outing and we watched black and white films, memorably *The Hasty Heart*, a tearjerker set in a jungle army hospital, and *Mrs Miniver* who I recall discovered a ravenous German prisoner of war on the run eating out of her kitchen fridge. However, the films were incidental because it provided the cloak of darkness that we needed so that we could daringly smoke our packet of Player's Weights cigarettes, finishing off by spending our precious sweet coupons to buy liquorice laces or lemon sherbet dabs to disguise our breath. We may have won the war in 1945 but sweet rationing, at six ounces per person each week and introduced in 1942, remained in force with only a short interruption until 1954, the same year that food rationing ended and also the year I left school at the age of eighteen.

Fancy cakes and cookies were scarce during the same sweet-rationing period and I clearly remember the ecstatic joy when, as girl guides, we arrived for a summer camp in the Devonshire village of Bow where the only bakery was crammed with mouth-watering cakes waiting to be purchased. We all wanted to assist and so urgent phone calls were made home to plead for the dispatch of the coveted bread units (BUs) – such gastronomic delights made the camp an outstanding success.

Carefree holidays were also spent in Troon in Scotland, home to the Open Golf Championship, residing with the hospitable and loving Russell family, a household always filled with good conversation and great laughter. Mrs Russell and my mother, Mrs Mitchell, were related and, as Elizabeth and I were close in years and like cousins, we enjoyed a lifelong friendship, sealed when Elizabeth was my chief bridesmaid when I got married. As young teenagers we would cycle through the surrounding and hilly Ayrshire countryside, walk and picnic in the Fullerton Woods, explore the rock pools, follow the Boys' Open Golf Championships, play tennis, and brave the elements to swim in the sea where the temperature was a challenge to us human mortals but seemed to be attractive to the shoals of jelly fish whose painful sting we wished to avoid at all costs. Another memorable holiday was spent in 1952 at the end of the Ordinary level GCE exams in the home of my German pen-friend who lived in Feuchtwangen, a most attractive Bavarian village some thirty miles south of Nuremberg. During my third year at Latymer, our German teacher gave us the opportunity to have a pen-friend and in distributing the names he had obtained from their school, the Ansbach Gymnasium, he tried to match the various families. By chance, one of the potential German correspondents was the daughter of a dentist, so I was automatically paired with her, Evelyn Hofer. In her first letter to me she asked if I was any relation to Margaret Mitchell who had written *Gone With The Wind* but, alas, I had quickly to dispel her of this intriguing thought. So, after two years of correspondence, all was set for us to meet and there was great excitement as some thirty sixteen-year-old pupils left Edmonton to make the journey by train to Germany to spend three weeks with our respective families and then, together with our pen-friends, return to Edmonton for another three weeks in our individual homes. Friendships were truly forged or broken after such an intensive time together. Mine turned out to be a fortunate pairing, because our friendship has endured and we regularly send greetings cards. Even more rewarding is that friendships have blossomed with the next generation and exchanges continue. Introduction in this way to the German way of life was without equal, especially in the close-knit community of Feuchtwangen where the father was the dentist, with his surgery in the home, so the familiar 'perfumes' abounded. Downstairs the aunt owned a dress shop and the family also ran the Konditorei where I savoured for the first time the gigantic strawberry flans oozing gorgeous whipped cream. I had also been brought up to believe that the hot daily meal was not complete without potatoes, but here the family did not serve them daily and this too was a quirk that Evelyn had to come accustomed to when she came to stay with us.

The three weeks sped by, meeting up on occasions with the other Latymerians, some likewise happily settled in to the new routine while for a few there had been an insurmountable mis-match – a risk lurking with all friendships initiated through the pen or electronic medium. With Evelyn and her sister, Inge, when off duty working in their father's practice as a dental nurse, we cycled to the neighbouring villages without mishap – once I had mastered how to action the brakes on the pedals. We swam in open-air lidos surrounded, not like our local pool in Barrowell Green with concrete, but with lush lawns, shady trees and picnic areas. To venture further afield to old towns Rothenburg and Dinkelsbühl with quaint buildings and cobbled streets, we were driven in the exciting green Beetle, the Volkswagen, with a flower holder on the dashboard, a car not yet familiar on the British roads.

When I left I was given presents, which I still treasure: a silver friendship bracelet and a Hummel figurine of 'Toothache' interestingly stamped on the bottom as by W. Goebel – Western Germany. At the end of the war, Feuchtwangen found itself in the US Zone and although the army still had a visible presence when we were there in 1952, certainly compared to the other military zones and notoriously the Russian sector, there had been a return to an acceptable way of life with little day-to-day interference. Amazingly, my fluency improved by leaps and bounds but the experience awakened in me the tragedy of war when innocent and loving families like the Hofers witnessed similarly the destruction of their beautiful and historic buildings and churches and experienced the ignominy of living with the occupation troops and tanks patrolling their streets. And yet, they welcomed me royally into their home. Friends were keen to meet me, despite some of their memories of England being not from a holiday perspective but as prisoners of war. I was acutely aware of the need for forgiveness and tolerance on both sides. I returned home, viewing the world from a different perspective – I had grown up.

Then it was our opportunity to return hospitality and cousin Elizabeth was recruited to assist as we toured the notable London landmarks and met up with Evelyn's school friends at events organised by the school. The planned highlight was to take Evelyn on her first visit to the seaside because the German countryside is landlocked, despite its beautiful lakes. Why we chose Southend in Essex where, when the tide is out, is exposed nearly a mile of mud, I shall never understand. However, with the purchase of a rare stick of coloured seaside rock, the visit was declared a success.

The summer holidays were soon at an end and, even after gaining ten O levels, entry into the sixth form was a culture shock. The intensity of covering and also undertaking practical work in the four subjects, physics, chemistry, botany, and zoology, to advanced level within the two-year slot, brought home the need for meticulous planning if there was to be built-in time for pleasure pursuits outside school life. I also found myself in a shrunken sixth form, as at that time many pupils left school at sixteen to pursue other careers for which O level grades were more than sufficient.

Leadership skills were kindled in my final year at Latymer when, to my great delight, I was nominated as Head Girl Prefect by the staff. This role carried a spectrum of responsibilities and privileges, some onerous and others very enjoyable. I was never quite sure which I should have considered the ultimate accolade – receiving the beautiful silver head girl prefect badge, or the most enormous bunch of keys with masters to every door in the school. One of my first official tasks was to give the vote of thanks to the guest speaker, Dr George Cansdale of London Zoological Society fame, at the junior speech day and this, in front of parents, staff and pupils, was a daunting prospect. Under the eagle eye of Miss Satterly, I worked and worried hard in drafting a possible response, completely unaware of what the speaker might actually say. The critic's report in the school magazine was eagerly awaited and the verdict was given as 'an excellently proposed vote of thanks' so there was relief all round. This first successful foray into public speaking led to another engagement – proposing the toast to the Latymer Old Students' Association at its annual black tie dinner in Firs Hall. This time, extremely helpful coaching was forthcoming from Miss Strubell, our somewhat eccentric art teacher who cycled to school each day, often with her dog perched aloft in her handlebar basket, ready to provide the real life composition for her class. Again through repeated drafting and rehearsing out loud, my ten-minute contribution was well received – although it did dampen my enjoyment of the preceding meal, an interesting effect that has never left me.

I could not have wished for a better early training in public speaking, which has become an integral part of my professional life. I tried to record not only my gratitude to the school some years ago with the gift of the oratory prize, but also to underline what I believe to be an important extracurricular pursuit, worthy of recognition alongside the traditional academic subjects. Today, it is reward enough to witness that Latymer has an active debating society which I understand is a force to be reckoned with in the English-speaking Mace Competition, which is the foremost debating schools' event in the UK.

The choice of house captains, one boy and one girl, was left to the pupils to decide. I was thrilled to be elected captain of Keats House, named after the romantic poet John Keats who lived in Edmonton. Our House shone at most sports, but our coveted reputation was for swimming, as we had secured the Bird trophy for six consecutive years. I was determined that in my year this record should not be broken and so set about collecting an unbelievable number of points, even before the swimming gala took place. This was achieved through encouraging the whole House to swim a distance for which points were awarded. Never has a mile been swum by so many. The strategy paid off – we won the cup.

In the final term even the most notorious slacker became, overnight, a compulsive swot. Heads were down to concentrate on revision for the rapidly approaching A level examinations. The practicals in each of the four subjects were taken in advance of the written papers and, with the exception of zoology, all exams were taken on our school premises.

We spent hours dissecting the lowly earthworm's central nervous system, the vascular supply of the dogfish, well pickled in tear-jerking formalin and, for one day only, displaying each internal system in turn of a freshly deceased rabbit. Then the appointed day arrived when our form members made the great trek to the examination halls, then located in Exhibition Road in South Kensington, to sit the zoological practical exam. The June day was hot and humid, the windows were open but while not much breeze entered, the large bluebottle flies did, and in great numbers. There, laid out ready for us to reveal our dissecting talents, was a rabbit. To this day I believe mine was short-changed on the chloroform because it twitched and bled profusely, even at the gentlest approach with scalpel and tweezers in hand. The practical was not a happy experience – more akin to a nightmare – for many of us, who made the homeward journey not best pleased with our performance.

My entry to study dentistry was dependent on passing the four A levels and a place in the dental school was waiting for me at my father's and brother's Alma Mater, the London Hospital Medical College in the University of London. My acceptance had been judged on an interview and the glowing array of school subject reports, predicting passes with flying colours. The long wait for the results of the exam was filled with endless rounds of parties, dances, excursions here and there, and, after the final and emotional singing of the school song with a promise to meet on the steps of Trafalgar Square in ten years' time, we all settled down to wait. The day of reckoning arrived. The envelope containing the slip of paper carrying my destiny was torn apart and my worst fears were confirmed. I had failed the practical – I had failed zoology.

Just where did this leave my dream of becoming a dentist?

Chapter 4

Will it be dentistry?

INTERMINABLE DISCUSSIONS TOOK PLACE within the family as to the next step after I had made such a spectacular examination failure in my best subject. Even the unexpected poor performance of some of the brightest of my fellow Latymer pupils brought little consolation. Amidst the despair, a phone call from the London Hospital lifted our collective spirits dramatically, because an interview was on offer at the dental school. Here was a chance to redeem myself: I was sure that the panel would understand the trauma of the Zoology practical.

I am reliably told by one of my fellow interviewees, Barry Jonas, that I arrived escorted by my mother because, in the 1950s, Whitechapel, in the east end of London, was not viewed as a nice place for young ladies to be on their own. In retrospect, I wonder if, secretly, she thought she could put in a good word for me, although thankfully she remained firmly ensconced in the safe haven of the waiting room until the interview was over.

It is amazing how some events remain as clear today as fifty years ago and that interview is one of them. As I entered the room there were assembled around a large oval table eight dark-suited men, and the dean, Professor Max Horsnell, introduced himself and his panel members. I was asked at the outset if I had any idea why I had failed zoology. I recounted, in all its gory details, my brush with the rabbit as I struggled to display its vascular system. 'I can assure you there will be plenty of blood in dentistry!' exploded one professor, and a great titter went around the entire panel as they all obviously enjoyed the joke. I meekly smiled in response and by now was convinced that my dream of becoming a dentist was shattered for all time.

However, the remainder of the interview went off without mishap and I must have made a sufficiently good impression, as I was offered a place, along with four of the young men being interviewed. This meant that for the first three months I would attend Queen Mary's College of London University and retake the biological subjects in the December. As the College was just about fifteen minutes' walk away along the Mile End Road, I was also able to enter the dental school in October 1954. This allowed me to mix with the main group of twenty-five dental students, attending as many of the lectures as I could fit in without damaging my chance of passing the crucial A level subject of zoology – failure this time would definitely be the end of the road.

The change in learning style at university was a memorable experience. Gone was the didactic approach, which I was used to, and it was replaced with the colourful and entertaining hour-long lectures from equally colourful learned professors. The eccentric Professor of Botany improved our appreciation of the subject beyond all botanical parameters and gave an insight into matrimonial disharmony caused by keeping a pet alligator in the family bath, especially as he happened to be completely intolerant of his wife's objection to this practice.

The five of us, Barry Jonas, David Wine, Peter Maddox and Alexander Plucinski (a recently domiciled Polish Count) sailed through the retakes with flying colours and, with much relief, we became a closely-knit tutorial group for the remaining four years and one term of our dental course leading to the degree, Bachelor of Dental Surgery of the University of London.

Our year was something of a novelty in the dental school because there was a total of five women students. In the year above us and, as it transpired, the year below us there were no women at all. This was not due to the iniquitous quota system, which had operated in English medical schools until the early 1950s in order to prevent the medical profession being overrun with women. As far as dentistry was concerned the reason was that it was viewed as an unsuitable career for women, as it was believed that brawn over brain was needed to extract teeth.

My Alma Mater, the London Hospital Dental School, has yet to celebrate its centenary as it was established on 3 October 1911. However, many of the founding members of staff have become legends: Professor Evelyn Sprawson, MC, Professor Harold Chapman, and Mr George Northcroft particularly, as their names are attached to subject prizes and eponymous lectures. I was honoured to deliver the Evelyn Sprawson Memorial Lecture at the Old Students' Annual Meeting in 2001 and so was able to acknowledge the influence of 'The London' on my life in so many ways. As an aside, it is also interesting to note that the London Hospital established its training school for doctors some 125 years before the dental school, and the authorities were only driven to establish a dental school when they discovered that patients needing dental care were being transferred to Guy's Hospital – rivalry, even in those days, was very much alive and well.

To achieve in the traditional subjects – anatomy, physiology, embryology and biochemistry – depended on an ability to memorise factual information and this never presented me with problems. As many lectures were shared with the medical students I could find myself crammed in a lecture theatre with over a hundred undergraduates. Dental students also shared a cadaver, although we were only required to dissect the head, neck, thorax and abdomen, leaving the would-be-doctors to display their dissecting prowess additionally on the upper and lower limbs. We also absorbed intimate details of the dentition of mammals, reptiles, crustaceans, fishes and birds, all encompassed in the grand-sounding title of comparative dental anatomy. I also became acquainted with every cusp and fissure of our thirty-two teeth, as I sculptured a representative selection of incisors, canines, bicuspids and molars out of a block of greeny-grey beeswax, although the shavings from working with the Lecron carver seemed intent on embedding themselves in my clothes, despite every effort to take all precautions to cover up.

But it was not all work and no play. Sport was encouraged and Wednesday afternoons were jealously protected and, from 12 noon onwards, hordes of students, myself included, would take off to pursue our favourite pastimes. More often than not I would find myself travelling to the London Hospital Sports Ground sited at Hale End in Tottenham and, fortuitously, conveniently situated some four miles from home. I soon found myself recruited into the team for hockey and tennis matches and these normally occupied Saturday afternoons. It was at Hale End that I was introduced to the thrills of being a spectator at the rugby football matches and witnessing the true ferocity of the game when watching the final match for the inter-varsity cup, at Twickenham. Emotions ran high and propelled student pranks of pre-match flour bag fights on the hallowed turf and the soaking of innocent pedestrians with water pumped out from the hospital coach as it crossed the City en route from Whitechapel to Twickenham. These antics, to which many a blind eye was turned, became a regular feature of the University Rag Week when large sums of money were raised for numerous charitable causes.

I was thrilled to be chosen to play badminton for the University of London Ladies in their massive Sports Hall at Stamford Hill and, again with good fortune, this was a mere five station stops along the railway line from home. I continued to play badminton matches long after I qualified in the building with the highest roof on the London Hospital site – the outpatients' hall. The quicker we could clear the benches of waiting customers the sooner we could get down to the energetic business of the evening – badminton.

But there were other equally energetic student activities concentrating on the ability to raise a glass or drink the traditional yard of ale. Professor Francis Fish, in his excellent history of the dental school, chronicles the impact of Whitechapel pubs on student life. He writes that 'the pubs became a part of the experience of both staff and students – certainly students discovered the inside of them in connection with the ritual celebrations associated with the passing, or not passing of examinations'. Women in pubs did not sit comfortably with my Presbyterian upbringing and a public bar was viewed as a refuge for working-class men. The pubs close to the hospital rose and waned in popularity for the rumbustious Friday evening revelry. Taking their turn were Murphys in the Whitechapel Road, The Good Samaritan (Sammys) on the corner of Turner Street and Stepney Way and The Blind Beggar which courted notoriety in 1966 when the Kray Twins walked into the bar and assassinated Cornell at point-blank range. However, the popular hideout during my time for students to meet up with staff after hours was The Black Bull, an elegant mock-Tudor building which belied its shabby smoke-filled interior, standing majestically on the corner of Whitechapel and Vallance Road. Warm beer or lemonade shandy never appealed but I discovered ice-cold lager which has remained my 'tipple' of choice to this day.

Once I had passed the second Bachelor of Dental Surgery (BDS) examination, I exchanged the dissecting room attire for a smart well-starched short white jacket, the 'uniform' of a clinical dental student. But first, along with other members of my group, I had to pass through the hoops of an introductory and phantom head course before I was let loose on real live patients. So it was that I met an enthusiastic and gifted teacher, Douglas (Dougie) Shepperd, whose fund of stories was remarkable (though some not repeatable) and who clung to many of the hallmarks associated with active war service in the RAF. Within no time at all the young men in our group appeared with 'short back and sides', and dangling jewellery was definitely not encouraged under his tutelage. It was he who impressed on me and countless students who attended his courses the need to drive for perfection and seek the highest standards in our chosen vocation. But Dougie also commanded great respect and affection and his organisational skills were utilised in compiling each year clinical parts of the Old Londoners' or former students' study days. Inevitably lifelong friendships were forged and he demonstrated to us the importance of work-life balance before it was so named. Every Friday, at the end of his busy day in his West End general practice he would drive down to Port Navas in Cornwall to spend the weekend with his family, sailing his beloved boat. On one occasion, when I was invited to sample this pleasure along with my friend Joan Roberts (later Fountain), I stowed my plastic raincoat out of the way on what I thought was a shelf. He never forgot to remind me on countless occasions that, not only did his back hurt after giving us piggy-backs to shore to visit the local hostelry, but also that he had spent countless hours removing scales of plastic from my coat which had melted on to his engine casing. Many years later, Dougie came into my office in Wimpole Street clutching two bottles of prized Bushmills Whiskey that had parted company from a flimsy paper bag. In no time these bottles were secreted safely in a stout plastic *British Dental Journal* bag, which was normally destined to hold books. Chortling at the humour of the situation he was soon on his way, a contented man.

At the end of his phantom head course I had mastered placing a cement lining or an amalgam filling of differing shape or size into the twenty-eight perfect plastic teeth which were anchored in a yellow stone material in upper and lower metal jaws, which were firmly attached by screws to a polished wooden head. As we learnt to handle the instruments and manipulate varying dental materials, we progressed to test our cutting skills on real teeth, garnered from the hospital extraction rooms. All too soon it seemed the time had arrived when I was going to treat my first patient.

I still marvel at the stoic nature of the East End cockney who was destined to fulfil this role. At eighteen stone, he had to shoehorn himself into the dental chair which in those days remained mainly in the upright position with stoutly padded armrests. My mixed emotions of extreme nervousness and excitement gradually disappeared during the one and a half-hour long appointment allocated for his first visit. So intent was I not to penetrate the tooth pulp, I discovered to my horror that I had barely traversed the tooth enamel, leaving the intervening dentine layer intact. Thus at the end of this first appointment the tooth was sealed with a temporary dressing and the patient uncomplainingly returned for a second visit when he was thrilled to become the proud possessor of a highly-polished and well-carved amalgam filling – and for free.

Even during my student days there were rapid advances in the techniques and materials used in dentistry. As a senior student some two years later, my reliable electric engine working at a speed of 2,500 rpm was replaced by a fast, although deafeningly noisy, airotor, capable of speeds of up to 250,000 rpm. Inventors were hard at it and soon there appeared a quieter and cleaner air-bearing turbine rotating at up to 500,000 rpm. For patients, it meant that both the time taken to drill teeth and the pressure exerted by the drill on the tooth were greatly reduced, which was a bonus for the dentist as well as the client.

During the dental course we were introduced to and became absorbed in many subjects, some catching our imagination more than others. The lectures on medicine and surgery were always eagerly awaited and well attended, as our teachers were experienced hospital consultant physicians or surgeons who embellished the theoretical teaching with tales of their dramatic encounters. A large amiable grandfather-like figure was the surgeon Mr A. M. A. Moore, known affectionately to students as 'Dinty'. Always with a ready eye for the young ladies, he told us of the occasion when an attractive young lady (whose legs were obscured by tightly fitting long leather boots) sat opposite him on a London bus. Suddenly, he observed blood spilling out over the top of a boot and, realising something was amiss and uttering the words, 'pardon me', he thrust the offending leg in the air – thus impressing upon us how to stop serious bleeding, which in this case was from a ruptured varicose vein. An apocryphal story, maybe, but we took it at face value and no one ever failed a viva when asked how to treat serious haemorrhage.

Studies in general pathology drew me to the college museum with its shelves stacked with hundreds and hundreds of specimens of every organ and disease imaginable, displayed in perspex pots, and certainly not for the faint-hearted. Renowned as one of the finest museums of its kind in the world, the pride of place belonged to the skeleton of Joseph Merrick, popularly known as 'The Elephant Man', about whom numerous films, plays and TV documentaries have been screened over the years. Alongside the skeleton was a cast of his head on which was displayed a large black cap from the edges of which hung a curtain of grey flannel with a slit to enable him to see and yet cover his deformities so that he could venture forth from the London Hospital where Sir Frederick Treves gave him sanctuary, saving him from his previous degrading existence where he was put on display as a freak.

As you will have gathered, throughout my career I have been fortunate to be assigned some outstanding teachers and I believe that is a highly influencing factor, in my particular case in relation to prosthetic dentistry (false teeth). Our consultant in charge, Mr A. G. Allen, was a previous director of the dental school but during my time he concentrated on teaching the students and running a highly successful West End practice. A tall, handsome man, with thick horn-rimmed glasses and a shock of neatly trimmed, wavy white hair and a stylish moustache, he demonstrated the power of a good chairside manner, as his patients responded to his every bidding and never seemed to complain – at least not till out of earshot! 'AG', as we called him to distinguish him from another colleague on the staff called S. G. Allen, was an accomplished water colourist and his skill in constructing dentures brought forth his artistry as he provided false teeth for patients who had been cast off as failures and gave them back their confidence and dignity to speak and socialise once more.

Later, when undertaking my studies in the children's department, I was allocated a little boy, John aged just over four years old and without any teeth, whom the teacher in charge of the clinic thought would benefit from dentures. It was a challenge to treat a frightened child whose memory was still scarred by the pain and trauma of his carious teeth and their removal. Trust was established and soon his dentures were in place – a dour child started to eat and smile again. Gifts to students were not encouraged but at his last appointment John arrived proudly bearing a box of Milk Tray chocolates and a hand-crayoned note, 'Thanks for giving me my teeth.' I still treasure the photographs of his happy smiling face and handwritten note but the chocolates have long since been devoured!

It is not surprising that happy memories of my early days of enjoyment in model-making at my father's laboratory workbench were aroused by my prosthetic studies and not only did I gain the first distinction in prosthetic dentistry of the University of London awarded to any London Hospital dental student but it also convinced me that I would seriously consider specialising in prosthetics after I qualified.

Due to the endless hours standing at the dental chair, a recognised occupational health hazard was to suffer from varicose veins and often-intractable leg ulcers, causing great pain and discomfort. Sadly these afflicted my father during his latter years and, while intent to soldier on if I was going to take over his general practice, we all knew that the only permanent cure was retirement. Flushed with my prosthetic success, my sights were now firmly set on a hospital career, which had full parental support, and so my father sold his practice and family home, moving to a new house at Athole Gardens some half a mile away. There was no turning back for me.

The final undergraduate year was a delightful mixture of cramming for examinations and enjoying the fruits of student life, such as receiving a coveted invitation from one of the medical Cambridge undergraduates to go to his May Ball at Corpus Christi, always a magnificent affair, and to take part in the annual Christmas Show held in the medical college library, where the installation of a temporary stage and wings permitted actors to exit through the open large library windows. Great ingenuity was the hallmark throughout and the satire built round the professors and consultants was legendary, with members of staff using as a measure of their popularity their inclusion in the script.

It was also at this time that I met the Barnardo medical students who were descendants of Thomas Barnardo who came in the late 1870s to the London Hospital to train as a medical missionary and then, while still a student, started first his school and then his now famous Children's Homes. The Barnardos introduced me to the Student Christian Medical Fellowship, whose outreach activities involved leading worship on Sunday afternoons in hospital wards at Bethnal Green and the Mildmay Mission hospitals. I attended the evening house groups and one of the staff nurses brought along her boyfriend, David Sheppard, later to become the inspirational Rt. Revd David Sheppard, Bishop of Liverpool, after leading the England Cricket Team as captain. There were also weekends away to learn more about the word of God through study and prayer interspersed with vibrant songs of praise. This was a new evangelical world which tested my traditional low-key Presbyterian style of worship, just as did attending the intensely emotional Billy Graham Crusade at Haringay arena and at the Royal Albert Hall. I am sure that these early forays into other Christian experiences showed me the importance of the ecumenical movement and encouraged me to try to be understanding of all faiths and creeds in today's multicultural society.

Soon, the final third BDS examination arrived, and after a hectic round of written papers, oral examinations, clinicals and practicals, the results were eagerly awaited. At noon on the appointed day the official results, in alphabetical order, were posted outside the Senate House of the University of London in Mallet Street. So, on a fine July day in 1959 I made my pilgrimage to Senate House and scanned the extensive list of successful candidates – but 'Mitchell' did not appear amongst the 'Ms'. I recall a sense of panic, followed by the swift realisation that the list was divided into two, with the top list carrying the names of the handful of candidates who had been awarded honours.

There was my name, 'Margaret Helen Elizabeth Mitchell' – Honours in Prosthetic Dentistry. I had fulfilled my dream.

Chapter 5

Decisions, decisions

QUALIFIED AT LAST, BUT WAS I ready to leave the protected environment of my Alma Mater. Some of my peers did not enjoy the luxury of choice, as they had to complete their deferred, but compulsory, two-years' National Service in the armed forces. Others could not wait to enter the world of general dental practice and start earning real money, understandably necessary for those with family commitments or pressing student debt.

For myself, approaching twenty-four years of age and still single, I could afford to seek further clinical experience at the London Hospital. The preferred way to achieve this was to secure one of the seven coveted house officer posts so that over a period of six months clinical practice could be undertaken in most of the specialist hospital departments. One of these was graded as a senior house officer post and was a resident job, so competition for this was fierce, especially amongst those seeking a career in oral surgery. The job entailed living on site and, as all of my student days had been spent living at home, this presented itself as a very attractive proposition. When I discussed the possibility of submitting an application for this post, I was firmly told by one of the registrars 'Forget it, the job is always given to a man.' Sensing, indeed seeing, my indignation, he continued to explain that the hospital consultants, all men, would never approve of a woman being appointed, because they viewed the incumbent of the post as the perfect partner to accompany their daughters, of eligible age, to the grand autumn and spring hospital or college balls, always held in luxurious surroundings, like the Grosvenor Hotel in stylish Mayfair. An additional obstacle, I was told, would be the accommodation provided in the spartan residents' mess, which was located unceremoniously next to the hospital incinerator. As the given reasons seemed grossly unfair, in went my application form for the job. Looking back, this was possibly my first serious encounter with gender discrimination, years before the advent of the Equal Opportunities and, later, the Sex Discrimination Acts. It turned out to be worth the challenge as, with a pleasant surprise to myself and others, I became the first woman to be appointed as the resident dental house officer at the London Hospital. The culture shock was real when I found myself attired in a long and heavily starched white coat, carrying a bleep for constant contact and on a steep learning curve as I wrestled to come to terms with my new role and responsibilities. I was fortunate to have an overlap, even though only of seven days, with my predecessor John Pidgeon before he departed for the Antarctic survey expedition acting as its dental officer. 'You are at the beck and call of all the dental consultants and registrars, so you won't get much sleep,' he warned me. Then he outlined the various duties: organising the admissions of patients for operation, assisting the surgeons in theatres, looking after the patients when in the wards, and arranging for them to be seen in the relevant consultants' clinic after discharge. In addition to the planned work, the resident was also responsible for the emergency admissions and operations when patients had suffered trauma from car accidents or, as the hospital was near the busy London docks, from horrific industrial injuries. The resident was also expected to offer an emergency dental service in the evenings and at weekends after the dental department was closed. A corner was reserved for the resident in the receiving room of the main hospital, now more grandly entitled the accident and emergency department. Here stood a solid, upright and leather upholstered dental chair, which was firmly anchored to the floor and, if only given the gift of speech, I am sure would have many enthralling stories to tell about its occupants over the years. The sister-in-charge, Miss Nora Elvy, who wore a distinctive blue uniform, and on high days and holidays sporting the unique London Hospital lace tails attached underneath her cap, ruled her domain with a rod of iron, but, as I was quickly to find out, had a heart of gold and a sense of fun, attributes also displayed by the vast majority of ward sisters. However, there was a quick way to win Sister Elvy's approbation and that was to allow her to extract the occasional wobbly tooth. Initially apprehensive, I was assured she was accomplished in the art and had been indulged by my predecessors, so I admit I did eventually succumb – she never let me, or the patient, down. If I was looking for experience, there can be no doubt that my evening clientele provided me with many challenges, especially as they would frequently arrive with police escorts after having been involved in fights, or, as usually explained by an inebriated client, 'Oh Miss, I just walked into a revolving door the wrong way!' Many of my 'regulars' were hardened methylated spirit drinkers and professional wanderers who took up residence in the many neglected and overgrown bomb sites, which, in the sixties, still scarred the landscapes of the East End of London.

Although each consultant had a dedicated time for his operating sessions, it fell to the resident to negotiate the operating time for an emergency. This entailed a face-to-face encounter with the superintendent-in-charge of theatres, Miss Ida Latham, whose features, mannerisms and voice could have been mistaken for the actress Peggy Mount, who at that time was playing the formidable mother in the West End of London stage production of *Sailor Beware*. It was easy to find oneself intimidated, resulting in the acquisition of a late operating slot, which did not please the registrars who were then forced to wait well into the evening before operating in theatres. The secret to success, I was told, was to stand up for your registrar and get a good deal, not only for him but also for the benefit of the patient. So, I did just that, even surprising myself to go willingly into battle against such a stalwart of hospital authority. Perhaps, in retrospect, these encounters helped me to understand the importance of negotiation and certainly at the time securing a good slot not only thrilled the registrars but also resulted in Miss Latham and myself forming a good working relationship based on mutual respect, especially as it was crystal clear that life as a resident in any speciality without the theatre superintendent on your side would be intolerable.

The European Working Time Directive, or junior doctors' hours, limiting the number of hours which staff could work in a day or week, did not yet exist. Nevertheless, the resident houseman was entitled to take off alternate weekends, but otherwise needed to be available, on call, twenty-four hours a day. It was a treat to creep into bed before midnight, although by seven o'clock I was well on the move again. Even nights were not sacrosanct, as there could be a knock on the door from the hospital porter with a summons to deal with a sudden emergency. This pattern of working was endured by all housemen and sleep deprivation took its toll, so that on a weekend off my parents were left bemused as I spent most of my visit home sleeping. However, the experience gained from being 'on call' can never be underestimated. I was on the spot to observe an impressive variety of cases, which far outweighed even the best colour photographs that could be found in numerous textbooks. Occasionally, phone calls were received from an outlying hospital annexe and one such contact took place early on a Saturday morning from the maternity unit at Hampstead in North London. The urgent request was to remove a tooth from a newly-born boy which was causing intense pain and trauma to the mother's breast each time he suckled. I have to admit to a degree of apprehension, as the baby's mouth was so small and slippery and even my children's-sized forceps, carefully carried from The London, suddenly appeared to be designed for giants. A wise sister produced a pair of more delicate Spencer-Wells forceps and in no time at all the offending neo-natal tooth was removed, to the great delight and comfort of all concerned. A more dubious privilege which befell the resident dental house officer was to offer up his or her bedroom as a party venue, although, to be fair, the aftermath was never as bad as feared. In fact, the sleeping facility on site was envied by many and there was no lack of willing volunteers from the rugby fans to cover my weekends off, particularly if the rugby team was playing a home match with the likelihood of a win in the inter-hospital cup match to celebrate.

All aspects of hospital mess life were to me exhilarating: listening to the interminable discussions amongst medical housemen concerning the patients in their care, learning about the exciting career options and forging friendships which have stood the test of time. But the six months of close-knit communal living passed all too quickly. It was decision time again. Should I pursue the speciality of prosthetic dentistry, or train as an oral surgeon? A defining moment came when early one evening a young man with a fractured lower jaw was admitted under the duty general surgeon, Mr Gordon. I was just about to phone dental duty senior registrar, Gordon Seward, to alert him to the need for a theatre when Mr

Gordon told me not to phone him until his last train to London had departed from Ilford, where he lived. Rather, he would take me to theatre and let me do the treatment necessary. What an opportunity to put into practice all I had learned during the past few months assisting in wiring numerous broken jaws. Thankfully, the operation went smoothly, and with a perfect result. I was sure I wanted to make oral surgery my career. Dr Francis Fish, second-in-command in the prosthetic department, told me that a glittering career lay ahead of me in dental academia. 'Go and work in the prosthetic department in the world-renowned research centre at the University of Malmö. I will arrange it for you.'

Now, totally confused, I confided in my senior registrar, Gordon Seward. He was firmly of the opinion that, in order to keep my options open, I should take my fellowship in dental surgery (FDS) before contemplating any move to Sweden. My parents concurred with this advice, but it did raise the question of how I would get the further necessary experience to pass the fellowship examination, which comprised two parts. The first or primary examination demanded a serious return to the well-thumbed textbooks, as well as many more advanced ones, but the final examination required in-depth clinical and dental surgical experience. Thus, if at all possible, it would be a sensible approach if I could continue to work in a hospital environment. I coveted a junior registrar job in the oral surgery department and was delighted to secure such an appointment at The London for a period of six months. With great delight I passed my primary FDS at the first attempt, and within less than a year, so I was greatly encouraged to focus on the next hurdle – the final.

Fortunately, at this time, I was promoted to become a middle-grade registrar, again in the oral surgery department but working part-time. Then, to my great surprise, I was invited by the House Governor of the hospital, Captain Brierley, to become dental officer to the nurses for two days a week. I was even more amazed when I discovered that I had been recommended for the post by the consultant dental surgeon in charge of the nurses, none other than the head of prosthetic dentistry, Mr A. G. Allen, so I realised that no hard feelings were harboured against me for turning down the opportunity to further my prosthetic career in Malmö. The dental surgery for the nursing staff was located in the nurses' sick room, which was on the top and fourth floors of the private wards. This greatly appreciated service was provided by the hospital authorities and organised as a general dental practice. My clientele varied from probationary nurses through to the matron, bringing me collectively a wealth of clinical experience. So far, my domestic activities had been limited and I was challenged by the nursing staff on the fourth floor to take up knitting, which could ensure that, if a patient failed to attend, I could put the valuable half-hour to a more productive pastime. It was a struggle, and perhaps due to insufficient cancellations it took me nearly a year to complete my first and, as it turned out to be, my last pullover in an attractive lovat green colour, which was worn conscientiously by the lucky recipient, my future husband, until his expanding girth and the inquisitive moths deemed that the masterpiece should be discarded.

Study was intensive for the final fellowship and it was a real challenge not only to understand and recognise a wide canvas of diseases and their treatment, but also to recognise their macro- and micro-pathology. Urgent expert help was certainly needed and I was fortunate to discover that in the oral medicine department at Guy's Hospital, the outstanding teacher, Brian Cooke, was willing to let some prospective FDS students attend his department and outpatient clinics, which I did in the company of Peter Banks, a very bright dentist, who was also pursuing a medical degree, as it was beginning to emerge that this qualification was essential for a career in oral surgery. Assisting in the department was Tony Naylor, another bright and recently-qualified dentist, whose communicative skills revealed to me the many histological wonders to be seen through the microscope and how to explain them to the satisfaction of an inquisitive examiner.

This foray outside The London, and to Guy's Hospital in particular, opened up a new world of learning and resulted in my enrolment on the famous Cooke's crammer course. This was held on a Sunday afternoon at the home of Brian Cooke, for a dozen or so hopeful FDS students, and lasted for almost three hours with a welcome break for refreshments. The stack of square-boxed individual Lyons fruit pies or sugar-sprinkled bath buns, which miraculously appeared halfway through the afternoon in the arms of Mrs Cooke, is still a deliciously happy memory. The copious note-taking and answering of sample questions filled numerous ring binders and became invaluable and greatly envied as superb reference material, which continued to be used throughout my career.

But it was certainly not all work and no play. I had decided that the time had come to learn to drive a car. My beloved Grandad, when he died in 1957, left me the handsome sum of £900 with which I opened my first savings account with the Enfield Building Society. So I was well placed to buy my first car, but what to buy was the quandary. I was encouraged by a neighbour in Athole Gardens to go and look at a new model recently arrived in his garage showroom, the two-door Triumph Herald. I immediately fell in love with this very handsome smoky-blue car, with grey leather upholstered seats and polished mahogany dashboard. In no time at all I was the proud owner of this magnificent car but it was destined to sit in our family garage if I did not learn to drive. To supplement my lessons I needed practice and soon found a string of volunteers, provided that they were permitted to take the wheel in order to put the Triumph through its paces, including the highly-acclaimed turning circle equivalent to that of a London taxi.

The test date was issued and a day off from the hospital had to be negotiated. Then disaster struck for, on arriving at the Test Centre for an early morning appointment, I found it had been cancelled because the examiner was ill. I protested and was offered a test in a neighbouring area in the afternoon but gone were the well-practised routes and hill starts; instead an encounter with more roundabouts than I ever thought existed in the whole country. Nevertheless, and to my great relief, I passed and in no time at all my Triumph and I were constant companions, although at times it could give me uncomfortable surprises. My consultant at The London knew that the North Middlesex hospital was on my drive home, so I was asked to take a clinic for the indisposed consultant, Arthur Freese. This assignment lasted a few weeks and on one afternoon, making my homeward journey along the North Circular road, I came (with a deafening clatter, attracting the attention of pedestrians and drivers alike) to a terrifying and abrupt halt just short of a busy junction with traffic lights at every corner. Even I, a greenhorn in car mechanics, realised on lifting the bonnet that the radiator should not be resting on top of the fan blades. It turned out that I was not alone in experiencing the consequences of a design fault and so all the cars were recalled to have fitted a simple modification, which consisted of soldering on a cross-bar to keep the two vertical stays supporting the radiator firmly in place. Undeterred by this driving adventure, I adored my Herald car and drove countless miles, until water lapping round my feet after even a moderate shower convinced me that the time had come for us to part company.

During this time, even more exciting events were happening at the hospital. One morning the sister in the dental department, known to us as Sister Honey due to her endearing form of address, called me in to her office in the outpatient department. 'Margaret, have you seen Gordon Seward? He is looking for you.' I finally tracked him down at lunch-time and, much to my surprise, discovered that it was not work that he had in mind but an outing. He invited me to go with him to see *Ben Hur*, not necessarily my choice of film, but it was running to much acclaim in the West End at the Odeon Cinema in Leicester Square. It sounded a good proposition, especially as a meal beforehand was also on offer. This was the first of several outings but in the close-knit hospital community, gossip of a romantic nature can quickly get out of hand, so precautions were taken to keep the fledgling courtship under wraps. Sister Honey's assistance was enlisted and a fellow registrar, Colin Parker, acted as a brilliant decoy on many occasions. I still permit myself a smile when I pass by St Martin's Theatre, lights sparkling outside, announcing that Agatha Christie's great 'whodunit' is still running since its first performance in 1952. The secret of its success is that the audience remains loyal to the request at the end of the show to keep the plot to themselves, however tempting it may be to share it with others. I did obey this request but for a totally unexpected reason. On leaving the theatre, Gordon sprang the ultimate question and asked me to share his life – to be his wife. Although I had begun to admire greatly this gentle, calm and frighteningly intelligent dentist, who, although he had also qualified as a doctor and gathered up many of the hospital and university prizes, above all, had remained endearingly modest, suddenly the truth dawned – I loved him enormously and could hear myself say, 'Yes, please.' Then we parted and each hurried down into the underground to catch our last trains home. Little wonder that the plot of the play was completely forgotten!

My parents were thrilled. 'Now I know why Gordon didn't want you to go to Malmö,' observed my father wisely. Then the hunt for the ring was on, and arrangements made for announcing the engagement, which we knew would take the hospital world, family, and local friends completely by surprise. As the engagement columns in the *Daily Telegraph* were avidly read by the hospital staff during the coffee interludes, this newspaper seemed a wise choice in which to announce the engagement. On Friday, 16 February 1961, readers in the hospital could hardly believe their eyes when they read of the engagement of Margaret Helen Elizabeth Mitchell to Gordon Robert Seward. How had they missed the stirrings of this hospital-based romance with a senior registrar falling for his houseman? The news spread like wildfire through the hospital and my morning clinic in the nurses' sick room did not shield me from the well-wishers, or the disappointed nurses who told me that they had hoped to catch Gordon for themselves.

Fixing the date for the wedding took some thought, because Gordon was very keen that I should complete my FDS studies before we married, so we settled on a date some fifteen months hence: 5 May 1962. I was now fortunate to have expert tutelage on hand and after the clinic on a Saturday morning we would make our way to my fiancé's home in Ilford for some enlightenment on the radiological and surgical delights of mouth and jaws, followed by tea with Gordon's parents. Freshly-baked cakes were on offer as his father was a retired master baker who, after the closure of his family shop, Seward & Sons in Dalston Lane in Hackney, kept his hand in with a regular Saturday morning bake.

In tandem ran the normal wedding day preparations and, as my mother wanted the best dress possible for her daughter, a trip to Harrods was organised. 'Bridal Department,' my mother requested the lift attendant in her soft Scots accent and then exclaimed in disbelief when we alighted from the lift to be surrounded by horses' headgear and adornments for riders. 'Well,' retorted the attendant, 'it is what you asked for – the bridle department.' Eventually we reached the correct floor and I was measured for the most gorgeous ivory-silk wedding dress of my dreams, complete with a small train and flowing veil. As the wedding momentum increased, so did the intensity of study for the rapidly approaching examination and, within two months of the wedding, I was able to claim that I had satisfied the examiners and was now the proud possessor of the Fellowship in Dental Surgery of the Royal College of Surgeons of England. Today it would be impossible to complete this exam within three years of graduation because there exists a longer and more formal training pathway, but I like to believe that none of my patients were compromised due to the less structured examination procedures at that time.

My parents gave me a perfect wedding: the gentlemen in morning suits, ladies in outrageous hats, the church – St Paul's Presbyterian Church in Enfield –

decorated throughout with heavenly-perfumed white and purple lilac blooms, and a sumptuous wedding breakfast, which was rounded off in true Scots fashion with an eightsome reel. The excitement in the church was palpable, as I arrived with my father. My two bridesmaids, cousin Elizabeth Russell and great friend Joan Roberts (Fountain), were resplendent in lime green brocade, ignoring the doom merchants who claimed that green courted bad luck. The Oldershaw clan was represented by my six-year old niece, Sue, carrying a beautiful flower basket, and my nephew Peter (of similar age) smartly attired in a kilt as a page boy. Kneeling as vows and gold rings, which we had cast for each other in the dental school laboratory, were exchanged, I suddenly heard myself reverse the order of my Christian names. Dismayed that I could get it so wrong, I was also concerned that this might render the marriage null and void. However, a kindly smile from the minister, the Revd Alex MacDonald, reassured me all was well. Then Gordon, as the attentive new husband, decided to help me to my feet but found resistance. Wondering if I was fainting, he gave me another mighty heave. Still firmly anchored in place and with my headdress now tipping and sliding off sidewards, I, unladylike, exclaimed, 'Get off my train!' much to the merriment of those around.

Returning from a glorious honeymoon in Guernsey I knew it was time to contemplate the next stage of my career. Now, as a married woman, and both of us with ideas of a family sooner than later, I realised that it was not practical to return to study medicine, as Gordon had done before me, if I was seriously contemplating a career in oral surgery. Perhaps I was also ready at last to leave the London Hospital, especially as I realised that when the *British Dental Journal* arrived fortnightly through the letterbox, I had been studying first the advertisement section. Then one day the perfect post appeared. This was for a senior hospital dental officer to work for five sessions a week at the local Highlands General Hospital, barely a ten-minute walk from where we now lived in Cotswold Way in Enfield. I sent off for the information package, made some enquiries, and submitted my completed application form.

Was this to be the time I would at last spread my wings?

Chapter 6

The Highland years

After having made the decision to apply for the post at Highlands General Hospital, I was encouraged to be called for an interview, which was held in the sombre concrete office block of the regional health authority in Eastbourne Terrace, directly behind London's Paddington mainline railway station.

In an effort to assemble some background information for this encounter, I took myself off to visit my prospective workplace and to arrange an informal meeting with the consultant-in-charge, Theodore Schofield, who was based at the Royal Northern Hospital in Holloway. He was the epitome of a London west-end private practitioner, immaculately attired in a black jacket with a matching black waistcoat and pinstriped trousers, and he most helpfully explained to me the intricacies of the prospective job.

On the day of the interview, in his role as chairman, Mr Schofield introduced me to the fellow members of his panel, John (Jack) Pilbeam, the consultant dental surgeon at the nearby Barnet General Hospital, and James Hudson, who was in charge of the dental department at the neighbouring Harefield Hospital in Hillingdon. These genial, and well past middle-age gentlemen were kindness personified and made me feel immediately at ease, and showed more confidence in my abilities than I certainly possessed myself. Undoubtedly, as I was told later, the acquisition of the fellowship in dental surgery and the fact that I had done so in record time after qualification, were the clinching factors in getting the job. Thus, I had even more reason to be grateful to Gordon for his advice to sit the examination before our wedding, although at the time, with all the competing preparations for impending nuptial celebrations, it was a close-run event. However, the greatest shock was contained in the papers I received confirming my appointment as senior hospital dental officer (SHDO) which, after specifying details of my salary and terms of service for the contracted four sessions each week, stipulated that I was not eligible for a salary increase until I had reached 35 years of age. This seemed an extraordinary long timescale for a 27-year-old to contemplate, but as I was so delighted to secure the job, it never occurred to me to challenge this blatant age-discriminatory rule which so obviously disregarded the incumbent's performance or increased responsibilities which could take place during the intervening eight-year period of service.

My future workplace, Highlands General Hospital, was situated at the top of the World's End Lane in Winchmore Hill, north London, and had originally been built by the London County Council as a hospital for infectious diseases, housing patients with afflictions requiring isolation, for example scarlet fever and tuberculosis. The wards were located in two-storey pavilions set well apart from each other in extensive grounds, with each of the eleven pavilions commanding stunning views of the rolling Hertfordshire countryside. Without a doubt, I kept fit walking between the wards to visit patients, as my dental beds were separated into those for males (pavilion 5) and females (pavilion 8). However, it could prove unnecessarily bracing for patients in inclement weather when they had to be wheeled on a trolley in the open air along to the operating theatres situated in two converted pavilions. The not uncommon sight of a theatre orderly holding an umbrella aloft over a patient lying on a trolley never failed to bring a smile to one's lips at such a Heath Robinson way of protecting patients from the rain.

The dental unit was self-contained and housed in a bungalow-like building, strategically placed at the apex of the two main sweeps of the road skirting all the pavilions, and had originally been built as the admissions centre for the isolation hospital. I have never worked before or since in premises with so many doors, although, for the waiting patients, it acted as a welcome distraction because they never knew where a person was going to next appear. The reason for the seemingly superfluous number of doors was that the highly-contagious individuals would be brought in through one door and, following confirmation of the diagnosis, would be decontaminated and then dispatched through a further door into a departure bay, before transfer to their assigned ward.

When I arrived at Highlands, on a typically misty autumnal morning in 1962, a warm welcome awaited me because the post had been vacant for nearly a year. My predecessor, Douglas Munns, although employed full-time as a senior hospital dental officer, carried dual responsibilities for orthodontics and oral surgery. After his departure, continuity for the orthodontic care of the patients was provided by a locum consultant, Ron Willcocks, whose main working base was Whipps Cross Hospital, but there remained no senior cover for the much needed hospital referral service for local practitioners. As a result, on my arrival, I was inundated with patients seeking treatment, so there was no problem in filling to capacity my four outpatient clinics and my one allocated Monday afternoon operating session. But care of human beings cannot, and did not, fall into circumscribed working times. So, as a single-handed senior hospital dental officer (SHDO), I accepted as normal practice being called out for patients involved in traffic accidents, although, as a consequence of living on the outskirts of rural Hertfordshire, there was also the occurrence of facial trauma resulting from encounters of riders or bystanders with overexcited horses.

Because I was now working in an area where I had spent my schooldays, it was inevitable that some of my patients were former classmates at Latymer. However, I was taken aback when checking the patients' notes ahead of my Friday morning outpatient clinic to find the name, Percy Blackwell, on the top of the pile. It could have proved to be a stressful encounter, but my revered chemistry teacher was a model patient, and he took great delight in subsequently bantering with friends and colleagues, 'Guess who I was sent to see at Highlands Hospital about my teeth?' After some inaccurate suggestions he would continue, accompanied with the characteristic twinkle in his eye, 'Margaret Mitchell of Latymer days, and she's better as a dentist than at chemistry.' I felt I had won my spurs and this mode of personal recommendation to my mind remains the preferred way of advertising, despite the frequent use by dentists today of the telephone directory's yellow pages, or the rapidly growing and favoured computer websites.

Although there was no shortage of patient referrals, I was aware that I was still an unknown quantity as far as many of the local general dental practitioners were concerned. I had yet to gain their trust. So I decided to hold an 'Open Evening' and invite the local dentists to come and meet the Highland team. The evening programme included a talk from the orthodontist Ron Willcocks, the hygienist Ms Winley-Green, and Gordon but I allowed plenty of time for discussion following each presentation. Trade displays and table clinics were organised, not only to provide up-to-date information about new dental products and materials, but also to finance the essential refreshments for the attendees. 'It will be nice to put faces to names' was the enthusiastic response of my staff when the proposed new venture was shared with them. Pavilion 12 was already often used for postgraduate medical activities and so it was identified as the venue, safe in the knowledge that it could seat comfortably up to sixty people and had projection and catering facilities. Invitations had been sent to the local dentists with the request for a reply, and so we were excited to get just over thirty positive responses, but this certainly did not prepare us for the eventual turnout. On the appointed evening, as 7 p.m. approached, my state-enrolled nurse, Iris Skinner, rushed into my office to report that a steady stream of cars was snaking its way up the drive from the main gates in World End's Lane. Shortly afterwards, this was followed by a degree of panic as, with still fifteen minutes to go before the scheduled starting time, all the chairs were occupied – it was standing room only. The support staff, nurses and technicians, were fantastic in raiding the waiting room in the dental unit and hospital outpatients for additional chairs, finally packing eighty people into the postgraduate centre. Many of the dentists echoed the same sentiment. 'This is the first time we have been given something free by the dental unit and we thought it a great idea to come and check you out!' Whatever the underlying motive, it did show me that if you put on an evening of talks relevant to the busy dentists in general practice, they will turn out and support you.

But there was yet more excitement in store. Minutes before the start, my auxiliary nurse, Gwen Aupers, appeared in my office with her bare arm outstretched exclaiming, 'Mrs Seward, look – I have been bitten by fleas.' Contrary to how I felt, I tried to utter calming words while taking a closer look at the collection of ugly-looking red weals on her forearm. Then the penny dropped. Gwen had been helping to unpack a new instrument designed to ease the pain of local injections by raising a blister on the gum. Inadvertently, when assembling the parts together, she had pointed the nozzle towards her arm and unwittingly pressed the trigger! Not an auspicious start for a newly launched dental instrument.

On the occasions when I did drive to work, I was able to park in the hospital consultants' car park located near the outpatients' pavilion, just across the road from the dental unit. I had by now finally pensioned off my beloved Triumph Herald and had replaced it with another brand new model, a four-door Hillman 1800, in a dashing cherry red colour with a cream roof and a matching cream flash along the sides of the bonnet. Imagine my consternation when one day on leaving the unit after my morning clinic, I saw a man opening the door of my new car and proceeding to get into the driving seat. I was soon at the window remonstrating with this car thief, whom I believed I had caught red-handed, when the occupant bellowed, 'How dare you? This is my car – out of my way!' Fortunately he agreed to open the glove compartment in the dashboard and on being confronted with an array of ladies toiletries he admitted that indeed he was in the wrong car. The commotion had gathered a small crowd in the car park and the sister-in-charge of outpatients enlightened me that the 'car thief' was the senior orthopaedic surgeon, Mr Baillie. Our paths did not normally cross but, following this unconventional introduction, we became good friends and he retold this anecdote to the assembled crowd at my retirement party, to the great amusement of all. However, in a more serious vein, we were both left wondering how many other Hillman cars our keys could unlock – so much for security!

But during my time at Highlands, the car's paintwork acquired more than its fair share of scratches through the lovingly administered car-wash by a man called Joe who had lived in the hospital for nearly forty years. Each Friday morning I would be obliged to drive to work because I knew that Joe would be eagerly awaiting my arrival, perched on the steps outside the front door of the dental unit from early morning, irrespective of the weather, armed with a pail of soapy water and a rather old grimy and grit-laden cloth. There was a modest payment for this car washing service but for Joe it was prized pocket money.

So how had Joe and nearly sixty other men and women come to reside in Highlands Hospital? It is the heartbreaking story of shunned and forgotten people who contracted sleeping sickness, encephalitis lethargica, in a pandemic which first appeared in Vienna in 1917 before sweeping the world and affecting nearly five million people before it suddenly, and as mysteriously, disappeared in 1927. When the disease initially arrived it caused diagnostic confusion as the clinical symptoms varied from person to person. But most profound and terrifying were the variations in the long-term afflictions. Some individuals would sit motionless and speechless all day with the absence of any motivation to eat or to take part in any activity. For others, the aftermath was the burgeoning of Parkinsonion disorders which included an involuntary or uncontrollable tremor and a faltering gait, as well as a range of neurotic and psychotic problems.

The tragic aftermath of this sleeping sickness meant many were unable to work or care for themselves and, unbelievably, were abandoned by family or friends and consigned to live out the rest of their lives in chronic hospitals, nursing homes or lunatic asylums because, not only was no treatment available but, even more disturbing, no cure was on the horizon.

Joe, at the early age of 21 years, was fortunate to be sent to Highlands Hospital where originally some 250 afflicted men and women were housed in separate pavilions, with the freedom to wander, if able, in the extensive grounds and fortunate to have loving nursing care lavished on them, coupled with the provision of expert medical attention. In 1962, when I arrived at Highlands, this was the sole remaining community of post-encephalitic lethargica (PEL) in England, and as the senior hospital dental officer I was responsible for their dental care, although their overall medical care was in the very capable hands of the medical superintendent, Dr James Sharkey, a geriatrician by speciality, as the majority of the PELs were now within the older age group.

On my first visit to the pavilions to see Lillian and Dora who had been identified by the sister-in-charge as needing attention to their ill-fitting dentures, I was completely unprepared for the scene that greeted me. While the pervading atmosphere was open and cheery, here were people slouched in high-backed leather chairs, immobile, with their mouths' hanging open and saliva drooling uncontrollably from their lips, making it so difficult for them to wear dentures, let alone eat food with them. I desperately wanted to provide a solution and explored the idea of implanting a recently manufactured magnetic mesh frame into their mandible with matching magnetic studs fused into the flanges of their lower denture so as to aid stability. My wonderfully gifted dental technicians in the dental unit, Arthur Day and Ken Osborne, were willing to help, but for this research to take place protocols had to be prepared and passed by the relevant committees. The time needed for this procedure took its toll and as a result the idea was never implemented.

Despite the broken lives of the PELs, as they were affectionately called, most exhibited a loving and endearing personality, rooted in a childlike fervour, and looked forward to a visit from the dentist and the change in routine that it would bring. I soon gathered up my friends from the badminton club at St Paul's Church to provide entertainment in the evenings, and at Christmastide to sing carols, when they loved to join in our party games as far as their abilities would allow.

Many years later Pamela, my daughter, and her friends from Christ Church in Cockfosters, befriended these PELs at Highlands, visiting regularly, including sending letters and greeting cards. One elderly and frail lady, Dora, who had been admitted to Highlands when only twelve years old, took great delight in sharing with Pamela that she remembered me as the dentist at Highlands who provided her with dentures, although she was too discreet to comment on whether they had helped her to eat.

In 1968, Dr Oliver Sacks, a clinical professor of neurology at the Albert Einstein Hospital in America, began to administer a new drug, L-dopa (laevo dihydroxy-phenylalanine) to a group of twenty out of the eighty survivors of the sleeping sickness epidemic, who still lived at the Mount Carmel Hospital in New York, USA. The results of Dr Sacks's work were reported in a letter published in 1970 in the Journal of the American Medical Association, when he vividly recounted the astonishing awakening of individuals from their frozen state. However, the joy was short-lived as sadly he began to report the occurrence of relapses, many with traumatic consequences.

A six-week trial of L-dopa was undertaken in 1969 amongst some of the Highlands patients, but there were no startling accounts of the miraculous transformations that some of Dr Sacks's patients experienced at the Mount Carmel Hospital. Individual stories of patients from the community in New York were told in great detail in his book *Awakenings* which is now accepted as a medical classic. Since it was first published in 1973, it has been the subject of many radio and stage plays and, in 1989, was adapted into a major feature film starring Robert De Niro who played the part of the patient, Leonard Lowe. The cast in the film spent time both at Highlands and Mount Carmel hospitals, observing the many unique mannerisms of the patients and portraying these with incredible accuracy. So much so that when I watched the film with my son Colin in the London Odeon cinema in Leicester Square, I was transported back in time and deeply moved. It was good to be able to share some of my work at Highlands with my son as we watched the courageous struggle of the PELs, and the dashed hopes of liberation from a frozen state by a much-trumpeted wonder drug.

Human tragedy is never far from us if we care to look and at the beginning of this twenty-first century we are being alerted to future pandemics, the Asian bird and Swine flu. My sincerest hope is that in addition to the protection and treatment regimes already being formulated by the health officials at the highest levels around the world, cognisance is taken of the human dimension of suffering from these diseases. Never again should ignorance dictate the fate of patients like the PELs who were coldly abandoned without hope by family and friends to institutions where, thankfully as evidenced by the health care professionals at Highlands and Mount Carmel hospitals, they were nurtured with dedicated love and caring denied to them by their relatives.

During my time at Highlands I was thoroughly enjoying my newly married state and was taking time out to brush up on my long-neglected culinary skills, although competing with my Scots relations to produce mouth-watering pancakes, scones and the traditional scotch bun was definitely an uphill task. At the same time, Gordon was building me a dream kitchen and his 'do-it-yourself' expertise became much admired and sought after by family and friends. However, he temporarily lost the empathy of some of his male friends due to them being continually nagged by their wives, 'Why you can't build me a kitchen like Gordon is doing for Margaret?'

Gordon had also turned his attention to learning to drive a car. Although he had won countless medals and prizes for his academic achievement, gaining a driving licence still eluded him, despite three attempts at the test. Now the tables were turned when I announced that I would not start a family until he passed his driving test. 'This tale is not apocryphal – I witnessed it at first hand' recounted Professor John Langdon, a colleague from our London days, when he gave many years later the public oration when I received the Colyer Gold Medal from the Faculty of Dental Surgery.

Fortuitously, our next-door neighbour in Cotswold Way, David Morgan, was a police driver and, sympathising with this ultimatum, took Gordon under his wing. In the shortest of time, Gordon successfully passed the test with flying colours. The family was now on its way. Some time later I was told suspicions had been aroused amongst the dental unit staff as my girth began to expand. My nurse, Iris, who assisted me in theatres, was encouraged by Arthur 'to keep a watchful eye and report back' as I changed into my operating gown. Eventually the secret was shared and as the news spread the patients in the occupational therapy department began making me a layette basket, beautifully lined in a diplomatic yellow satin material.

Time was taken up with attending the antenatal clinic and being a member of the very first group to use the pristine bedding and equipment in the brand new health clinic conveniently built in Merryhills Road, which lay at the end of our road. The health visitor was a cheerful Irish lady who was to prove to be full of down-to-earth common sense for us probationary 'Mums'. On learning that I was a dentist, she quickly exclaimed 'That's good – you can tell us all about teething!' – a chance remark which was later to play a significant part in my professional life.

Highlands dental unit was getting welcome publicity in the national dental scientific journals with the publication of two papers reporting on patients I had treated while still working as a registrar at the London Hospital. I shall be forever grateful for the kind and patient tuition given to me by one of the demonstrators in the conservation clinic at The London, Donald Derrick, who was also the editor of the journal *The Dental Practitioner.* He convinced me that there were no shortcuts to the writing of an article. Patience and diligent research was the key to success, as well as the realisation that a paper had to metamorphose through many drafts before it was in a suitable form to be submitted to a journal for possible publication. This sound advice at such an early stage in my career was invaluable, and I hope I have been able to pass these pearls of wisdom on to subsequent budding authors.

The patient whom I wrote about in that first paper, in 1962, I can recall clearly as though it was yesterday. A young coloured man presented in the outpatient clinic at the London Hospital complaining of numbness of the lower lip and a painful swelling at the angle of his right mandible. Because he had been given a local injection by his dentist for fillings a few days before, the senior registrar Peter Barton had diagnosed secondary haemorrhage due to post-injection infection and sent the patient to have a general anaesthetic, with the instruction to evacuate the pus from the swollen area of the jaw. However, as I explored the area, I found no pus but instead a large oozing blood clot, which I carefully removed.

It was evident that further investigations were needed and, sadly, the results of the blood tests confirmed the diagnosis of acute leukaemia. The paper I wrote reporting this most unusual mode of presentation of a fatal blood condition was accepted for publication because it drew attention to the fact that the other symptom of a pale complexion was masked by the patient's natural dark skin. It was rewarding to me that in writing the paper I was able to provide a reference to an article which my father, John Mitchell, had written some twenty years previously together with a notable ENT surgeon, George Quivst, recording the tragic death from asphyxia of a haemophiliac for whom he had removed a tooth during treatment at the Royal Free Hospital in London.

The second article, about a problem in the differential diagnosis of anaesthesia of the lower lip also appeared in the dental press in December 1962, highlighting the fact that I was now working at the dental unit at Highlands Hospital. Proudly, I published both of these papers under my married name, although there was, and still is, a school of thought that women should use their maiden names when authorising papers for publication, or indeed for everyday working in a profession.

Just before I started work at Highlands Hospital, Professor Sir Robert Platt had published his report on *Medical Staffing in the Hospital Service*. For a number of years, there had been disquiet about the grade called senior hospital medical or dental officer, because generally it was believed that the employing hospital authorities were getting consultant labour on the cheap. The posts up and down the country were becoming increasingly difficult to fill as the position was also branded as a cul-de-sac with no opportunity to the top job – the consultant. One recommendation of the Platt report was that regional hospital boards should review their medical staffing and the controversial position of senior hospital dental officer. As a result, my dental unit was visited by a senior dental team, amongst whom was notably Desmond Hayton-Williams, a highly influential oral and maxillofacial consultant from the John Radcliffe Hospital in Oxford. Following a full assessment of my clinical roles, responsibilities and service provision, the visitors recommended that my post be regraded as a consultant.

Already, in 1963, a newly created consultant post had been established in the North-West Metropolitan region of London, and Jimmy Leitch was appointed as consultant at Watford, Mount Vernon and Barnet General Hospital, succeeding at the latter hospital Jack Pilbeam who had retired in 1962. I was now delighted to have nearby the support and advice of an experienced colleague who had also been senior registrar at the Central Middlesex and Mount Vernon hospitals, a leading plastic and burns unit in the region.

The upgrading proposal took time to implement, but it was gratifying that my successor, Nina Shotts, a doubly qualified oral surgeon (a doctor and a dentist like my husband) was appointed consultant at Highlands in 1967, Charles Dundas undertaking a locum consultant post in the interim period.

Amongst the usual collection of a lifetime of trinkets residing in my china cabinet at home there is a pair of hospital scissors. These cut the ribbon when Nina kindly asked me back to Highlands to open refurbished dental accommodation. However, later in the 1990s I was delighted to open the state-of-the-art dental department at Chase Farm Hospital in Enfield where Nina transferred her clinics when Highlands as a hospital was closed in 1995. In its place is a flourishing Highland Village, with the grand administrative block and pavilions converted into much sought after apartments. Weathered over the years, the black pavilion number ingrained in the keystone of the arch entrance to the apartments remains. I wonder if the present residents realise the tales that could be told of yesteryear?

Gordon and I had decided that my dental career would be put on hold while I had our baby and so I handed in my notice to retire from Highlands. In the early 1960s it was still regarded as unusual for professional women to return straight away to work after giving birth to a baby and paid maternity leave did not exist. Indeed, women in the armed forces and the diplomatic service were obliged to resign when they got married, let alone when they became pregnant. The view was supported by my mother, and generally by my parents' generation, certainly until the child was old enough to go to school.

Ted Sycamore, who had also recently been appointed a consultant at the neighbouring North Middlesex hospital, was outspoken about the move I was contemplating. 'Don't resign: if you step off the ladder you will never get back on the same rung when you return.' This, to my mind, was a negative view. I had surely proved my worth in the two years at Highlands. The post had been upgraded to consultant; the local practitioners were highly supportive of my work and innovations. Theo Schofield provided me with a glowing reference to be used for future job applications so, of course, I would find it easy to step back on the ladder, and even possibly on a higher rung.

Was this to be the misplaced optimism or arrogance of youth? Without a second thought, I left my job at the hospital and spent the month of May gently hoeing in the garden, patiently awaiting the arrival of our first child.

Chapter 7

Taking time out

'It's a girl'! truly magical words to be heard by a first-time mother, deemed to be old by the medical fraternity at the grand age of 28. Our daughter, Pamela Elizabeth, chose to arrive on a Sunday evening, on the last day of May and in the middle of a most spectacular thunderstorm. Soon she was tucked up in her cot by the attentive midwifery staff at the London Hospital and parked safely alongside my bed. It was not long before admiring nurses, medical and dental colleagues were peering into the cot. Bearing in mind that Gordon's hair was fair and mine a very dark brown, they all screamed with delight when they spotted the auburn-haired baby. 'So, Margaret, tell us who the milkman was that week?' After considerable repetition from members of the family and well-meaning friends, the joke did wear thin. Throughout Pamela's early years, strangers would stop us in the street, stroke her hair and remark to me, 'Oh, what gorgeous coloured hair. Isn't she lucky?' Pamela and I found this unsolicited attention embarrassing, and I for one vowed not to embrace this adulation of infant parts. Just why should hair be singled out? Perhaps perfectly formed ears should also command admiration and respect.

In the early 1960s, fathers were not encouraged to be present at the birth and paternity leave had not even been thought about. However, in line with common practice I thoroughly enjoyed my ten-day 'holiday' in hospital, which ensured the luxury of learning from highly trained midwives the dos and don'ts of baby care, as well as successfully mastering the London Hospital culture of 'Breast is Best'.

Sleep deprivation is one of my abiding memories of the first few weeks after arriving home with our bundle of joy when the day, and indeed night, revolved around the demands of Pamela, who seemed to have an insatiable appetite and a desire to survive on minimal sleep. It is salutary to watch succeeding generations enduring these broken nights and broken routines. Despite the medical advances in child care and explosion of nursery equipment available to them, 'baby rules – okay' is still the mantra of today for most households. But as the months passed, nothing prepared us for the effects of the appearance of a florid countenance, excessive dribbling and contorting of the face in pain, all accompanied by much screaming and disturbed sleeping. However, the diagnosis was swiftly dispensed by wise grandparents: 'Pamela's teething.' I was suddenly reminded of the comment from the health visitor during the antenatal classes when she discovered my occupation – 'A dentist – that's good, you can tell us all about teething.' The remark at the time had sent me scurrying to consult the leading textbooks on children's dentistry, but I found all of them dismissed the topic in less than half a page, so I had concluded that it was considered by the experts as a non-event.

Perhaps there was more to teething than reported? I was experiencing some of the symptoms at first hand and decided to explore the topic in more detail. The luxury of a web-search did not exist but, as a British Dental Association member, I was able to contact their library, which is renowned as the repository of the largest collection of dental books in Europe. Indeed, when the first female dentist, Lilian Lindsay, qualified in 1895, she subsequently became assistant librarian at the BDA. She had the novel idea of collecting published papers and magazine cuttings on specific topics and assembling them into a package distinctive in its navy blue, A5, hard-backed cover with the subject title inscribed in white lettering. Fortunately, Lilian Lindsay had compiled one on 'teething', and I was sure that once I had read the contents thoroughly, all my questions would be fully answered.

My confidence was soon shattered, because neither in the included articles from the medical literature, nor in those papers from the dental press, were there any details of a scientific study. Rather, the papers referred to accumulated experience, based at best on clinical observation, strong parental views and a goodly selection of myths and folklore. I found out that Hippocrates in 460–370 BC wrote in some detail on the subject in his seminal work entitled, *On Dentition*, while, in the UK, the first textbook on paediatrics was written in 1530 by Thomas Pharye, and he termed teething 'the breeding of teeth'. His reported symptoms make for interesting reading: 'the child is sore vexed with sundry disease and pains, as swelling of ye gummes and jaws, unquiet crying, fevers, cramps, palsies, fluxes, reumes and other infirmities', a list not unfamiliar to us today.

I also discovered, much to my surprise, that as recently as 1906 a total of 2,175 infant deaths were assigned to teething in the Registrar General's annual report. As I read through the literature, diversity of opinion was clearly evident. Some people stoutly maintained that teething was responsible for a great many disturbances, both in general health and locally in the mouth. Others believed that children, when their teeth were erupting, did become irritable, lost their appetites and experienced disturbed patterns of sleep. Finally, there were those who claimed that the eruption of primary or deciduous teeth caused no disturbance at all: 'Teething produces nothing but teeth,' they boldly pronounced. This attitude seemed to me to be of little comfort when a baby appeared 'out of sorts'. Suddenly, it dawned on me that, as many of my peer groups were becoming mothers, I was uniquely placed to test the hypothesis that eruption of primary teeth can be accompanied by certain local and general complications. But where or how to start?

First, I sought to enlist the support of Cherry Goad, my cheerful Irish health visitor who had sowed the seed for this avenue of research. Obviously, I could not confine the study only to my friends, because I needed to have a representative sample of the population, embracing all the designated social classes. Therefore the next step was to obtain permission from the medical officer of health for the Borough of Enfield so that I could attend the welfare clinics and enlist some of the mothers into my teething study. Sensing that I was embarking on a substantial piece of work, I consulted Professor Geoffrey Slack, director of the dental health study unit at the London Hospital, who advised, even at this early stage, that I should register my study for the highest degree awarded by the University of London: Master of Dental Surgery. So within a couple of months, my germ of an idea had blossomed into a full-scale research project. 'Taking time out' seemed to be deferred. However, this project fitted comfortably with my home-based status because it was possible, with baby-sitting arrangements in place, to travel a couple of miles to spend an afternoon interviewing parents at one of the two clinics involved. I found it especially easy to establish a rapport with other parents as I was identified as one of them, rather than as a dentist.

With great relief, it took only one year from June 1965 to enlist a total of 275 mothers willing to record the necessary data for their infants at the time each primary tooth (baby tooth) came through the gum. This meant a substantial commitment from the mothers for nearly three years but, fortunately, there was great enthusiasm to take part, many expressing delight that someone was at last taking teething seriously, and they all believed that their experiences should be invaluable to future generations of mothers. Information gathered ranged from baby's general health, including the incidence of commonly reported symptoms, such as irritability, disturbance to sleeping patterns, reduced appetite and intestinal upsets. Additionally, data was gathered about local symptoms and mothers were encouraged to phone me if their son or daughter presented with a facial rash or a lump on the gum around the erupting tooth so that I could make a swift visit to their home to take a photograph for use later in illustrating my thesis.

Aware that many parents do resort to giving their baby a teething ring, rusks, or Bickiepegs to chew on, I also asked a further question about these teething aids, as well as enquiring about the use of a teething jelly or lotion to rub on the gum around the erupting tooth. Thankfully, the project was well underway by September 1966, when a delightful addition to our family arrived, Colin Robert Seward, who proved to be a popular playmate for Pamela, now an enquiring two and a half year old. In view of our expanding family I was very fortunate that my study population was locally based, and it was a bonus that I could recruit Colin into the project. Unsurprisingly, this action increased my already good rapport with the mothers.

Then a bombshell. Gordon was told by his superiors that, unless he took leave of absence from the hospital and went abroad to study at leading oral surgery centres, he had little chance of promotion to professor. This seemed a harsh prediction because he was already gaining an enviable reputation as a meticulous surgeon with an encyclopaedic knowledge, and an innate skill to master and introduce new techniques to improve patient care. Naturally, I did not relish a separation for even a few months but I was only too aware how much hard work and dedication my husband had expended to attain his current position as Reader in the University of London. To fall at this last hurdle would be a great disappointment for everyone concerned and a total waste of years of investment of time and money. After qualifying as a dentist at the London Hospital, Gordon had completed his obligatory two years' National Service and then embarked on a further five-year course to train as a medical doctor. To fund these medical studies he had worked in the evenings as a dentist in the practice of an Old Londoner, C. W. F. Thomas, nearby in Hackney. So it was without question that in the spring of 1967, Gordon, funded by the Waldorf Astor Foundation, and granted leave of absence by the Governors of the London Hospital, departed for an eight-week visit to America, first spending time with Dr Fred Henny at the Henry Ford Hospital and Dental School in Detroit, followed by time at the dental school in Ann Arbor. Next, he moved on to two dental schools in Canada, Montreal and Toronto.

His absence abroad coincided with the publication in the *British Dental Journal* of my article, bringing attention to the importance of dental health education during the antenatal period of pregnancy which until then had been given scant attention. As a consequence, I received invitations to talk to various women's groups about my work, and this usually took me out and about locally, which in turn focussed more attention on my teething work. This helped, I am sure, to secure an impressive response rate from the study participants of 84 per cent.

After two months in the USA, Gordon returned home, but just as Colin and Pamela were getting reacquainted with their father he was off again, this time to Switzerland, to spend a month with Professor Hugo Obwegeser at his world famous oral surgery unit in Zurich. His homecoming was, however, particularly sweet as he brought for Pamela and Colin an intriguing set of building blocks called 'Matador', which soon became a firm favourite and the envy of their friends. Thankfully, all this study abroad brought its reward when, in 1968, the University of London conferred the title of Professor of Oral Surgery on Gordon Robert Seward and, needless to say, there were great celebrations all around.

Now, it was time for me to redouble my efforts and begin to write up my research findings. The amount of data I had amassed was daunting, because it represented a total of 4,480 separate, and individual, eruptions of the primary teeth. My battery-operated desk calculator, a thoughtful birthday present from my husband, was completely inadequate for the task. However, I was fortunate to be awarded time on the sophisticated IBM 360 computer at the University College Computer Centre, with the statistical evaluation being overseen by a talented statistician, Paul Goddard. Thirty years later, the use of computer programs for this task is taken for granted but at that time I realised I was privileged to see the potential of computers at first hand and enjoy an experience which raised my awareness and also led to my commitment to computerisation in future work situations.

For nearly three hours each morning, while Pamela was at nursery school, I would sit writing at the dining table, with Colin alongside amusing himself happily by running his cars up and down the slopes or bridges built from my reference books. I do harbour still a sense of guilt, because Colin's vocabulary was severely limited to 'yes', 'no' and 'thank you' until his third birthday. It may be that he enjoyed the benefit of an elder sister who could speak on his behalf, but I think it is more likely that it was the hours of silence he endured while I beavered away at my thesis that led to his reticence to speak. However, handwriting was not appropriate for the finished manuscript and I was lucky to be able to recruit my bridesmaid friend, Joan Fountain, now herself at home expecting and so with time to type the wax stencils from which the four copies for the University could be produced. This was a labour-intensive procedure, now changed by the arrival of the 'all singing and dancing' photocopiers and computers.

Due to my frequent visits to the welfare clinics, the mothers held no inhibitions in probing me for information, and a recurring question related to the effectiveness of the various teething lotions and gels on the market. However, there was a dearth of scientific evidence, so was this another avenue for research? Further, if I could complete it in time, it would be possible to submit it along with my thesis, but as I was unemployed I realised quickly that I needed financial support for any new enterprise. Wondering if a pharmaceutical company might be interested in the project, I wrote to W. Woodward's Ltd in South London, the well-known maker of gripe water. I was pleasantly surprised when I received a reply by return from the chief chemist, inviting me to meet him and discuss my idea further. I found the tour of the factory fascinating and enjoyed thoroughly my first business lunch. This was my initiation into the commercial world and the beginning of a harmonious relationship, as they not only provided me with the necessary supply of the research materials for the clinical trial of Woodward's teething drops, but also awarded me a fee as a professional adviser and a grant to the dental health study unit at the London Hospital, because Professor Slack continued in his role as my supervisor.

After the findings of the trial had been published in the *British Dental Journal*, I was greatly flattered by the comment in the editorial in a subsequent issue of the highly respected *British Medical Journal*. 'This was a good, simple but scientific study of a common problem and it has given guidance to the doctor who wants to provide relief for a baby with painful teething.'

The experience of fruitful cooperation with a trade company again expanded my horizons away from the narrow environs of hospital and academic dentistry. It was the beginning of a lifetime of respect for and enjoyment in working with colleagues in the dental trade or industry, who sadly can so often be treated with contempt rather than the cooperation they deserve.

On occasion the Royal Mail can bring extremely exciting news, and this is exactly what happened on a cold winter's day in 1968. An invitation arrived for Gordon to tour Singapore, Australia and New Zealand in the summer of 1969, as the guest lecturer of the National Dental Associations of those countries. The rider in the letter was of particular interest. 'If you come on your own we will cover business-class travel, but if you want to bring your wife we will provide you with two economy tickets.' Gordon readily forsook the luxurious mode of travel in order to take me, but we were concerned about leaving our children for nearly three months as neither set of our elderly parents enjoyed good health. After being reassured by Pamela's primary schoolteacher that her schooling would not suffer from missing half of the autumn term, we decided to go as a family. We have never regretted this decision for, instead of following the staid sightseeing routes, we visited beaches and zoos, cuddled koalas, watched kangaroos with their joeys on board hopping at speed across the bush, peered in water tanks at the antics of the duck-billed platypus and watched for a glimpse of the nocturnal kiwi as it scurried out of the light of day for the comfort of its dark habitat.

Gordon had an enormous amount of preparation to undertake, giving 123 lectures during the 68-day tour. The format in each venue was similar and consisted of a two and a half-day seminar, which gave me and the children ample time to explore most of the capital cities: Singapore, Perth, Adelaide, Melbourne, Sydney, Dunedin, Christchurch, Wellington, Palmerston North, Napier, Rotorua and Auckland. Gordon travelled on alone to Brisbane and Townsville as I had settled for a weekend with the children at the nearby Sydney seaside resort of Manley, to provide a respite from continued attention and to get back some normality to their lives. We all became veterans of air travel, clocking up 70.55 hours in the air, crossing the date line twice, and travelling a total of 30,233 miles. This was made possible by limited car travel, twenty-one journeys by air in eleven different types of aircraft and, when sleeping on the ground, in twenty different beds. This factual information was recorded in a scrapbook and diary of the trip, which took the form of twice-weekly airmail letters to my father, who was now living on his own as my mother had died suddenly in the June before our departure.

Details of the trip could fill a book on its own, but here I will limit myself to the defining moments, which undoubtedly influenced my future specific areas of dental interest. First I will recount the flight to Singapore for an intriguing reason, which will soon be revealed. Our departure from Heathrow was on 18 August, mid-afternoon, on the well-used Boeing 707. On each side of the aisle was a row of three seats, so Pamela, Colin and I sat in one row, and Gordon in the seat on the other side of the aisle next to a young girl of 12, flying out on her own to spend her summer holiday with her parents who lived in Singapore. 'You look a nice family,' chirped the air hostess. Could you please look after Jill when we are in transit in Rome?' – a duty which we were delighted to accept. Compared with journeys by air today, the designated route must appear circuitous but it is worth remembering that the later preferred carrier for long-haul flights is the Boeing 747, which had only started flying a few months before we went, and Concorde had only just passed its first half-hour test flight in June that year. First, we headed for Zurich and then it was Rome, where we chatted to Jill as we toured the transit lounge and duty-free shops. After a further six hours of flying we arrived at Karachi and, although we were allowed off, it was now well into sleeping time so, seeing the military presence, with soldiers guarding not only every exit but also every wheel, we decided to stay put. This we also did when we touched down in Calcutta in the midst of a monsoon storm. Finally, as dusk fell for the second night, we alighted in Singapore, saying farewell to Jill, while we were whisked away by Gordon's colleagues and deposited safely in the delightfully colonial Chequers Hotel in Thomson Road, away from the noisy bustle of the centre of Singapore.

Some eight years later our family was taking an Easter break at the Waterford Lodge Hotel in Mudeford, a secluded seaside resort on the south coast, near to the New Forest. After we had finished breakfast on the day of departure, an attractive young lady enquired of Gordon, 'Were you aboard a flight to Singapore in 1969?' Rather taken aback he nodded and the lady continued, 'I am the little girl, Jill, whom you kindly took under your wing, and I am so pleased that I can now say a proper thank you to you all.' We were astounded that she had recognised us! 'You see, I recognised you all by your daughter's beautiful auburn hair.' Surely this distinctive feature must be without equal.

Although in Australia and New Zealand my husband was the guest lecturer, once the local press discovered that I too was a qualified dentist, I was in great demand for interviews for the local newspapers or regional radio stations, or on TV channels. This unexpected interest arose because in that part of the world it was taken for granted that a dentist would be a man, while a woman was more likely to contemplate dental nursing or dental therapy as a career. The fact that I possessed a fellowship in dental surgery, which was rare in New Zealand at that time, added even more to the media interest.

My recent research on teething and my talks on dental health education during the antenatal period were popular topics for discussion at the interviews, and seemed to produce fertile ground for the strap-line editors: 'Yes, Mother – There is Such a Trial as Teething' ran the *Dunedin Herald*, which complemented its generous coverage with a fantastic photograph taken by them of Pamela (5) and Colin (3) in the home of Dr Donaldson. Elaine herself was one of the exceptions, a lady dentist, so well able to understand and help me cope with the intense media interest.

Another interview that I can vividly recall was in the studio in Adelaide. Just before I went on air I heard the announcer say, 'Welcome to the first day of spring' – to me this proved the country was upside down as the date was 1 September.

There is no doubt that this exposure to media, which I confess I enjoyed, provided exceptional experience and allowed me an insight into the importance of cordial cooperation with the news seekers and, I am sure, built my confidence by enabling me to deal with TV and radio interviews, which later became an integral part of some of my jobs. On this tour there was also the awakening of interest in the use of dental auxiliaries and this stirred my commitment to raise awareness of their unique contribution to providing oral health, and to mitigate against many of the then current misgivings and misconceptions, rife in the UK, surrounding their training and utilisation within the dental profession.

My first visit relating to the training of dental auxiliaries abroad was while in Adelaide, to the School of Dental Therapy, the brainchild of Hugh Kennare, a lecturer at the dental school. While the course lasted for two years, just as at the experimental training school at New Cross in England, it was more comprehensive than the latter, providing training in pinned amalgams, extracting all primary teeth, permitting injections of local anaesthetics, and operating exclusively with the use of rubber dam. The patients were children: either they were brought in by coach to the dental school or treated in clinics specially built in the grounds of their schools.

In Wellington, New Zealand, I visited both the training school and the specially built school clinics. There were three schools throughout the country, training each year over 200 school dental nurses (known in the UK as New Zealand school dental nurses). It was like stepping back in time to watch, in Wellington, sixty-five nurses in the conservation room, working in the standing position with patients seated on rather uncomfortable-looking wooden chairs. Of particular interest to watch was their expert handling of a most difficult material, copper amalgam, which was predominantly used as a filling material. During the time that I was visiting the schools there was great excitement because the school dental nurse scheme was celebrating its 50th anniversary. Each school clinic throughout the country was uniformly equipped, and the qualified school dental nurse wore a distinctive white tunic, white shoes, and a red cardigan. Uniquely, the dental nurse was treated as a member of the school staff and was under the jurisdiction of the head teacher of the school. The integration resulted in appreciation of their work by people outwith the profession, so that the status and attraction of a two-year course, compared to the five-year training to become a dentist, undoubtedly contributed to the dearth of women in the dental profession.

In the middle of October, we arrived home and the excitement of three months travelling was over. We had been fêted in every city, dined, and welcomed by a fruit basket in each hotel room, with delicious contents previously unknown: tamarillos, kiwi fruits and paw-paw. Our children had taken in their stride jumping in and out of strange beds, and boarding planes as though they were the normal mode of transport, but they exclaimed on arriving back home in Cotswold Way, 'Can we stay in this hotel longer? These are better toys.' The primary school headteacher had been proved correct: 'the trip would be an education without equal' – and indeed it was, for all of us. However, we felt unsettled. Gordon had been invited to apply for chairs in oral surgery in Australia and New Zealand. But while the open-air way of life with beaches, barbecues and sun held its attraction for us with a young family, we did not feel able to desert our elderly parents, or deprive our children of grandparents, so, instead, we moved house from our modest and comfortable residence in Cotswold Way, Enfield, to the larger and attractive Tudor House in Beech Hill Avenue, Hadley Wood, Barnet, with three lawns and a spinney backing on to the Hadley Wood golf course, although the interior especially was in much need of renovation: plenty to keep our minds and hands well occupied.

Then there was another diversion. Before I had gone abroad, I had submitted my thesis, with the grandiose title of 'A survey and statistical evaluation of the complications attributed to the eruption of the primary dentition' to the University of London, and now I received the summons to attend for a viva voce. I read up the relevant literature again and, with great relief and delight, I was awarded the Master in Dental Surgery. I also learnt, to my surprise, that I was the first woman to gain this degree. Never again should it be said that 'teething produces nothing but teeth'.

On hearing of my success, a dental friend locally, Judy Wicks, who worked at clinics in Hoddesdon and Hertford, said that the chief dental officer of Hertfordshire was looking for a dentist to undertake four sessions a week at a clinic in Cheshunt, some four miles from where we lived. A meeting with Mr Millett was arranged and, after a few preliminary questions he enquired, 'Can you start next week, please?' I was taken aback. I had not held a dental handpiece for five years. Sensing my concern he added, 'It's just like riding a bike – you never really forget how to drill.'

Poor patients! Was this really the way I was going to return to dentistry?

Chapter 8

A gentle return

'This is Mrs Seward, our new dentist,' announced Mrs George, my dental surgery assistant, as my first patient Tracy was towed reluctantly by her mother towards the dental chair. Mrs George's brief introduction obviously did not satisfy Tracy's mother, who viewed me as far too young to be properly qualified, so she settled herself into a chair tucked in the corner of the surgery, intent on keeping an eye on me.

'Oh dear,' I thought to myself, 'is there to be a confrontation on my first day?' I had been taught that during treatment parents should be left in the comfort of the waiting room. Fortunately, Tracy's mother acceded to my request to retreat outside, and the visit went without mishap. A successful relationship was sealed with the gift of a coloured sticker for Tracy's jumper, depicting a smiling crocodile with shiny white teeth.

By the end of my three-hour long morning session, seeing some ten patients, I was exhausted. Yes, Mr Millett was correct in that the basic skills, albeit somewhat rusty, were still there. More worrying to me was that there were areas where my knowledge was grossly lacking, for example, the advances in the technique of restoring teeth, and the understanding of how to use the many new filling materials on the market. Was trial and error on the job really the way for the patients, let alone the dentist, to learn? Although there was no colleague on the premises, because there was only one dental surgery in the health clinic, I was fortunate to have two very experienced dental surgery assistants, Mrs George and Mrs Moody, who had grown-up families and a wealth of experience to impart. In the early 1970s, only one in eight of the UK dental practitioners was female, and they were likely to be found working in the scantily-regarded school dental service, notorious too for low salaries. Inevitably, when a parent of a new patient entered the surgery, the parent would turn to the oldest lady for information. Thus it was to my assistant and not to myself that they turned, especially as we were all addressed as 'Mrs'. The use of the courtesy title 'Doctor' for dentists, which is commonplace today, would have saved many mistaken identities and tedious explanations.

Cheshunt was a happy clinic, seemingly well organised, with a stream of patients to treat. Each Friday, at the end of my clinic, I would drive to the nearest 'Little Chef' restaurant along the A10, and rendezvous with my friend and fellow dentist, Judy Wicks, who worked down the road at Hoddesdon. However, I always seemed to be the first to arrive because my last patient on an otherwise busy Friday morning seemed to have the happy knack of cancelling. Finally, sensing that there must be more than coincidence at work, I made enquiries of my dental assistant. 'Mrs Seward, it is an imaginary patient in case we over-run because I must not miss my hair appointment at 12.30 p.m.' came the honest reply. Needless to say, there were some changes in this creative working practice, but it was also a useful learning exercise for me.

I will be forever grateful to Mrs Doris Moody who instructed me in the mysterious art of school inspections. She not only had a grown-up family and understood the needs of young mothers, but was also a Councillor and past Mayor of Hoddesdon, so was known by and knew everyone. This certainly paved the way as we went into schools, meeting head teachers and members of staff. I quickly realised that the arrival of the school dentist and entourage was not greeted with universal acclaim, rather as a distinct diversion from the work in hand. My first school visit was to a junior school for ages seven to eleven year olds. We were ushered into a small room, crammed mainly with filing cabinets, but with enough room to wedge a chair and a small table on which to lay out the tools of the trade: mouth mirror, probe, and tongue spatula. Additional light was provided by an Anglepoise lamp. As time passed, and more visits were made, I discovered this provision was luxurious, compared to later situations which included draughty corridors in wintertime. After a rudimentary inspection, a decision was made as to whether it was necessary to refer the youngster to the clinic for further assessment and treatment or whether the youngster needed to be seen by the orthodontist. At the mid-morning break, we were hurried in to the staff room for tea and a delectable sticky bun. To my horror, I discovered that these treats were not confined to members of staff, as I witnessed tray loads of these carcinogenic items being descended on by the children in a manner akin to a plague of locusts. Just where did dental health education (as it was called then) fit into the picture? Naturally, I protested, but the teachers politely explained to me that many of the children were dispatched off to school by working parents without breakfast and that the only way to ensure the youngsters' attention in lessons was to provide, at a nominal charge, a carbohydrate infill. I quickly realised that one's desire to 'practise what you preach' in relation to diet and oral health has to be tempered with a modicum of practicality.

As a result of this experience of school inspections, my heart sank whenever I was told it was time for a visit to school x, y or z. How could such a cursory glance at the teeth be of benefit to a youngster, beyond the fun provided by having lessons interrupted by the school dentist. Fortunately, the chief dental officer, Arthur Millett, was aware of all these shortcomings and launched the first 'oral health campaign' in the county, with the catchy title of 'Healthy Teeth for Herts' imprinted on a glossy red heart on an adhesive backing. As the slogan was also emblazoned on T-shirts, balloons, pens and other products, the imagination of youngsters, parents and teachers was fired, and a demonstrable change in tooth brushing habits and oral health was shown by a survey conducted at the end of this high-profile initiative. Sadly, a follow-up twelve months later showed that old habits had begun to return. To me this proved that however imaginative a dental health education programme may seem to be, the effect is not long lasting and, instead, it is necessary to have continuous reinforcement of any change in lifestyle.

Within six months of taking up my post at Cheshunt Clinic I felt I was getting the hang of drilling and filling teeth, undertaking school dental inspections, and conquering extracting teeth for ten or more children during the weekly general anaesthetic (gas) session, overseen by a consultant anaesthetist. The catchment area for the clinic in Blindmans Lane, a name, I felt most unfortunate, included many less well off Italian families, who worked in the nursery glasshouses which filled the Lea Valley Region. In the Second World War, Italian prisoners of war were detained in the South Mimms area of Hertfordshire, and at the end of the conflict some decided to work in the market gardens. As a result it was not unusual for a small child to arrive for treatment accompanied by a mother or grandmother who could not speak a word of English, and it always amused me that many young patients had to shoulder the responsibility to translate my request to the guardian for permission to treat them.

It was not long before the bush telegraph was activated, and the local practitioners learnt that I had been in charge of the dental unit at Highlands Hospital. The result was that I was sent patients with oral surgery problems, and I acted as an unofficial referral point for problem patients from neighbouring clinics. This provided me with the welcome opportunity to brush up on my dormant oral surgical skills, although I was still very uneasy at this haphazard approach to retraining. As a caring profession, surely it could do better and positively assist colleagues who intended to return to practice?

Also working at the clinic was a dental auxiliary, later called a dental therapist, who carried out treatment on children to a prescription provided by the dentist. She (at that time all were women) deeply impressed me with the high quality care she gave to the most difficult children. This early contact with auxiliaries, and respect for their contribution to oral health care, left me with an abiding wish to resolve the many inequalities which they experienced. I also wanted to raise the profession's awareness of this undervalued dental ancillary personnel; the dental team concept had yet to be discovered.

During my visit some three years previously to the School Dental Nurses Training premises in Wellington, New Zealand, I had been extremely impressed at the ease with which they had used copper amalgam as a filling material to insert into the deciduous or primary teeth of children. In the UK, silver amalgam was the material of choice, but in New Zealand copper amalgam was highly favoured, due to exhibiting less corrosive properties. So I decided to find out its potential for myself. I sent off for a trial pack of copper amalgam which contained not only the pellets of copper but also a crucible at the end of a long handle, in which the pellets had to be melted over a gas flame. I quickly discovered it was a highly sensitive procedure, and I ended up with strange shapes of molten metal but not in their correct location, namely the teeth! I had failed miserably, but as a consequence my admiration of the clinical mastery shown by those New Zealand dental nurses increased by leaps and bounds.

I slowly began to feel a degree of professional fulfilment working at the clinic, and my family commitments seemed to fit in well alongside the sessional working, although I was aware that I needed to improve my knowledge of children's dentistry. So I joined the south-east group of the British Paedodontic Society which met monthly from October to June at the Royal Dental Hospital in London's Leicester Square, and reputedly in the very room where the famous Ciro's nightclub operated in the 1950s. The talks varied from clinical topics to research papers, but of even greater importance was the fact that I got acquainted with colleagues working in the specialist field of children's dentistry. Unfortunately, postgraduate courses or courses leading to a diploma in child dental health or an M.Sc. in paediatric dentistry did not exist at that time.

Within a year of attending these meetings on a regular basis, a volunteer was sought to stand for the post of honorary secretary of the group, because Stanley Parkin of University College Hospital had completed his distinguished three-year term of office. By now, I was gaining confidence in my new-found field of children's dentistry, and so indicated that I was willing to let my name go forward. Thus I found myself elected honorary secretary, a post I held for three years until 1975. This was my first taste of the workings of a serious committee, learning again on the job the role of secretary, and observing not only the chairman at work, but also the chemistry and dynamics at work among committee members. I cannot recommend strongly enough this sort of exposure, which gave me a grounding in basic committee and chairing skills, which have played such an important role in my life within and outside dentistry. The message is clear: to join local or national organisations is not sufficient; full participation and involvement are the only way to make progress.

Once a year, a national meeting was held when the members of the regional groups came together. These were family-oriented occasions and Gordon, Pamela and Colin would come along to explore, over the weekend, intriguing city venues like York, Sheffield and Edinburgh. During my secretaryship our son and daughter, now ten and eight years of age, had become proficient 'envelope stuffers' of circulars, which went out to members of the south-east group of the Society. It was enlightening for them to put faces to names, as well as meeting offspring of other colleagues, and no doubt share the downsides of being dentists' children.

One day, as secretary, I received in the post a call for clinical or research papers, table demonstrations or films, to be presented at the International Children's Dentistry Association, planned to be held in Paris in the summer of 1973. I considered that submitting a film based on my teething research would be a good idea. The drawback was that, as yet, I had not made one! So I set about exploring methods, not only of how to make a film, but also how to finance its production. I was convinced that a film on this topic was needed because I was frequently asked by mothers and health visitors for up-to-date information and advice on teething. Literature was scant on the subject and audio-visual aids non-existent. I recalled that while researching the various treatments for teething there was a local firm in Welwyn Garden City called Bickiepegs, whose teething biscuits were made of flour and wheatgerm with no added sugar or sweetener. They had been developed by Dr Harry Campbell, a paediatrician, at the time when he was editor of the respected medical journal, *The Lancet*, and in 1925 Dr Campbell had, with Miss Millington Lymn, a dietician, founded the firm 'Bickiepegs Ltd.' These teething biscuits were peg-like in shape with a small hole at the top end through which a ribbon could be threaded: blue for a boy and pink for a girl. Today this colour-coding is dispensed with, because it was soon discovered that boys and girls are not born in equal numbers, so there were uneven sales. The ribbon, irrespective of colour, was crucial, because it secured the teething biscuit to the infants' clothing, enabling them to grab it from the age of three to four months. This they did when wanting to chew or suck on something to relieve the pressure on the gums from the erupting teeth.

Imagine my delight, when I received a prompt response from the managing director of the company, Norman Miller, who wrote on 17 November 1972, 'I am most interested to learn of your proposed lecture in Paris and we should be very pleased to consider having a small film produced. Do you think you could give me some rough idea of how much it would cost to sponsor, or what you have in mind?'

What a positive reaction! I was on my way. After preparing an outline of the film I was thrilled to receive £2,000 to make a 15-minute 16 mm colour film with sound. Thirty plus years ago, this was a generous sum. But, after the euphoria, it was down to the hard work. I contacted a local film maker in nearby Boreham Wood, Stewart Hardy Films Ltd., who was engaged to prepare for me a 'shooting script'. Then permission was obtained from the Medical Officers of Health to shoot film sequences in the local authority clinics in Enfield and Hertfordshire. There was no shortage of volunteers wanting to take part, parents and infants, but also health visitors and doctors sensing a chance to achieve stardom status, and then perhaps contemplate a change of career. The first few scenes needed to be taken in a home environment, so the friend who had stoically typed my thesis on the topic, Joan Fountain, volunteered her home for use, in nearby Little Heath, Potters Bar. The film crew duly arrived on the appointed day with all their paraphernalia, which took up a great deal of the living/dining room area. A bedroom was designated for the nappy-changing scene, the kitchen identified as the place in which Joan's son Ian, aged four, was to take a fluoride drink out of a slanting cup, the Doidy Cup, (another Bickiepeg product), and the bathroom for my daughter Pamela, aged nine, to give a demonstration of effective tooth brushing. Pamela was thrilled to have an afternoon off from Hadley Wood Junior School, all with the blessing of her teachers.

Then, just as filming was getting underway, there was the realisation that we were without the man necessary for our opening shot, who was to be seen receiving a phone call from his very excited wife, announcing the arrival of baby's first tooth. We desperately needed a man's ear, but there was only one man in the room and he was operating the camera. Then, suddenly, as if on cue, a man's face appeared outside the window, precariously perched on a ladder. He started to clean the windows, and peered into this normally quiet household, now invaded with noisy infants and chattering mums in every room. With the promise of a 'cuppa tea' he was enticed to come down from his ladder and come into the hallway to hold the phone to his ear to take the imaginary wife's call. 'I don't know what's going on 'ere,' he growled. 'Hope there's no funny business with these ladies?' With the filming over, he beat a hasty retreat with his ladders – the rest of the windows didn't get cleaned that day!

The final scene of the film was to show a young child being introduced to the dentist at an early age, so Ian Fountain came to the Cheshunt clinic to be greeted by one of my colleagues, Harold Mercer, for his first dental examination, and ride in the chair. Today, Ian Fountain is a world-class concert pianist and the youngest winner of the Arthur Rubinstein International Piano Masters Competition when he was 19. It is fortunate that no agents or contracts were required for media coverage in those early days.

It took almost as long to decide on a title for the film as to make it. Various suggestions included; 'Teething Troubles'; 'Toby's First Teeth', and 'Robert has a Tooth'. But none seemed to inspire. Then a variant of 'Nothing but the Truth' became 'Nothing but the Tooth', and for this there was universal approval; we all felt it was a winner, which it proved to be. The film was completed in association with the Royal Society of Medicine Film Unit, who were also responsible for converting it into the video-film, which since has been translated into several languages.

So, in 1973, with only a couple of weeks before the appointed date of 10 July, the film was ready for showing at the 4th International Congress of Dentistry in Paris. Imagine my delight after the showing when I received a letter from the Italian Paedodontist, Professor Luigi Capozzi. 'Please send me a copy of the excellent film so I can show it at the October meeting of the Società di Odontoiatria Infantile to be held in Rome.' This was followed by an avalanche of requests for copies of the film from as far afield as Australia, New Zealand and USA. The bandwagon continued to roll with a screening during the FDI Annual World Congress in 1974, held at London's South Bank Arts Centre. This was the first time that a scientific programme had included dental health education promotional literature and films. Finally, the following February, came an invitation to show the film at the Old Londoners' postgraduate meeting, which really was rewarding as this was my Alma Mater.

The staff at the health clinic were badgering me to have an opportunity to see themselves on the screen, and Norman Miller came to my assistance again when he agreed to sponsor a private screening for the participants and provide an informal buffet reception. Looking now at the receipts from J. West Caterers, the finger buffet was 50 pence per head and VAT was at 10 per cent. A glass of Emva Cream Sherry cost 10 pence per glass and the Spanish Sauternes 20 pence per glass, so there was no excuse after 'wining and dining' not to enjoy the special viewing at the Prescott Hall in Cheshunt.

The preview was a great success with a guest list unashamedly compiled to include the great and good in paediatric dentistry, especially Professor Gerry Winter, Professor of Children's Dentistry at the Eastman Dental Hospital, the director of nursing in Hertfordshire, Cherry Goad, the health visitor, the Medical Officers of Health, and all those who had given permission, advice and encouragement along the way. The local and national press were in attendance, as was the executive editor of *Dental Practice*, Mary Newing, with whom I have remained firm friends over the years. The greatest disappointment was that our sponsors, now relocated from Welwyn Garden City to Aberdeen, were fogbound, and all flights grounded for the day. 'If you have time to spare – fly by air,' Norman advised me, when he phoned with his apologies. This is a maxim I have remembered and repeated on many occasions!

There was more excitement to come when a certificate of educational commendation arrived from the British Life Assurance Trust for Health Education, in conjunction with the British Medical Association. The publicity resulted in many invitations to talk on teething, and to show the film not only to groups of mothers and Women's Institutes but also British Dental Association sections around the country. All these were invaluable learning arenas for public speaking. I also developed networks with dentists in different parts of the country, as often an overnight stay was needed when meetings were held in the evenings.

A couple of years later, in 1977, Douglas Shepperd, who was in charge of arranging the table demonstrations at the annual Old Londoners' postgraduate meeting, contacted me. 'Margaret, have you got a table demonstration for the next meeting in February?' I did not have any clinical cases to show, especially as my brush with copper amalgam had not met with success. Perhaps my teething research could be squeezed one more time and presented as a table demonstration? These demonstrations were traditionally scheduled for the graveyard slot after lunch, so I wanted mine to be interesting as well as entertaining. I hit upon the idea of a demonstration of the various treatments that we advocated for the relief of the pain of teething.

So, according to my records, on 14 December 1976, I wrote to the marketing manager at the Glenlivet Distillery: 'The systemic use of alcohol has long been recognised, and many doctors over the years have advised their patients, when they have complained of sleepless nights with a teething offspring, to 'pour some whisky, rub on baby's gum, drink the remainder and both will enjoy a good night's sleep!' I was wondering if your firm would be able to support this demonstration in providing some whisky for display purposes?' This could be classified as a 'tongue in cheek' request but I have also believed that 'nothing ventured, nothing gained', a maxim I still adhere to.

Imagine my absolute delight, if not surprise, when I received a letter from Derek Taylor, the national sales manager of the Glenlivet Distillers in London. 'We will be very pleased to provide the samples and, if you would kindly let me know in due course the amount and where these should be sent, I will be pleased to arrange this.' There was a great deal of conferring to decide how much whisky was needed and six bottles was considered sufficient. Even more exciting was that Derek volunteered to bring them himself to the London Hospital Dental Institute, where he was encouraged by the warmth of his reception from the hundred dentists attending the meeting, and the interest aroused by his Queen Anne whisky in the treatment of teething!

Douglas Shepperd, noting the success, asked me if I would present the table demonstration again at the Annual Conference of the British Dental Association, to be held later in Aberdeen. Initially, I was dubious as to whether this was a serious enough topic to be cast alongside thirty other clinical demonstrations from cleft palate to cardiopulmonary resuscitation. More to the point, would Glenlivet supply me with more whisky, this time for nearly six hundred delegates? So off I sent another letter to Derek Taylor, who seemed undeterred by the large hike in numbers and enthusiastically offered support. He encouraged me to contact Martin Smythe, the sales manager in Scotland, which I duly did. Arrangements were then made for him to deliver the whisky to the exhibition hall, located in the zoology laboratories of the University of Aberdeen. Martin, on arrival, not only produced the bottles of whisky, but also a magnum of Queen Anne's best whisky. However, he was horrified when he saw that I intended to dispense his prized whisky in the paper cups normally reserved for pink mouthwash. Within a couple of hours, he had returned with several dozen whisky taster glasses, and a very smart black china Queen Anne water jug, which remains a much admired item in our china cabinet to this day.

More pressing at the time was what to do with the magnum? I hit upon the idea that each dentist coming to my demonstration should test for themselves the effectiveness of rubbing whisky on the gum (many of them then drinking the remaining liquid dispensed in the glass). They would then be issued with a 'certificate of attendance' in the form of a raffle ticket for the magnum, which would then be part of the BDA Benevolent Fund draw. Unsurprisingly, there was a continuous queue of delegates wanting to test this teething regime, and at the Saturday Banquet, to the skirl of bagpipes, there were squeals of delight when it was declared that the winning ticket was held by the chairman of the organising committee, Mungo Allan.

After all this excitement, life at the Cheshunt clinic was a much more humdrum affair. As a result of the 1974 NHS reorganisation, the school dental officers re-emerged as clinical community dental officers, with a new breed of dental managers, area dental officers. I thought that perhaps I should know more about management techniques, so signed up for a six-day course on 'Time and Motion Studies' at the Theobalds College of the Middlesex Polytechnic. A fascinating world full of jargon and sound bites was revealed, convincing me that clinical work was still at that time my preferred option. However, the smart and efficient working practices that I learnt were later invaluable.

Unlike some working parents, my work regime was not disrupted by the school holidays. I would load the portable black and white television set into the car boot and then set it up in the recovery room at the clinic, to keep Pamela and Colin amused, while I treated patients in the surgery. Many, many years later, I learnt that for some light relief they would slip out the other door of the recovery room, into the health clinic, and enjoy time on the waiting room slide or playing with any available toys. No wonder they preferred this regime to a baby-sitter at home!

In 1975, as my term of office as secretary to the south-east paedodontic group came to an end, I was nominated as Secretary of the national British Paedodontic Society. As this was the time of its Silver Jubilee in 1977, there was to be a great deal of activity, with a major meeting in Manchester under the presidency of Professor Leslie Hardwick. At the meeting a scroll of honorary membership was awarded to Professor Geoffrey Slack, who had been my thesis supervisor, and an inspiration to countless other budding children's dentists. Indeed most of the professors who subsequently headed up dental school children's departments were trained by Geoffrey Slack at The London. I produced a special Silver Jubilee booklet, with a brief synopsis of the origins of the ten groups of the Society. This was sponsored by Oral B, then a dental health division of Knox Laboratories Ltd.

Locally, the Enfield and District section of the Middlesex and Hertfordshire Branch of the British Dental Association had been closed for several years, and I found myself encouraged to re-open the section, now that there was a brand new postgraduate medical centre at Chase Farm Hospital in Enfield. Again using my now honed technique of finding a sponsor, Oral B agreed to provide the buffet supper and wine and show the film 'Control of Dental Plaque'. One of my husband's former students, Michael Wise, had returned from successful post-graduate studies in America, and was now part-time in general practice and a lecturer at the Eastman Dental Hospital. He was a fresh face on the scene of restorative dentistry, and readily agreed to my invitation to be the speaker to relaunch the section with the result that an unusually large crowd of practitioners flocked to the meeting.

Throughout my gentle return to work I made every effort to keep up-to-date by reading the dental journals and there was one particular article in the *British Dental Journal* (*BDJ*) in July 1973 which aroused my interest: 'The Career Commitment of Female Dental Graduates'. The author, Tony Friend, had conducted a study of the women dentists who had graduated from Birmingham from 1950 to 1965, gleaning information about their practice experience from the year of graduation until the end of 1971. To write a letter for publication was a new experience for me, so after many drafts I sent the finished masterpiece off to the *BDJ*, with some trepidation. In my letter I commented how pleased I was to see the paper dealing with the subject of women dentists, grossly neglected on this side of the Atlantic. Aware that there was in operation a women doctors' retainer scheme, I posed the question: 'Why not a women dentists' retainer scheme?' This, to me, seemed an admirable way for women, unable to practise dentistry because of domestic responsibilities, to remain in touch with professional activities and, in the long term, assist their return to the dental workforce.

A couple of days after the publication of the *Journal* including my letter, I received a phone call at home. 'Is that Mrs Seward? Come and see me. I would like to discuss your letter.' I fixed an appointment and as I made my way on the train to London, I was more than a little apprehensive. Just what had I said in that letter that resulted in a summons from the postgraduate Dental Dean, Dr Desmond Greer Walker?

Chapter 9

Stirrings of women's issues

My anxiety level rose as I trudged my way from King's Cross station up the busy Gray's Inn Road which seemed to possess more than its fair share of uneven paving stones and potholes. Thankfully, and without mishap, I was soon checking into reception at the British Postgraduate Medical Federation (BPMF), which was easily identified as it nestled on the corner of Guildford and Millman Streets. Without delay, I was ushered upstairs and my escort knocked on a door identified by a grand looking plaque with words embossed in gold lettering 'Regional Postgraduate Dental Dean'. In awe, I entered the room, but fears were instantly dispelled because the most genial man in his sixties rose slowly from behind his desk and, after placing his pipe on the table-top, he peered over his half-rimmed glasses with twinkling eyes, exclaiming in a soothing Irish brogue, 'Margaret, thank you for coming. I want to help you to get a women dentists' retainer scheme – it's a great idea!'

I had to pinch myself. Was it really true that Dr Desmond Greer Walker, an acknowledged giant within the dental profession, a consultant oral surgeon at the Middlesex and Stoke Mandeville hospitals, as well as the postgraduate dean, was offering to help me achieve my objective? It was not long before I was making frequent trips to the BPMF and, interestingly, as familiarity grew, the walk became shorter and the potholes less obvious. 'Father', as he was affectionately referred to by his ever attentive staff, suggested that we should write a paper together explaining the need to retain women dentists in practice and put forward ideas as to how to achieve this. Imagine my delight when the paper was accepted for publication in an October issue of the *BDJ* in 1974, and how proud I was, and how envied by my friends, to have the privilege of joint authorship on the masthead of the article. In the paper, details were provided about a scheme for women under the age of 55 years who held an expectation to return to NHS dentistry when domestic responsibilities permitted. Briefly, the arrangement proposed was that the postgraduate dental dean for the region in which the woman lived should interview and assess her for participation in the retainer scheme. On acceptance, the woman's name would be entered on a central register, although, sensing more local liaison would be needed, experienced women dentists would be designated as liaison officers from within or without the established regional postgraduate committees. Also on offer to the registered woman would be a mix of educational and operative dental sessions, with access to home-based learning, either through radio cassette or videotape. In return for this commitment to keeping in touch with dentistry, the Department of Health and social security would award a financial contribution. This would assist with payment of the retention fee to keep the woman's name on the Dentists Register held by the General Dental Council, to maintain membership of a protection organisation, and to subscribe to a professional journal. In many respects, the format mirrored a similar initiative launched in 1972 for women doctors, although for dentists there was the added challenge of ensuring that a sufficient number of appropriate clinical sessions were available, so that professional skills could be maintained.

The positive response to the appearance of the article was encouraging, but without funding it was clearly impossible to convert a dream into reality. So an approach for financial support was made to the chief dental officer at the Department of Health, Mr George Gibb, by Dr Greer Walker, with the unanimous support of the conference of postgraduate dental deans and advisers of the UK, which he chaired. Their support was based on the fact that I had the previous year, while still working as a community dental officer at Cheshunt, spoken about the problems which could face the increasing number of women entering the profession and about how many of us found it difficult to get postgraduate education for further career enhancement, due to a lack of part-time posts, or the need to have passed a certain level of income to become eligible for Section 63 NHS courses. My high hopes were short-lived when George Gibb replied pointing out, 'facts and figures will be needed if I am to convince Ministers to support this initiative'.

But how could I acquire the 'facts and figures' needed? I had already scoured records and collected all the available data from registration and postgraduate bodies. However, I did know personally some women who had taken a career break and had not returned to work in their chosen profession for a variety of reasons, children, ill-health, looking after elderly parents, to name a few. So I was convinced that there must be more women in retirement around the country than those accounted for in the records of the dental registration body. The only way to discover the true picture was to undertake a survey. Again, there was the stumbling block of funding. Who would sponsor such an inquiry? Dr Greer Walker suggested that an approach should be made to the Nuffield Provincial Hospitals Trust to support a survey entitled 'the postgraduate retraining and further education of women dentists'? My hopes did not have much time to rise as a swift response was received. 'Owing to present financial stringencies we are unable to offer support,' a comment which continues to have a familiar ring.

I learnt a great deal from Dr Greer Walker and in particular one lesson of lasting relevance, never take 'No' for the final answer. So, undaunted, he wrote again to the chief dental officer enquiring about the possibility of a small research grant, and, at the same time, requesting information about projects currently receiving monetary support. This was a clever move for it revealed that nearly a dozen projects had been favoured with the department's support, from sums ranging from

£54,000 to £3,000 and a few appeared to have slim relevance to present-day problems. This bold strategy paid off, because an eighteen-page formidable application form arrived at the beginning of September 1974 for me to complete. Advice was also proffered, suggesting that there would be a greater chance of success for the bid if the emphasis shown in the project's title was shifted away from continuing education to the activities of women dentists in delivering dental services.

Naturally, I followed this advice and renamed the survey: 'The provision of dental health care by women dentists in England and Wales.' I also indicated on the application form that I intended to undertake the survey while based at the central office of the BPMF in a part-time capacity for four sessions a week over a twelve-month period. I now note that the total support requested, which included secretarial and statistical assistance, amounted to £57,220 with the proposed starting date of 1 January 1975. It is relevant to reflect that, at this time, women formed only 29.3 per cent of new graduates, although my survey was also to give advance warning that some thirty years later this would rise to 50 per cent.

The wait for a response seemed interminable, and as Christmas passed, I began to imagine the worst possible scenario – another rejection. However, my luck had turned and, with great relief, a letter arrived from Mr Forsdick, of the research branch at the Department of Health and Social Security, informing me that I had been awarded a grant for a twelve-month period starting on 1 February 1975. After waiting so long for an answer, it seemed extraordinary that he assumed I was going to start immediately. Again, Dr Greer Walker came to my rescue and phoned Mr Forsdick to explain that I was currently in the employment of the Hertfordshire area health authority, and would be expected to work out the agreed notice to terminate my contract. Even more importantly for me, I wanted to try to complete as many courses of treatments as possible for the delightful youngsters in my care. There were also arrangements to be made in connection with the forthcoming survey: recruitment of secretarial staff, activation of the agreement with Professor Curnow at the University of Reading to provide statistical assistance through the deployment of his assistant director of the health services operational unit. Personally, there was the challenge to juggle the childcare arrangements for Pamela and Colin who, although they were now eleven and nine years of age, would be arriving home from school before me. At the grand age of 39, I was all set to become a London commuter.

My new post, as senior research fellow, was no joke, despite the starting date of 1 April. There was also encouragement from the conference of postgraduate dental deans and advisers, to hold an event to launch the project, and raise its profile. So, on 23 April, a one-day symposium was organised at the Royal Society of Medicine, with one hundred invited participants. Looking back at the names of the delegates, they included the 'movers and shakers' of that time as well as people who were to rise in due course to the top of the profession, and whose influence undoubtedly contributed to many of the recommendations being implemented. So who was there? Sir Robert Bradlaw, the president of the British Dental Association, and the editor of the *BDJ*, Archie Donaldson. The dean of the faculty of dental surgery at the Royal College of Surgeons of England, John Hovell, and Professor Gerry Winter, the vice-dean at the Institute of Dental Surgery. The undergraduate dental schools were also well represented by Professors Duckworth, Emslie, Howe, Renson and my own husband, Gordon Seward. Also present was Stanley (now Professor) Gelbier who was the first to provide clinical opportunities for women returning to work. Kindred spirit support was provided by Dr Jean Lawrie, secretary of the Medical Women's Federation. The ancillary dental personnel were included: Sally Verity a dental auxiliary (therapist) as a speaker, and a couple of hygienists and dental surgery assistants. Most importantly, nearly forty women dentists were on the guest list. After all the day was about them and their aspirations. Again, thirty years on, names are still well-known in the profession – Edwina Kidd, Elizabeth McEwen, Penny Vasey, Marilyn Gelbier. Dr Desmond Greer Walker chaired the day and he was supported by other postgraduate deans, Reg Dinsdale, Ken Ray and Professor Howard Tonge, who delivered a comprehensive summary of the day's proceedings. There was also a good contingent from the Department of Health, which was not surprising, as they were financially supporting the project.

The symposium was a healthy mix of short presentations, examining the problem and looking at current retraining schemes and further education requirements. I can well recall feeling some apprehension when faced with such a distinguished gathering, after previous audiences of mums with teething babies.

The afternoon was designated as a discussion period, with participants in six groups examining problem areas – career counselling, part-time work, and the objective of retraining. It was unanimously acclaimed that encouraging the proposed Retainer Scheme was a possible way of keeping women in dentistry, and Professor Tonge said it was clear that women wished to play their full part in the profession, but felt that they were not being given the opportunities to do so. The Equal Pay Bill and Sex Discrimination Bill were in their infancy at this time, but great hopes were held that once enacted they could make a difference in improving the working lives for women.

The main part of the study involved sending out questionnaires to all women dentists on the 1975 Dentists Register, so formulating the questions occupied me fully in the first few months of my job. I was incredibly fortunate that Dr Don Neal, the statistician and assistant director of the operational unit at the University of Reading, had been deputed to assist me. Don Neal was a larger than life character: six foot-three tall, weighing in at seventeen stone and normally attired in shorts, open-neck shirt and sandals, irrespective of the extremes of the British weather. He was understandably reticent about travelling to our central office in London because it meant 'dressing up', and so I found I was making frequent journeys to his university office, in a Victorian house within White Knights on the outskirts of Reading. But he was able to 'clear the fog' for me in relation to statistics, and even excited me when explaining the various statistical tests on offer. Of lasting importance, he convinced me that time spent on questionnaire design pays dividends later. 'Many studies,' Don would explain, 'start off with good intentions, but flounder because insufficient time and energy were put into compiling the questions.' I have repeated this sound advice on many occasions to colleagues, who have told me that it will just take them a couple of hours to put together a questionnaire. From bitter experience I have discovered that, even if the questions are tested in a pilot or dummy run, questions which were believed to be straightforward were found to be ambiguous, and therefore failed to elicit the information needed.

A most important outcome from the project was to find the missing women, that is those women who had withdrawn their names from the Dentists Register, held by the GDC. I spent a great deal of time endeavouring to trace these women. I wrote to the secretary of every branch and section of the British Dental Association throughout England and Wales, each of whom dutifully read out the letter at their relevant meetings. This undoubtedly not only raised the profile of the project but also raised my own profile. Encouraged by a positive response, I next wrote to deans of dental schools and alumni organisations of dental schools, the editors of dental publications, and then to women's groups such as the Soroptimists, the Townswomen's Guilds, the Women's Institute's National Federation, and the Society of University Women. As you can imagine this involved a great deal of secretarial work, and I was incredibly fortunate to have Mrs Marjorie Gillate as secretary to the project. She had recently returned from overseas with her husband Don, who had just completed a tour of duty for the British Council, teaching in schools. Not only did she understand and sympathise with the demands of my family life, but she also had two young sons of her own. Above all, she possessed a most cheerful disposition, so nothing was too much trouble, and she took the ever-increasing workload valiantly in her stride.

Having exhausted all my known dental contacts, it became clear to me that I had to throw the net wider and engage the general public in the hunt for the lost women. A glossy A4 leaflet was printed, with the eye-catching headline, 'Where Are You Now?' Underneath the silhouette of a lady dentist, seated while treating a patient, ran the caption, 'Can you help us complete this picture? Thank you.' It was with great relief that I discovered that the topic was of interest to journalists, so interviews with lady dentists appeared in many regional newspapers with intriguing headlines: 'Wanted: women who still know their drill'; 'Hunt on for lost women dentists' and 'Big search to fill those gaps'. The south-east Thames Health Authority issued its own press release to coincide with the dispatch of the questionnaire on Monday 20 October, with the comment, 'Mothers whose children are now at school or grown-up are being urged to think again about putting down the vacuum cleaner and taking up drill again.' This is an insight into the perceived role of women in the home in the 1970s, and was even more surprising because 1975 had been designated as International Women's Year.

Then there was great excitement when I received an invitation to go on the BBC *Today* programme. 20 October was fast becoming a red-letter day for me. It did mean a very early start, as a car was sent by the BBC to pick me up at home at 5.30 a.m., so that I would be ready for the live studio interview with John Humphreys at 6.45 a.m. He was gentle with me, enquiring why I was looking for women dentists, and asking if it really was a suitable career to combine with raising a family. Unscathed, I beat a hasty retreat to the canteen, to take up the offer of a cooked 'Auntie Beeb' breakfast. However, to my great surprise, before I ate I was handed £5 for my effort. I was even more pleasantly surprised to discover just how many friends and colleagues had heard me describe my sleuth-like activities so early in the morning. As a result we did trace a few more women through this media coverage.

But there was to be more excitement. The very next day, in the post, I received a letter from Edwina Kidd, containing a newspaper cutting. Unfolding it, I discovered it was the entire page three of *The Sun* carrying a photograph of a most gorgeous pin-up – a lady dentist – but from Sweden. *The Sun*'s editor had certainly done his bit towards giving publicity to the hunt for missing women dentists, albeit in an unconventional way. This portrait captured on a 2 × 2 slide brightened up many of my factual presentations on the survey and its results. I especially remember on one occasion speaking at a BDA Section meeting in one of Oxford's leading hotels. After a splendid meal and with the tables still stacked with wine glasses and coffee cups, the lights were dimmed and I launched into my talk on women dentists. Just as I had projected the slide of the lovely page three dentist onto the screen, in order to explain and emphasise the power, and humour, of the press, the door opened. 'Can we come in and clear the tables?' requested a couple of the waitresses. They continued to enter the room until their eyes alighted on the screen, when, with confusion, they hastily withdrew muttering to each other, 'Funny sort of dental meeting going on in there. We'll come back later!' I often wonder what they told their dentist at their next visit, that is, if they ever plucked up the courage to go again.

Once, each year, the conference of postgraduate dental deans and advisors opened their morning session to all those interested in continuing dental education. Dr Greer Walker asked me to prepare a poster display, to give information about the progress of the women's survey and also to encourage the return of the questionnaire. In Barnet, just adjacent to where we lived in Hadley Wood, I found a firm who could supply mobile poster display boards but they were going to be expensive and outside the budget for my project. Also in the town lived the area dental officer, Alan Lawrence who, with his wife Judith, also a dentist, had been most supportive of the survey. They were fully aware from first-hand experience of the problems facing women dentists, especially those who did not have a dental husband or partner. A visit to their home was most fruitful, as they showed me a photograph of their group of dental students in their clinical years at Bristol University dental school. We all agreed that this would make an eye-catching centre panel to the display. It is interesting also to reflect that 1963 was a vintage year, as many of the young hopefuls in the group rose to eminence in the profession: Brenda Fox, Keith Osterloh, David and Anne Phillips and, of course, both the Lawrences.

My next task was to find a sponsor, both for the display boards and the artwork. Recalling the previous coup with pharmaceutical companies, I wrote to Knox Laboratories-Oral B. By return I received a message that the sales manager would like to take me out to lunch so that I could tell him about the project and exactly why I needed the company's support to provide display boards. Basically, what was in it for them? At twelve noon precisely, a very presentable young man arrived at Millman Street and whisked me away in a waiting taxi-cab to his chosen venue for lunch. I was aware that we were travelling north, away from London, when Islington appeared on the signpost. Shortly afterwards we alighted at Camden Passage and entered the renowned Robert Carrier restaurant. The meal turned out to be the most sophisticated and delicious fare that I have ever tasted, and was exquisitely presented. My escort agreed sponsorship within the span of the first course, and then we were able to turn our full attention to the meal and wines at hand. To finish, during coffee, he selected the fattest of cigars, and not wishing to make me feel excluded from this extravagance, he ordered a copy of the acclaimed book by Robert Carrier, 'Cooking for You'. Imagine my delight when the owner appeared with the book at our table and inscribed it, 'To Margaret Seward with every good wish from Robert Carrier'. This book, full of coloured photographs and step-by-step instructions on how to prepare his delicious meals, certainly lived up to its claim, 'even the most timid of cooks can make them'. It instantly supplanted my Elizabeth David's heavy prose and became my 'Bible of Cooking'. It still remains a well-thumbed copy on my kitchen bookshelf. This, and the other extravagant items, were added to the bill, and I later learnt that the young man had some explaining to do to his finance director for an unusually large lunch bill to discuss display boards.

I arrived, somewhat late and flushed, back at the office and had to give a blow-by-blow account of where I had been to the BPMF dental administrators. Sheila Bird (later Light) and Sara Hall were full of surprise, if not a little envious at the turn of events to a sponsorship request. I managed to return home just in time to collect the children from school (this should have been one of my 'days off' but rapidly the part-time job was becoming a full-time one with extra hours unpaid). To allay my conscience, I bought my children the biggest two ice-lollies from Blakes, the local newsagents in Hadley Wood.

Another extra activity was to discover the reasons for the success of the Women Doctors' Retainer Scheme introduced in 1972. I quickly found out that women doctors were well organised as a group, and had in place a lobbying and negotiating body, the Medical Women's Federation (MWF), complete with its own office and secretariat. It was proposed that I should attend one of their committee meetings and see if they had any ideas to help me with my survey. I was scheduled to attend under the first item of business following lunch and was duly ushered in by the secretary, Dr Jean Lawrie, whom I had previously met. She had attended, while representing the MWF, the women dentists' symposium at the Royal Society of Medicine. I was greeted by the chairman, Dame Albertine Winner, TD, who was attired in a wide-brimmed hat and long white gloves. Noting similarly dressed middle-aged ladies around the table, I felt decidedly underdressed for the meeting, albeit wearing my most respectable summer frock. In a powerful deep voice, Dame Albertine asked me to explain my survey and how I thought they could assist. The parting advice from the chairman rang out, 'Get yourselves a Women Dentists Federation like ours. It's the only way, if you want to be heard.' I learnt later that this formidable lady had been an army colonel, and was therefore used to getting things done her way. But she did add, with nods of agreement from all there, 'Let me know if we can help you set one up.' A wave of relief swept over me as I bade my farewells and expressed my thanks, finally escaping into the brilliant sunshine of the July summer day, wincing at the thought of assembling a gathering of women dentists. We just did not fit into the 'hat and long gloves brigade'. But, giving the idea more thought I began to wonder if there was merit in having a women's organisation to put forward a corporate view, and admired how much they had collectively achieved. Was it time for women dentists to follow suit?

Some months later, I had the good fortune to meet Dame Albertine again but not under such daunting circumstances. She had organised a week-end symposium to discuss employment and educational problems facing the increasing number of women doctors in the profession and had persuaded the Rt. Hon. Barbara Castle MP, the Secretary of State for Health and Social Security, to attend. Her presence was remarkable because at this time there was the threat of industrial action by the medical profession throughout the country on a scale unprecedented since the inception of the NHS in 1945. Barbara Castle was a labour politician who favoured more of the stick than the carrot, and in order to persuade hospital consultants to accept whole-time contracts, she threatened to withhold merit awards from part-timers. The consultants' fury erupted and they began to work strictly to rule for sixteen weeks. Their actions were swiftly followed by the junior doctors who were disappointed over their stalled negotiations on reduced hours, two disputes in combination which could close many casualty and hospital departments, increasing waiting lists and jeopardising patient care. Another threat looming on the horizon was action by thousands of general medical practitioners who were fearful that the ministers would renege on their anticipated pay award.

So, I was excited when Dr Greer Walker told me that he had managed to get an invitation for the two of us to attend the symposium which was to be held at Northcote House, the impressive Civil Service College in Sunningdale, a place more famous for its championship golf course than the civil servants' halls of residence. I began to wonder what this powerful politician would be like as we waited for the conference to start. As it transpired, I was charmed by the attractive red-head, who oozed personality and who responded with a nod when Dr Greer Walker suggested in the question and answer session that women dentists needed a Retainer Scheme like the women doctors. Naively, I thought this action signalled approval: the deal was done. In due course I was to discover that this was far from reality because in Government, secretaries of state and ministers come and go and continuity is very much in the hands of the department's senior civil servants.

After the questionnaires had been dispatched on the red letter day, 20 October 1975, there was a hiatus as we anxiously awaited the return of the completed forms. So I began to thumb through the job section of the *BDJ* because I was conscious of the fact that I was now past the halfway mark of my research grant and needed to begin to contemplate my next move. My interest was aroused when I saw an advertisement inviting applications for the post of director of the New Cross School for Dental Auxiliaries, which was shortly to become vacant due to the retirement of the current director, Tom Liptrot. I considered this job could utilise my academic and clinical skills. The more I thought about the post, the more I began to relish the challenge which it could offer, in not only raising the profile of dental auxiliaries, but also in increasing their acceptability because, sadly, many leaders in the profession were not supportive, claiming that they 'diluted the profession'. My husband encouraged me to send in an application for the job, but only after I had tested the practicality of travelling to and from Hadley Wood to the auxiliary school situated in the grounds of the New Cross General Hospital, which meant crossing London using a daily combination of train, tube and bus. While waiting to hear if I would be called for interview, I was surprised to receive a letter from one of the lecturers at New Cross, Murray Hinton, and I quote: '. . . we generally believe that better direction and development of the course of training for dental auxiliaries is long overdue and I see you as the only person who can provide this. The lecturers and tutors are now more united in their views of the training scheme but need a new director with an open mind and reasonable attitude to bring it to fruition. I therefore offer you my best wishes for a satisfactory outcome to your interview . . .'

Unfortunately, the interview panel did not share the same unsolicited view of the lecturer and I was not offered the post. Theo Schofield, my boss from my days at Highlands Hospital, responded to this outcome with the comment, 'It must have been an exceptional person if you did not get the job.' In truth, I knew it was the right person who was appointed, Ted Seal, who had recently returned from running an auxiliary school in Papua New Guinea and obviously possessed first-hand experience, which I lacked.

My disappointment was transitory because both my part-time working and my spare time became fully occupied when the questionnaires began to return. Overall, a total of 2,454 questionnaires had been posted and replies were received from 86 per cent of the women. One thousand eight hundred and forty-six useable questionnaires were received, a response rate of 79 per cent, which is commendable for a postal survey. But this success brought its own problems with the tremendous amount of data to be sorted. Don Neal indicated that although he had received the questionnaires for coding by the middle of December, the presentation of relevant data would not be available until March, which coincided with the end of my research grant. Back I went to Mr Forsdick requesting a three-month extension for myself and Marjorie Gillate so that we could write the report and, thankfully, this was swiftly given. Unfortunately, I had still underestimated the time needed, so writing the report continued through the summer months and tapes and typed copy passed back and forth between Marjorie and myself, with the postal exchange continuing throughout the fortnight of our family summer holiday in Minehead, although I caution that intrusion into vacation time should be used only rarely. But this final push was rewarded as the report was delivered on 27 September to the Department of Health for its approval before final printing.

So, do I believe the research and effort was worthwhile? Unequivocally, yes. I now had assembled a surfeit of facts and figures for the chief dental officer over a wide range of issues. Of particular importance was the discovery that an increasing number of women in the profession had indicated that they were likely to withdraw from practising dentistry for varying periods at some stage in their careers. A dentists' retainer scheme could certainly make a significant difference in the retention of women in the workforce. However, it took a further three years for the Department's Circular HC/7 to appear, which officially launched the Women Dentists' Retainer Scheme in England, in July 1979, with Scotland and Wales quickly following with their own versions of the scheme. This experience gave me a deeper understanding of the true meanings of the words patience and perseverance whenever the implementation of a scheme, approved by the department, seemed to take a lifetime. But the intervening period was not wasted because there was convened a 'Working Party on Women' by the BDA. Was it possible that at long last our professional body, the dentists' trade union, was taking women's issues seriously?

The findings from the survey also quashed the long-held belief that women dentists would follow the often given advice of the 'Five Ss'. 'Enter the salaried school service – safe and satisfying.' In fact the survey findings showed the contrary was true; that is, more women entered general dental practice than the school or the now renamed community dental service. However, some of the findings were disturbing. For example, the revelation that it was difficult for a woman to get a part-time post if she wished to study for a specialist diploma, especially in orthodontics. Dr Rosemary Rue, the regional medical officer in Oxford, whom I had also met at the Sunningdale conference, had pioneered part-time training and employment (the original job-share scheme) for women doctors in her region, and provided a worthy role model for me and I know also for countless women doctors. She was rightly awarded many honours and Dame Rosemary also became a much admired president of the British Medical Association, a very male-dominated organisation.

More than thirty years on, my report's fourteen recommendations still make interesting reading. There was a call for a diploma in child dental health, obviously remembering my ambitions in this direction when at Cheshunt dental clinic. Also, one proposed that postgraduate study should be feasible from a financial point of view and so a study period of one year was advocated for any diploma and also recommended one in general dental practice. Further suggestions included the formation of a central agency to coordinate information about the Dentists' Retainer Scheme, retraining courses and proposals for tailor-made refresher courses to be available for women returning to work after a short absence from practice. Another recommendation was the compilation of a Central Register of Women Dentists in England and Wales, embracing those working and not working so as to ensure that in the future there would not be required a massive hunt for missing women dentists. Career counselling was similarly an area for development and it was proposed that this should be encouraged with the appointment of specific dental advisors to take on this role to cover undergraduates and postgraduates. Also highlighted was the need for paid maternity leave to be more readily available for women dentists, as well as suggesting that the expense of providing child care while practising dentistry should be allowed against tax.

In the final section of the questionnaire a blank page had been provided for women to express their own thoughts and anonymity was assured. I believe that a staggering response by 909 women dentists underlined how much they welcomed this unique opportunity to have their say on a wide range of topics. These feelings appeared to be summed up by one woman in her comment, 'This is the first survey I have ever answered with pleasure.' There were also unsolicited comments from husbands, fathers, daughters and sons, which I hasten to add were not included in the official results, but nevertheless provided a further perspective on the various problems encountered by women in dentistry.

Unfortunately some of the comments revealed disturbing attitudes which made me appreciate why the Equal Pay Bill and Sex Discrimination Bill had been drafted: 'On applying for an associateship in general practice I was told by the principal that he did not intend to employ women because married ones were too busy thinking about the day's shopping and single ones were always having emotional upsets with their boyfriends.' Another stated, 'When applying for an associateship in general practice I was informed that women did not have the stamina or organising ability to work in practice.'

I also stumbled upon the confusion which can arise in the spelling of Christian names. Three questionnaires were returned from men who had the misfortune to have been given the female spelling of their name and one added, 'If I can help to improve your response rate, I would be happy to have a little operation.' I hasten to add that this humorous offer was not pursued.

The report also suggested three further areas for research, one of which was to look at the training, career pattern and work performance of ancillary dental personnel, utilising the same questionnaire and research team. George Gibb, the CDO, encouraged me to pursue this possible line of research and suggested that I should contact Professor Slack at the London Hospital Medical College, who was director of the experimental dental care unit exploring different ways of training and using dental health care teams. He did of course know my interests as he was my supervisor for my MDS thesis on 'Teething'.

This suggested meeting was further confirmed by George Gibb in the letter of 8 October 1976. 'I shall always be pleased to discuss this with you if you think it would help.' I thus was surprised to receive a letter from Professor Gerry Winter, asking for a copy of my questionnaire. It transpired that during the previous month, one of his M.Sc. students (Ruth Holt) at the Eastman Dental Hospital Institute of Dental Surgery, had been awarded a research fellowship in order to progress to a Ph.D. degree. John Murray, reader and honorary consultant in the department of children's dentistry, had already written to Jimmie Rodgers, senior dental officer at the Department of Health and Social Security, expressing the view that the evaluation of the clinical effectiveness of dental auxiliaries would yield some important and relevant information and, furthermore, had proposed a research project. Naturally, I was very disappointed at such a swift termination to my idea. Nevertheless, I was greatly flattered that the formulation of the questionnaire by Ruth Holt and John Murray was based partly on the one which I had designed. Even more approbation came when the researchers wrote to the dental auxiliaries on 16 April 1977 stating in their covering letter, 'You may be aware that a survey of women dentists was carried out last year by Mrs Margaret Seward. Most of the questions in the questionnaire have been phrased so that comparisons can be made.' As their study progressed I greatly appreciated being kept in touch, which compensated for my initial disappointment. I also soon recognised the tremendous ability and energy of John Murray whose many talents I have benefited from during various stages in my career.

Obviously, duplication of the study about dental auxiliaries was a non-starter, so I went to see George Gibb. He sensed my deep disappointment and came up with an interesting idea. 'What about applying for a Council of Europe Fellowship? I want to know about the training of a new operating ancillary dental worker in the Netherlands. Why not go and find out about them for me?' My spirits soared: a brilliant idea. To visit Amsterdam seemed an attractive proposition. Then I came down to earth, and to the point. How did I get a Council of Europe Fellowship?

Chapter 10

Spreading my wings

'Congratulations: you've been elected!' was the exciting news phoned to me on a depressingly damp summer's day. It was the registrar, Mr David Hindley-Smith, informing me that I had been elected to serve on the General Dental Council (GDC) for a five-year term.

It was not a phone call that I had anticipated receiving, as this was my first attempt to break down a male-dominated bastion of the dental profession. Through my contact with the registration department of the GDC, when I trawled numerous registers for the names of missing women dentists, I had become aware of the workings of the Council and observed how decisions affecting men and women were taken only by male dentists. As I discovered that an election was pending in July 1976, I asked Mrs Jean Dineen to send me the nomination papers and information about its current membership. Looking through the names, it was obvious that those dentists promoting a single issue stood the best chance of election. I noted, for example, that Ian Simpson promoted the 'Legalised Use of the Title of Doctor' (LUTD) campaign and Alan Fearn vehemently opposed any extension of the working practices by dental ancillaries, saying that this would be detrimental, not only for patients, but it would also result in 'the dilution' of the dental profession.

It became clear that my name was now associated with a single issue, 'women in dentistry'. This was despite the fact that I had never intended to make it a crusade. Rather, as a woman with higher qualifications and so with no axe to grind, I had wanted to highlight the areas of inequalities of opportunities. Nevertheless, I accepted that my name was recognised by many of the women in the England constituency, because I had sent a letter with the questionnaire to them the previous year. Further, it was fortuitous that I also held the post of honorary secretary of the British Paedodontic Society, and of the section of odontology of the Royal Society of Medicine. Both of these raised my profile further with the profession. However, I was not lulled into complacency because I realised that there was tremendous competition to get a seat on the statutory governing body of the dental profession. I strongly hold the view that, even after all these years, it is easier to change things from inside, rather than agitating from the sidelines. But this means that you must be prepared to accept the ignominy of failure, and that possibility must not deter entry to any election or competition. So, after dispatching my completed nomination papers, I began to explore how I could get my wider views across to the electorate, as I wanted to avoid being dubbed as a 'woman issues' candidate. A number of the contestants went to the personal expense of sending mailings out to every one of the 16,000 dentists on the Register. Fortunately, I discovered a method with 'no cost', because the editor of the *British Dental Journal* (*BDJ*) made some of its pages available for candidates to publish their election addresses. I readily took advantage of this offer, and so, in the June issue of the *BDJ*, my contribution appeared alongside those from the other seventeen hopeful candidates.

I began my address on the thorny issue of the retention (that is, registration) fee, which, although initially £13.50, was destined to be increased in 1977 to £22. I entreated dental practitioners to be concerned, and ask questions about how their monies were spent on the business of the GDC. Few of us had any idea why a 63 per cent increase was proposed, the largest increase since the retention fee was introduced in 1921. There was no choice about paying the fee, as it secured for dentists the licence or certificate to practise dentistry. I used this sudden increase to highlight the need for improved communication between the Council and the profession, and promised that, if elected, I would make that a priority. In common with the other potential candidates I was only permitted to write a maximum of 500 words. So, after the briefest reference to the progress of my career, I finished with the words: 'To complete my dental experience I am happily married to an academic!' Gordon, at this time was dean of dental studies at the London Hospital Medical College Dental School, as well as professor and head of the oral and maxillofacial surgery department. An 'academic' was definitely an understatement of his status within the profession. I have also been opposed to reverse sex discrimination and do not condone the idea of allocating certain seats for women to contest, even to address the imbalance of representation on male-dominated organisations. However, as I was the only woman competing against seventeen men, I thought it would not go amiss to nudge the electorate into appreciating how unrepresentative was the current membership. The concluding words of my address took up this point: 'During the next five years, the GDC will take decisions which will affect us all. It is vital that the decisions are taken by a Council whose elected members fully represent each and every member of our profession.'

More than 16,000 dentists living in England, the Channel Islands and the Isle of Man cast their votes to elect seven dentists to represent them on the General Dental Council. It was more or less a foregone conclusion that those dentists seeking re-election would be returned and, on this occasion, the five dentists currently on the Council did get returned for a further five-year period of office: Douglas Barber, John Farrell, Alan Fearn, Ian Simpson, and Desmond Greer Walker. The two vacancies in the English constituency were filled by newcomers – Gerald (Gerry) Holden and, with great delight, myself. Scotland had two representatives, Charlie Downie, and a new one, Tom Macadam. In Wales and Ireland the sitting dentists were returned, David Roberts and Frederick Bell respectively. The majority of the membership was made up of representatives from the universities with dental schools, the royal colleges, the departments of health, and lay members appointed by the Privy Council.

At the opening of the 44th session of the GDC, all the newly-elected members were introduced to the Council and welcomed by the President, Sir Rodney Swiss, who was the first elected member to become President. In his address, he wisely reminded us all that we must not think of ourselves as representing a particular constituency, or as furthering a political purpose or sectional interest, but act together and influence the future of dentistry in the United Kingdom. He then concluded his welcome in this way. 'I would have added a special word of congratulations to Mrs Seward on making history as the first woman dentist to be elected to the Council, if I had not been advised that to do so might quite well be construed as a breach of the Sex Discrimination Act, insofar as it suggests that there may be something untoward in such an event.'

The Council meetings were held in the magnificent panelled Council chamber in its premises in Wimpole Street, sumptuously and expensively furnished by Heals of London. Each member had the comfort of a leather upholstered armchair, with its own extending desktop and individual light. Facing the members, on a crescent-shaped podium, sat the President, in a high-backed, carved seat, with to his left the Registrar and on both sides other senior dignitaries of Council, the treasurer and chairmen of the committees who would present their reports and recommendations for approval during the day-long proceedings. It was in this grand, yet forbidding, forum that I rose apprehensively to deliver my maiden speech. The topic which had aroused my desire to speak was the proposal from the Ancillary Dental Workers Committee that there should be a change of title for dental auxiliaries, to 'dental therapists'. I considered this to be an eminently sensible suggestion and was bewildered at the strength of opposition. It is reported that I spoke saying, 'I do not follow Mr Fearn's arguments. Parents are well acquainted with the term therapist, for example physiotherapist, speech therapist, and occupational therapist.' So what had Alan Fearn remarked that prompted my response? In his jocular, but forceful, style he made the point, 'I can see no reason for change. I am sure the girls would not wish to be referred to as "DTs" [delirium tremens].' His persuasive manner carried the day and the GDC decided not to approve the change of title for dental auxiliaries. Thankfully, some years later, what was in my view a more reasonable approach prevailed, with the adoption of the title 'dental therapist'.

Following my first Council meeting, I was given unsolicited, but sound, advice from a fellow elected member, Ian Simpson, although we held disparate views on the topic of auxiliaries. 'Remember, Margaret, this is a public forum and every word, laugh, and even cough, is captured by the shorthand writer, so there is no room for an "off the cuff" speech.' I had already been warned by colleagues that reading from a script was frowned upon, so I wondered how I was to comply with

Ian's advice. Homework, I soon learned, was the answer. Every committee paper and report had to be read thoroughly, and these were presented on sheets of foolscap paper, a different colour for each committee. I practised speed-reading, and how to pick out the salient points well in advance of the Council meeting. I then spent time drafting possible questions or comments and committing them to memory so that I could use them as a framework for any interventions I might make during the meeting. I quickly realised that a woman making a poor speech could be damned forever. Unforgivable also was to deliver comments in a shrill, nagging or hectoring tone of voice – all acceptable from a man whose poor occasional performance was quickly forgotten. Without doubt, the technique and discipline of debating that I learnt at the GDC was to prove invaluable throughout my career.

In the Council chamber, I had been given the seat next to Desmond Greer Walker, who gently guided me through the intricacies of the debating procedures, and the importance of adhering to the Dentists Act, the statutory instruments, and rules and regulations, the legal parameters within which the GDC had to operate.

Tragically, within a year, I lost my guardian. In the course of an acrimonious debate on possible vocational training for dentists, Dr Greer Walker 'crossed swords' with the President, collected up his papers and walked out of the chamber. His resignation in this manner caused repercussions throughout the profession, and resulted in a by-election in which Brian Lux was the winner.

So what caused such a dramatic resignation? Desmond's vision was of providing a buffer state for the newly-graduated dentists between learning and practice. Unfortunately, he became increasingly frustrated as few shared his dream, or would support him in pursuing it. His concept of an experimental scheme was eventually instigated and today every graduate undertakes vocational training, a lasting tribute to this great man.

But there were other hurdles in store. I quickly discovered that, unlike all my male colleagues on the Council, I had not been allocated to a Council committee. I consoled myself with the thought that this must be a typographical error and so, albeit with trepidation, I picked up the telephone to inform the registrar about my omission. I was assured, firmly, that there was not an error, but that, as a new member, I would have to be patient and wait for a vacancy. Patience is not one of my virtues, and so I felt aggrieved, especially as the other new members for England and the one for Scotland had been favoured with a place on a committee. To his credit, the registrar, sensing the strength of my displeasure, said he would speak to the President about the matter. 'Have you a preference for a committee?' he enquired. Already I had learnt that membership of the education committee was highly prized, so I said I would like a place on that one. Whether, in retrospect he decided that it did indeed appear unfair, or whether it was better to accede to my request to keep me quiet, I shall never know. But, whatever the reason, I found myself propelled onto the august education committee, with, I must report, a degree of indignation expressed by several long-serving members who had coveted a place on this prestigious committee for years. Perhaps also to further placate me, I found myself with a second assignment, the committee of management of the school for dental auxiliaries, the training school for the dental auxiliaries at New Cross, to which I had applied to be Director.

Being dubbed as the 'first woman' inevitably brings unexpected problems for a male-dominated organisation. While ensuring that you stand your ground, it must be done with courtesy and good humour. On one occasion, at the lunch-break, I decided it was time for a visit to the cloakroom. Trying to locate it was a challenge, as most doors were unmarked. However, one was labelled 'Members', so in I went. Consternation broke out amongst the assembled throng, because all the men had taken it for granted that this was the 'boys' room'. Speedy arrangements were made to provide me with a ladies' facility, which, in one stroke, increased the GDC's financial burden of having a lady amongst its elected members.

I was further taken aback when I attended my first meeting of the education committee. There seated at the centre of the large oval, cabinet-style table in the impressive Sheridan committee room on the first floor of the GDC, was the chairman, Professor Arthur Darling, who was the dean of Bristol Dental School, and one of the doyens of dentistry. His opening words were, 'Good morning, gentlemen' and after a pause which felt interminable as all eyes swivelled to me, 'and Margaret!' He was obviously not comfortable in finding a woman foisted onto his prestigious committee and I realised that I would have to be sure of my facts if I did decide to make a contribution to the discussions.

While I was delighted to have been elected to the General Dental Council and appointed to a fascinating and high-profile committee, the truth was that, professionally, I remained unemployed and, more to the point, unpaid! My thoughts returned to an earlier suggestion made by the chief dental officer that I should apply for a Council of Europe fellowship, with the aim of visiting and reporting on an innovative new training establishment for operating ancillary dental personnel, currently taking place in the Netherlands, a country with a shortage of dentists.

I was beginning to realise that it took a long time to secure grants or fellowships, and it was no different on this occasion. I completed the application form by the closing date of 18 February 1977, but was informed that, if a positive decision was made, a visit would not be practicable until the following year. Information was also shared with me about the results of the 1976 awards, when only ten of the 350 applications from doctors, dentists, nurses, and other health professionals had met with success. The only redeeming factor appeared to be my age. Thankfully, at 42, I was well within the upper age limit of 55.

A glimmer of hope came when, after three months, I received a letter informing me that I had been nominated by the UK Selection Committee for a fellowship, although I would have to wait until the autumn when a final decision would be made by the European Committee. Imagine my relief when I was contacted in the late October with the news that I had been awarded a Council of Europe fellowship for fourteen days, tenable in 1978. I quickly started to assemble a programme, centring it on Amsterdam, where the training took place of the type of ancillary worker that I was to study, the *curative medwerkster* (CM). It was also fortunate that it was where the director of the project, Professor Neil Swallow, who had taught me paedodontics as a student, and his delightful wife, Barbara, also a dentist, lived and they offered me hospitality in their home. This was especially welcome, as the grant did not stretch to more than very basic accommodation. It was also extremely helpful to have a guide around Amsterdam, as well as someone who could provide me with a wealth of information, not only about the project, but also about the provision of dental care within the Netherlands.

To see this for myself, I made train journeys to Utrecht to view its new dental school and the school where hygienists were trained. I ventured even further afield, to Nijmegen, where, in addition to training hygienists, another experimental project was underway, producing a type of ancillary worker with the grandiose name of the *Kinderstandverzorgster* (KTV), which occupied a position in the dental team midway between the New Zealand school dental nurse and the New Cross dental auxiliary. Of particular interest was that this operator was permitted to operate on children and also was allowed to give inferior block anaesthesia and take radiographs without supervision, activities prohibited for the dental auxiliary working in the UK.

However, most of my energies were focussed on the management and organisation of the *Tandhelkundig Gezondheids Projekt* (TGP), and to achieve this I spent time with the dentists and sociologists at the Free University of Amsterdam, who established the scheme in 1975. In short, a hygienist was given further training for six months to become a *curative medwerkster* (CM) who was destined to provide the much needed dental care to individuals over twelve years of age, in a community where a shortage of dentists existed. In fact, the training school was conveniently located in the Jordaan area of Amsterdam, which was devoid of even a single dental practice. I was most impressed with the training and quality of work which I observed, and had the good fortune to be conducted round the clinic by a UK trained member of staff, Carolyn Taylor, who later became the president of the BDA Community Dental Services Group.

However, the Dutch Dental Association were singularly unimpressed. Their opposition was intensified when a progress report on the project stated, 'the restorations placed by CMs, while working independently, were at least equal to, and may be more acceptable than, those completed by other dental operators'. Also, it was not helpful that the project ran into financial difficulties, due to the fact that the initial costings had been based on the hours each week for which a CM was employed, and not on the amount of time spent in actually treating a patient and earning money. Thus on my return to the UK, I realised that delegating to auxiliary staff may increase availability to the community of dental care, with restorations provided of the highest quality, but it did not follow that it was a cheaper method to deliver dental care.

But my admiration for the Netherlands was sincere, because here was a country prepared to embrace change and conduct projects to test innovative ways in which to deliver dental care. My recommendations to the CDO, George Gibb, reflected this when I said that 'further experiments should be undertaken in the UK to assess the economic contribution which could be made by the "expanded duty auxiliary" in general dental practice'.

But my visit to Amsterdam was not exclusively work. I was captivated by this attractive city, criss-crossed by canals. On one, the Singel Canal, was the colourful floating flower market. The rich history was preserved in the seventeenth-century architecture as well as in the world famous museums, the Van Gogh Museum, the Rijksmuseum, overflowing with Rembrandts, and the home of the courageous Anne Frank. I have returned to Amsterdam many times for conferences, and, while there are still new places to explore, it is always comforting to revisit favourite gastronomic haunts: it is not only the infamous Red Light district that is on offer.

Despite the satisfactory completion of the Council of Europe's fellowship, and submission of not only a report but also a paper for publication in the *BDJ*, I was still without a paid job. Dr Elizabeth Fanning, a paedodontist from Australia, was visiting the London Hospital dental school for a three-month sabbatical. She spoke at length with me about my work on teething and women in dentistry. 'It's time you thought about building up the academic side of your CV,' was her advice to me. As a lectureship in the children's department at the dental school was becoming vacant, I decided to apply, indicating to Professor Slack, head of the department, that I preferred a part-time teaching post. The other candidate for the post was Ken Williams, a general dental practitioner who also indicated that he ideally wished to work part-time. Thus, we were both appointed, probably one of the first 'job-shares', long before the term had entered the dental vocabulary. Although I was not scheduled to commence work until after Christmas, I decided to go each Friday up to London to the dental school, so as to familiarise myself with the varying aspects of my new job.

One Friday, while I was having lunch in the staff dining room, the Blizzard Club, Ted Renson, Reader in the conservation department, came up to me. 'Just the person I want to have a word with. You know I have got the chair at the Hong Kong, Prince Philip, dental school so I will have to give up my role as editor of *Dental Update*. Would you like to take over?' He explained that, as editor, I would have a unique opportunity to raise issues which I thought needed debate within the profession. Reassuringly, he added, 'It's not onerous; you will only have to write an editorial six times a year.' This sounded an attractive proposition, particularly as there was an accompanying honorarium. I promised Ted that I would think about it over the weekend and give him a decision on the Monday.

Later, on that same Friday evening, Gordon and I were in the bedroom at home in Tudor House, changing to go out to dinner at friends, Brian and Rhianon Trowell, in Hadley Wood. The phone rang. 'Oh dear,' I thought, 'the baby sitter can't make it.' I picked up the phone on the bedside cabinet and, after listening to the caller, sat down quickly on the edge of the bed.

'Are you all right, Margaret?' Gordon gently enquired. I began to rerun what the caller had said. It had to be a mistake!

Chapter 11

The editor's chair

'How would you like to be the editor of the *BDJ*?' Was this a wrong number or a joke? Just a few hours earlier I had been approached by Ted Renson to become consultant editor of *Dental Update*, an easy-to-read and well-illustrated bi-monthly magazine for busy general dental practitioners, as well as being avidly read by dental undergraduates. Now, within hours, the stakes were raised to editor of the *British Dental Journal* (*BDJ*) published by the British Dental Association, with the enviable reputation as the leading scientific and general dental interest publication in the UK. Indeed, the position of editor of the *BDJ* was viewed as one of the top jobs in the dental profession. The editor was also in the fortunate position of having his finger on the professional pulse and was privileged to be amongst the first to read articles announcing new treatments, or ground-breaking fruits of research, or results of surveys.

The plummy-honeyed voice belonging to the caller, due to his frequent broadcasts on the Jimmy Young Show dealing with enquiries about dentistry, was instantly recognisable as that of Ronnie Allen, the secretary of the British Dental Association. Ronnie Allen explained that the reason for the phone call was that Ted Renson had just arrived at BDA Headquarters with the news that during lunch at The London earlier in the day, he had asked me to become consultant editor of *Dental Update*. However, aware of the problems in recruiting an editor for the *BDJ*, he had encouraged Ronnie to phone me to see if I might be interested instead in the *BDJ*. 'I can sense this is a surprise,' said Ronnie Allen, understating the situation. 'Phone me on Monday if you want to know more.'

With my head still in a spin, I finished dressing for dinner and departed with Gordon for the home of our friends the Trowells with barely a chance to recount to him this amazing and unsolicited phone call. The rest of the evening remained a blur – just what was I meant to do?

At the time of this unorthodox approach, I was actively exploring varying career options. In addition to paediatric dentistry, I was very attracted to the new administrative posts created in the reorganised dental public health or community dental services and had made an appointment for the following Monday to spend time with Donald Norman who was the area dental officer in Hounslow. He was generous with his time and gave me a grand tour of his clinics, and a detailed insight into his management role. I did not wish to appear churlish, and spurn his proffered hospitality of lunch, but as quickly as politeness permitted, I beat a hasty retreat home. I wanted to pursue the tantalising conversation of the previous Friday evening with Ronnie Allen.

While beavering away on the women dentists' survey, I had been oblivious to the events regarding the *British Dental Journal*. It transpired that in November 1975, at the meeting of the BDA Representatives Board, the Chairman of Council, Professor Geoffrey Howe, presented to its members a worrying picture of the financial position of the *Journal*. In particular, there was concern about the escalating costs of production and distribution, which threatened to undermine the financial stability of the Association. The chairman had taken preventative action by inviting tenders from alternative printers who could make use of new technology, because the *Journal* was still using the traditional letterpress printing method. A further eighteen months elapsed before the Board decided that as the present editor, Archie Donaldson, was due to retire early in 1979, an advertisement should be placed in the *BDJ* for his successor. The Board stated that 'the successful candidate should take up the post as soon as practicable due to the pressure of work on the present editor and the necessity of redesigning the *BDJ* to be of greater appeal to a larger proportion of the membership'.

Action this time was immediate, and the advertisement appeared in the 5 April issue of the *Journal* stating that the expectation was that the person appointed would take up the position of editor-designate in January 1978. It transpired that no appointment was made after interviewing the applicants for the post, so that a further, and this time full-page, advertisement appeared in the 6 September issue of the *BDJ*. Interviews followed and, again, no appointment was made. The Chairman of Council and the Secretary were alarmed at this impasse, especially as there was a sudden deterioration in the health of the incumbent, prompting them, on hearing the news from Ted Renson, to take the matter into their own hands and contact me. As far as I was concerned, I could see no harm in finding out more about the post and travelled up to London on the Tuesday to meet up with Ronnie Allen and Geoffrey Howe at the BDA Headquarters in Wimpole Street. On arrival, I was handed a copy of the information pack sent to those candidates who had responded to the advertisement and settled down in an ante-room, with a welcome cup of coffee, to absorb details of the job. I discovered that the person had to be a qualified dentist and would be the sixteenth person to fill the position since the appointments of Alfred Colman and Joseph Walker as joint editors in 1880. This was when the BDA acquired the *Monthly Review of Dental Surgery* which had claimed an unbroken record of publication since its foundation in 1872, so ensuring that the *BDJ* was older than the Association which it served. The *Journal* was published twice each month and sent to every one of its members: 16,000 at that time.

The post was not only regarded as being of prime importance to the Association and to the dental profession, but was also a full-time commitment. In addition to the editorial duties, there was the requirement to attend meetings of the Representative Board and Council, often held on Saturdays, and to make visits to branches and sections of the BDA throughout the country speaking about and promoting the *Journal*. Concurrently were the responsibilities associated with *Journal* production; work with printers and advertising agents and especially to explore how to bring a new look to the publication. Ideas began to well up inside me, although my enthusiasm was tempered by the acute awareness that my editorial knowledge was limited. Most of my contact with journals was from the perspective of an author of scientific papers and reports.

Over a delicious lunch with the secretary and chairman, I was provided with additional information and the promise of training if I decided to apply for the post. So as we parted, the ball was back firmly in my court. My daughter Pamela, then fourteen, tells me that I shared with my children my dilemma about accepting a full-time post in London. Both youngsters were helpfully now attending the same school, Latymer in Edmonton. The downside was that there was no direct public transport to the school from Hadley Wood where we lived, so several families, the Lehners, Trowells, Floyds and ourselves, had organised a school 'run' to take the children to the 'W8' bus stop at Chase Farm Hospital in Enfield. The bus, after a twenty minute or so journey, disgorged its pupil load at the end of Haselbury Road, just a couple of minutes' walk from the main entrance of Latymer School. I therefore offered to do the morning run and, in return, my friends generously agreed to take care of the homeward journey. Pamela and Colin were already experienced at letting themselves into our house on their own, rewarded by finding tempting 'goodies' in the fridge to satisfy their pangs of hunger. My parents, along with many of their generation, would have been horrified to think that I was encouraging 'latchkey' children, although I believe, and they concur, that it did not cause them lasting harm.

I am, however, convinced from this event that life-changing decisions, disrupting comfortable and familiar routines, should be fully and frankly discussed with all family members. It is only in this way that consequences, worries, or difficulties can be shared, and solutions worked through together. I admit that at the time the discussions which took place were more by good luck than judgement, but if I had to encounter this situation again, I would put this exercise near the top of a list of 'must dos'.

Once my family had been consulted, I decided to contact, in strict confidence, Archie Donaldson, the then *BDJ* editor. He willingly agreed. 'Meet me at Oxford Street tube station at 12 noon. Wait for me at the bottom of the steps where you would exit to the south side of Regent Street.' As planned, at midday, a tall, bowed and bespectacled figure appeared at the meeting point and was instantly recognisable as Archie Donaldson. We climbed the stairs together and, breathlessly, he disclosed our destination. 'I am going to take you to a small and family-run Italian restaurant, where we will not be disturbed by anyone from the BDA.'

That claim has remained true over the years in which I have frequented the 'Il Porcellino' in Blenheim Street, secreted away from bustling New Bond Street, and still serving the delicious *scampi provencale* savoured on that occasion and remaining a firm favourite.

Archie described his problems in producing a high quality journal, and the ongoing preoccupation of the BDA members with costs. He came across to me as an unassuming man, kind and thoughtful and disliking fuss about himself or his journal, which he had carefully steered from his office in Wimpole Street for eleven years. He also carried the responsibility of his first love, the BDA Museum, of which he was curator for thirty-four years, which included the time when he returned devotedly to the task after demitting office as editor. To me he gave a clear account of a failing journal crying out for rejuvenation and an input of commercial acumen to improve its financial position, just the sort of business challenge that I knew from my previous enterprises I would relish, although I was only too well aware that I was light on editorial skills.

'Nothing ventured, nothing gained' spurred me on to submit on 6 January my curriculum vitae in support of my application for appointment as editor-designate of the *BDJ*. I also let Archie know that I had decided to apply for the post. His reply was generous but cautious. 'I was genuinely pleased to have your news. On grounds of ability and personality, I hope you are successful, but I am not sure that I can unreservedly wish you success on account of the stresses involved.'

By return of post, I was invited to attend the meeting of the Advisory Appointments Committee, on Tuesday 17 January at 3 p.m. This comprised senior members of the profession: the Chairman of Council, Professor Howe, as chairman of the committee, and as members, Professors Bertram Cohen and Howard Tonge, Messrs Gil Daley, Tom Dowell, Gerry Wootliff and Gordon Fordyce. It remains a vivid memory of being shown into the smaller of the two meeting rooms on the first floor of the Association's premises, with heavy brocade curtains and the stern and bearded founding fathers of the BDA staring down at me from the heavy gilt frames housing their impressive portraits. The bucket-shaped green leather chairs were crammed around the large table and graced by the members of the committee. My chair was the solitary one at the end of the table, facing the chairman and with a welcome glass of water positioned in front of me, as I felt my tongue gradually glue itself to the roof of my mouth. After a reassuring smile from the chairman and the introductions of the panel, the questions started to be fired for the next forty minutes or so, and were all predictable. Then one member addressed me in a critical tone and asked me to explain what I would do if one of my children was taken ill. I could feel my hackles rise and sharply replied, 'I expect Gordon could take time out of his clinic.' I could sense the unease amongst the members who knew Gordon well and were aware that it would be unlikely for that to happen as he was head of the busy oral surgery department at the London Hospital. The chairman came to my rescue by bringing the interview swiftly to a close with the traditional, 'Have you any questions for the committee?' Buried in my bag I had several. But I decided that now these were irrelevant and unimportant. It was a relief to escape into the cold and dark winter's afternoon, and make my way into the beckoning and brightly-lit department store, D. H. Evans, at the Oxford Street-end of Wimpole Street. I browsed around the goods on display to cheer myself up, and then treated the family to the recently released recording of the soundtrack of *Star Wars*, which we had enjoyed seeing at the Odeon Cinema in Tottenham Court Road during the Christmas holidays. Then, feeling in a happier frame of mind, I made my way home to share with my family the nightmare interview, and how I had responded when provoked over my 'child-care' arrangements for Pamela and Colin. Never, I vowed, would I ask similar personal questions if I became a member of an interview panel.

Now, I was determined to direct all my energies into returning to paediatric dentistry and the job at The London was still on offer. I had plenty to keep myself occupied in this field, as I was the national secretary of the British Paedodontic Society and had been involved in arranging the programme to celebrate the 25th Anniversary scientific meeting, held at the Manchester Business School under the presidency of Professor Leslie Hardwick the previous year. I had assembled and found sponsorship to produce a sixteen-page souvenir booklet to mark the occasion but I could not claim this as evidence of editorial prowess.

But I did not even have the time on arriving home to impart my forebodings at the outcome of the interview when the phone rang. It was the cheery voice of Ronnie Allen. 'Thank you for coming this afternoon; your name will go forward to the Representative Board in February with the recommendation to appoint you as editor-designate.' Delight, fear, relief and apprehension would be a selection of words to describe my reaction to this unexpected news. Gradually it sank in that I was to be properly employed, full-time, and earning a salary. I earnestly hoped that I would not let down the people who had shown confidence in me.

The process gained momentum and I received a letter on 21 February from Ronnie Allen, informing me that 'the Board had agreed unanimously that I should be appointed editor-designate, and Professor Howe should negotiate with me detailed terms and conditions of service.' But his life was also moving forward at a pace, and he resigned as chairman of council on his appointment as dean of dental studies in Hong Kong, with the exciting task of building a brand new dental school, later named the Prince Philip Dental Hospital. The new incumbent, Gil Daley, completed the negotiations and my starting salary was £12,000 per annum, with the luxury of one fifteen-pence luncheon voucher for each day. These were relished as a form of pocket money by our youngsters, who enjoyed discovering the various eating houses which traded in these vouchers. But the detail of the contract was complicated, and reflected the unease expressed forcibly by some members of the academic fraternity in having an editor (or was it a woman?) of limited experience at the helm.

There are times to speak out and fight for change, but on this occasion I considered it would be wise to wait and aim to prove them wrong. Thus, although I felt it irksome, I agreed to four different hoops through which I would have to jump to gain true autonomy. From the starting date of 19 June 1978 to February 1979, I would be editor-designate, alongside Archie Donaldson, who would retire on 7 February 1979. Then, from 8 February, I would enter a probationary period as editor until 31 May 1980. Finally, from 1 June until a date decided by Professors Cohen and Tonge, I was to be editor, subject to advice, even although by then I would have been in employment for more than eighteen months. Having experienced this complex arrangement, it is not surprising that I think overlap or 'subject to advice' periods should be as short as possible.

With completion of these tedious negotiations of my contract, Gil Daley reported to the Representative Board that I would be taking up my appointment on 18 June. It fell to Bernard Caplan, on behalf of the Board, to welcome me, and he did this in great style. According to Chambers dictionary, he said, I should be called an editress. 'Further,' he said, 'an editor or editress compiled, garbled or cooked up into literary shape.' Bernard Caplan then offered some advice as to the cooking up for success in the pot-pourri which was the *Journal*. 'Take a modicum of scientific matter, a soup can of news and events and a large measure of articles of interest to general practitioners. Garnish with a yellow sauce newsletter and serve up on a platter to all members of the Association.' Delivered in his Scots brogue, this witty discourse earned him loud applause. It also caused my temerity to disappear and I rose to thank him for his cordon bleu menu to help me in the *Journal*'s redesign. 'It is an honour and a privilege to serve as editor of the *BDJ* and I hasten to assure the Board that I neither plan to run an Auntie Maggie's column nor introduce a page three.' Bellows of 'More's the pity' followed, which reassured me that at least I had the ninety or so members of the Board on side, even if I was not so fortunate with the academics.

I was also thrilled that the Association took the decision to waive the discriminatory rule in force for the BDA pension scheme. In the handbook it clearly stated that men could join the scheme on appointment 'but women will normally only be admitted to membership if they have had two years' service with the Association.' I really began to feel I was working for an enlightened organisation.

In order to activate a further stipulation in my contract, 'She will use her best endeavours to acquire training in all the skills in which she may be deficient and to review the format, content and production of the *Journal*', I signed up, at the Association's expense, for a course on journalism at the London College of Printing. Its building fronted onto the Elephant & Castle roundabout, and was reached after traversing a labyrinth of subways from the underground tube exit. I arrived to commence the day-release course of ten weeks' duration, and discovered that my fellow participants were recent graduates intent on pursuing a career in journalism. Most of them were already securely on the first rung of the journalistic ladder as editorial assistants on *Family Circle*, *Music Maker*, *Leatherworld* and the *Financial Times*. I was twice their average age, but they were incredibly friendly and, like the tutors, viewed me as a novelty, coming with a background of a traditional scientific journal of a professional organisation. However, on the first day, it was clear that to be less obtrusive I needed to dress down; my tailor suit was definitely not suitable attire! So, I decided to don my gardening apparel, including my favourite baggy jumper, fraying at the elbows. 'Are you not going to the college today?' enquired Gordon at breakfast. I quickly explained that I was going and the reason for my informal garb. 'Well, don't travel on the same train as me!' was his embarrassed riposte.

From the college we were sent out on a variety of assignments: to interview the passers-by in a shopping mall about a topical event; to describe a local parade or exhibition, and to produce copy, not only by a set deadline, but also within the required word count. All these tasks seemed alien to the skills required for a budding editor of a scientific journal, but as it transpired, they were invaluable, as I wrestled with introducing an informal style to the reporting of trade and news items in the *Journal*. It also gave me great 'street cred' when talking with people within the wider printing and journalistic circles.

I was also privileged to be there at the time of the unrest affecting the printing industry due to the scheduled move of production from Fleet Street to Wapping and the introduction of modern technology, with the inevitable loss of jobs. The might of the trade unions, the power of the father of the chapel, as the local trade union branch was called, and the allegiance of the card-carrying members of the union was an education in itself for me. This was all a million miles away from the genteel trade union of dentists, the BDA.

Ronnie Allen opened another fruitful door for me when he gave me a copy of the recently published book by Maeve O'Connor, *Editing Scientific Books and Journals*. This became my bible as it was aimed at beginners like myself and most rewardingly it led me to the author, who was the senior editor of the Ciba Foundation. Through her friendship I began to attend a series of helpful seminars and workshops organised by the Learned and Professional Society of Publishers, of which Dr Stephen Lock, editor of the *British Medical Journal*, was a prominent member.

On my appointment there had been a great flurry of news stories in the local press, as well as in dental magazines. Local friends were especially impressed that my appointment ('Chosen to be the *Journal*'s first woman editor') appeared on the front page of the 23 June issue of the *Barnet Press*, alongside a photograph of Margaret Thatcher, the MP for neighbouring Finchley, who at that time was leader of the opposition. She was opening the new premises of Michael Gerson Ltd., an overseas removal specialist, and joked that it was a pity that they did not work locally, because 'I may be able to put some extra business your way very soon'. Her prophetic utterances became reality when, on 3 May 1979, she became Britain's first female Prime Minister.

This local coverage prompted lovely personal letters from friends and elderly members of St Paul's Church in Enfield, many of whom recalled seeing me first entering church with Mr and Mrs Mitchell, as a toddler, with blonde curls. Margaret Simpson, in her letter, echoed my inner feelings. 'I can't help wishing your parents were alive to share in the thrill of your success.' It had indeed been a great sadness that my parents, who had given me so many opportunities, died in 1969, within four months of each other, so robbing Pamela and Colin, at the age of five and three, of two adoring grandparents.

However, as was to be anticipated, not all the press stories were flattering. Donald Gould, columnist in *The New Scientist* wrote, 'I do find that "Letters to the Editor" beginning "Madam" take me aback a bit. Editors should be "Sir", just like God Almighty is a Him and that's all there is to it!'

The Probe, the magazine of the General Dental Practitioners' Association (GDPA) joined the fray. In its June editorial it made a critical comment about 'the skeleton of divided loyalties' and warned against 'bringing them out of the cupboard'. 'Mrs Seward' Ken Brown the editor wrote, 'may feel it would be wise for her to resign from the GDC . . . she made a highly partisan intervention in the auxiliaries debate at the last meeting. As she was entitled to do. But would her entitlement to speak out be the same were she the editor of the *BDJ*?'

Elaine Mason, the vice-chairman of the Representative Board, was quick to write to me. 'I see you are already being slated by the GDPA – but hope that won't upset you too much. I reckon you can give as good as you get.' Providentially, on the day the article appeared, I was due to attend the college for a lecture on law and ethics in journalism, so I took along with me a copy of the offending editorial: 'Divided loyalties?' My tutor, on reading the article, got excited, and expounded to the group how my integrity was on the line. More to the point, he said that libel and defamation were difficult to prove conclusively. 'Even if you don't sue, keep the article in your drawer for seven years, in case you change your mind.' There were many occasions when I used teasingly to remind the author, Ken Brown, that I had his article 'on ice'. But, in fact, we became the best of friends, and his knowledge of journalism was without equal, having spent a lifetime as a reporter in Fleet Street, with the reputation as the fastest shorthand writer in town. However, I did take on board his comments about ensuring I did not limit my interests and, indeed, I championed many causes for British Dentistry through the *Journal* columns, and not narrowly those of dental auxiliaries. Today, we would refer to the issue he raised as 'conflict of interests' which, increasingly, would seem to affect people within the public gaze. Nevertheless, I did not resign. I believed it would be the electorate who could decide my fate, not the editor of *The Probe*.

It was reassuring to work alongside Archie Donaldson for the first eight months. He was far from well and had an oxygen cylinder and mask parked alongside his

1. The Oldershaw family in Weymouth, 1933

2. Derek (7) nearest the pram and Leslie (10) admiring their new sister, me

3. Installed in my new home with Mum

4. In my Palmers Green High School uniform and the Hat!

5. *Together with Grandma and Grandad Oldershaw in Lincoln*

6. *Latymer School 1st tennis team, 1954. Myself extreme right*

7. *Our Wedding Day, 1962; left to right: Elizabeth Russell, Michael and Alan Tyrrell, Ruth Seward, May and Jack Mitchell, Joan Roberts (Fountain). In front nephew Peter and niece Sue Oldershaw*

8. *With my brothers Dr Leslie and Major Derek Oldershaw*

9. Pouring Dr Douglas Barber his whisky at my teething demonstration at the BDA Conference in Aberdeen

10. Showing the Minister Edwina Currie MP the latest BDJ *book on Dental Photography*

11. Princess Diana with Gordon in 1988 after receiving the Honorary FDS. I am following with the Lord Mayor of Westminster Councillor Elizabeth Flack

2. In front of the statue of John Hunter at the Royal College of Surgeons of England receiving the Commemorative Medal from the Dean of the Faculty of Dental Surgery, Mr Derek Seel, after giving the Tenth Menzies Campbell Lecture in 1990: The Fair Face of Dentistry – from Anathema to Acceptance

13. Appropriately attired for the Benevolent Fund Duck Race at the conference

14. At the civic reception, the Mayor of Bournemouth, Councillor Ron Whittaker, receiving delegates attending the BDA conference in 1993

large and stylish desk. He placed a small table in his room for me, and to get me started gave me the manuscript of my article on 'Operating Ancillary Dental Personnel in the Netherlands' to mark up and take through to the proof stage. To learn the steps of the editorial process on one's own manuscript made the task more interesting. I was also introduced to the piles of unread copies of Hansard – the verbatim report of the Parliamentary proceedings for each day – and entreated to extract the items about dentistry, which would then be copied to act as 'fillers' for the *BDJ*. Another transcript which needed my attention was the record of the debates by members of the Representative Board, which usually stretched on interminably, as debate followed debate, and could last an entire Saturday. These 'Proceedings', as they were called, were distributed with the *BDJ* to all members of the Association. It was a costly and time-consuming exercise and most members were only interested in what they themselves had said. If the blue pencil was used too liberally on pronouncements made by senior members of the Council, or the Board, there were immediate complaints. However, reputations could be made or lost if there was less than judicious editing of a verbatim speech. This boring, almost soul-destroying exercise of editing the transcript did bring its reward, because it reinforced to me the wisdom of the advice which I had previously received, about the dangers inherent in making ad hoc speeches when recording is taking place.

But my prime task during this overlap period as editor-designate was to design a new format for the *BDJ*. It seemed sensible, initially, to consult the readers for their views, and this I did with the expert statistical assistance of Diana Scarrott, an assistant secretary on the staff at the BDA. Thus, the first readership survey was conducted during the autumn, amongst one in every ten members of the Association.

So what did the readers want? There was enthusiastic support for a change from the quarter crown size to the international A4 size, although the librarians protested that this meant a change in the height of their shelves. The overwhelming desire was to expand the general interest side of the publication, without compromising the quality or status that the *BDJ* enjoyed as the leading UK scientific journal, with a worldwide readership. In response to this request, invitations were extended to Patrick Moore (astronomy), Stirling Moss (car racing) and Ed Swanson (cricket) to contribute an article, but this initiative proved to be too costly to maintain.

Regular meetings were held with graphic designers and a mock-up of sample pages was produced using Latin letterset. The reasoning behind its use was that the eye would concentrate on the designs, and not be distracted by the content of the pages, unless, of course, you were fluent in Latin. I took these mock-ups to as many branches and sections around the country as possible so as to gauge members' support, and was most encouraged not only by their enthusiastic support, but also by additional ideas for improving the readability of the *Journal*. I was fortunate to be in post at a time when change was to be welcomed. However, it was made clear to me that to succeed I had to return the *Journal* to operating at a surplus. (Profit was not a word condoned by the learned Association.) The production, advertising, and sales side of the *BDJ* had been undertaken for several years by Professional and Scientific Publications (PSP), a registered company at BMA House. In charge was Tony Smith, with whom I established instant rapport, and impressed upon him and his team the need to secure financial rigour to achieve a dramatic upturn to the revenue obtained from the 'classified and display' advertisement sales so that our new designs and ideas for the *BDJ* could be affordable. Welcome assistance to achieve this goal was received from the BDA accountant, Anthony Pugh, who confided in me the traditional 'hidden costs' apportioned to the *Journal*; rates, office rent, and the percentage of salaries of BDA staff who did not work directly for the *Journal* but whose costs the *Journal* had to bear, despite their links being more than a little tenuous. Although, I understand, this is not an unusual commercial practice, to me it seemed grossly unfair, when I was endeavouring to establish the real cost of the production of the *BDJ*. At every opportunity I strenuously contested this practice but at the same time looked at ways to reduce costs in production. For example, on visiting the established printers, I discovered that the letterpress method used also meant that production of blocks for illustrations could be prohibitively expensive. It was obvious that we should embrace the new lithographic process, which permitted cheaper production of photographs, but also the introduction of colour, much desired by readers and advertisers.

The launch party on 3 July 1979 was a jolly affair as everyone was anxious to see the 'new-look *BDJ*'. The lecture theatre at BDA headquarters was crammed to capacity with scientific editors and advisers, editorial staff, contributors, dental press representatives, printers, advertising and sales staff from PSP, as well as BDA officers. It truly had been a major team effort to produce the first issue. Gone was the dull and monotonous buff-coloured cover, replaced instead with a bright and eye-catching sequence of colours: orange, green, brown, blue, yellow and red. The sequence was to stimulate the dentist to note the arrival of a fresh issue of the *Journal* and provoke a change in the reported habit of leaving piles unopened on the desk! New features were introduced alongside the core scientific papers: 'casebook', 'way to do it', 'finance', 'practice management', 'trade product news', and an interview with a leading dental personality, Ronnie Allen chosen as the first volunteer for this series.

Approbation for the new-look *BDJ* was given in glowing terms by the much respected and loved editor of *Dental Practice*, Colin Davis. 'If a "give-away" journal may be allowed to touch its forelock to the chatelaine of the Big House, we offer her our humble congratulations and wish her well.' With this endorsement ringing in my ears, I then came face-to-face with the reality of the situation. It is one thing to pull out all the stops to produce the first issue of a new-look *Journal*, but quite another to repeat the exercise twenty-two times a year, with only one full-time editorial member of staff to assist. How indeed had Archie Donaldson managed? No wonder he had warned me of the stresses involved. His long-serving secretary, Kath Allan, had also decided to take early retirement, I guess sensing the new winds of change, and I was fortunate that Marjorie Gillate, who had worked with me at the British Postgraduate Medical Federation on the women's survey, came to be my PA for many happy and productive years, until she reached retirement age. However, I was determined to make the case for additional journalistic help, not only to lighten my load, but also to assist Frank Tidman. He was a walking encyclopaedia on all BDA and *BDJ* matters, having worked at the Association for forty-six years, spanning more eras than any other employee, with a record unlikely to be broken. He had started in 1936 as a junior clerk/book-keeper and, on returning from the Second World War, he had assisted the *Journal* with the accounts and advertising revenue, finally assisting in the production of the *BDJ*. I became the fourth editor with whom he had worked and his meticulous checking of detail led him so often to discover errors hidden in long lists of references, or columns of figures. His punctuality over four decades was legendary, and he met the seemingly mammoth changes in the *BDJ* with good grace and humour. But it was imperative that he should be given assistance with the brunt of extra work falling on him with the enlarged publication.

So I embarked on making my case to the BDA finance committee for urgent investment in their *Journal* staff. At first, it was agreed that I could employ a part-time staff writer, Pamela Mann, to help with the non-scientific material and, after some months, add a full-time assistant editor, Keith Sugden. As time progressed and the health of the *Journal* finances improved, I was emboldened in my requests. I now note that my response to a letter from Anthony Pugh for my budget requirements for salaries in 1982 was: 'I wish an allowance to be made in the coming year for the purchase of a pocket dictaphone and transcribing machine. I consider this an essential tool for my work.' Also included was a request for 'the possible lease, hire or purchase of a word processor for the *BDJ*'. My requests were granted and, throughout my career, the pocket dictaphone became my constant companion. On my retirement, Sue Hayman, my long-suffering and highly efficient PA, compiled for me a treasured scrapbook of personal letters from colleagues and friends and Sue herself wrote, 'You have the ability to fit forty-seven A4 page letters on to one side of a forty-five minute tape! Not to mention places in which dictated: under tannoys, in tunnels, placed on top of a washing machine during a spin cycle, in a parade ground, to mention a few.' I have to confess that all my wonderful PAs over the years, Marjorie Gillate, Eva Lembke and Sonia Chadband, will recognise Sue's description of choice of dictating sites, and so belated apologies would seem in order for the discomfort endured in these ear-deafening locations.

Improvements in technology can be slow to be embraced, and often it is a sudden crisis which focuses attention. In one particular instance it was the protracted mail strike. At the *BDJ* we were dependent on the post to bring and take copy to our new printer, E. T. Heron in Witham, Essex. On occasions, when speed was of the essence, a motor-bike rider would be hired to courier the copy, although this was an expensive method. Unfortunately, it was not always a secure method of delivery, as one day the rider lost his valuable *BDJ* cargo from his pillion, it being strewn over the M11 and grass verges for several miles. I pleaded for the purchase, or hire, of a very new fax machine for the *BDJ* office, so as to circumvent any future disasters or delays. Luck was on my side and I took delivery of a brand new fax machine, the first within BDA, and this resulted in plenty of callers to the *BDJ* office to view this magic piece of equipment, which could send material back and forth from Witham at the touch of a button. Two decades on it has become almost an obsolete item of office furniture, such has been the impact of electronic communication aides.

But it is worth remembering that it was not only the dedicated editorial staff within Wimpole Street who kept the show on the road; there was also my band of unpaid, and unsung, scientific advisers and referees. During my thirteen-year tenure as editor, I was fortunate to benefit from the wisdom, insight and unfailing support of three gifted, and incredibly loyal, assistant scientific editors, Professors Tony Naylor, Frank Ashley, and John Murray. Their role was to review virtually every manuscript submitted to the *Journal*, and then, taking into account the comments from the external referees, submit to me with all these documents their views on the suitability of the article for publication. With the benefit of this collated information, it was then left to me to come to a decision: accept, reject, or amend, my decision being the final word. It is also incumbent upon the editor to ensure that there are no legal irregularities in the articles, because responsibility for the entire scientific and advertising content is vested in the editor. It is the editor, not the authors of the offending article, who goes to prison – it certainly concentrates the mind!

After a couple of years in the job, I could feel I was slipping into a 'desk job' and gradually losing the 'hands-on' clinical experience essential if I was to keep not only myself but also the *Journal* at the leading edge of dental science in the UK. I therefore decided to activate a further clause in my contract which permitted me to work for up to two clinical sessions each week. I was appointed honorary lecturer in the oral and maxillofacial surgery department at the London Hospital, and found the experience greatly stimulating and enjoyable. Imparting, on a Monday afternoon, to students, the tips for successful exodontia (tooth removal) and see them brimming with enthusiasm, accomplishing their first 'this or that', energised me for the remainder of the week. As I know from other teachers, the reward is to see your students achieve and, for me too, it has been reassuring to see so many happily settled in their chosen career pathway as well as some, like Paul Gallop, climb the political greasy pole at the BDA, while Len d'Cruz became a regular contributor to the dental press.

When I arrived to become editor, I inherited the incumbent eight honorary scientific advisers, as well as a fearsome *Journal* subcommittee of BDA members. Fortunately this latter was disbanded soon after my arrival, which certainly made life less complicated, with fewer meetings. However, it was imperative for the new-look *Journal* to refocus and rejuvenate the current group of scientific advisers, as I wanted an editorial board which would act as a sounding board, and advise on policy matters, with the *Journal* then benefiting from their wide and varied experience. I consigned to the history books the frequent, and what I considered tedious, meetings of advisers who discussed the minutiae of manuscript composition, or the suitability of those papers submitted. My mandate was change and the scientific editors and advisers were a valuable resource to effect that change.

The resulting select group of scientific advisers jealously guarded their position, but also exhibited a prized camaraderie. So much so that it led them, as a group, to embark on designing a '*BDJ* tie', to be worn by themselves, as well as for presentation to regular referees and to a selected few for acts of service to the *Journal*. I was astounded by the complexity and protracted nature of the meetings held to produce the finished item of clothing. All the advisers arrived at the table with their favoured designs, and John Rayne, with consummate skill, guided them towards an acceptable design comprising the BDA crest of 'lions, staff and serpent', beneath a pair of crossed quills stitched in yellow, on a navy background. But more dissension occurred among the ranks when exploring the fabric to be used: 'I do feel that the tie should at least be all silk,' said Ian Gainsford. 'My wife,' said Peter Sykes, 'reminds me that I am a filthy eater and only washable polyester is practicable . . .' 'Polyester/silk has perhaps a slightly higher coefficient of friction, and there is an advantage that it can be washed,' opined Robin Basker, at that time Professor of prosthetic dentistry, so he should have been conversant with the claims of differing materials. The discussion then shifted to the position of the logo and the width of the tie. In the end I was left to ponder if any scientific paper, throughout the existence of the *BDJ*, had enjoyed such scrutiny!

The *Journal* was a hard task master. A leader column had to be written every two weeks, bringing to the attention of members current issues, or making considered observations on the main recommendations in published reports or inquiries. During my tenure, I wrote most of them, totalling nearly 300 in number, and under the cloak of anonymity. I needed undisturbed and quality time to decide on a topic, and weave my comments within the constraints of 600 words, a task more often discharged satisfactorily early on a Sunday morning.

It was this area of my work which invoked comment from Professor Bert Cohen, who would write to me, expounding my faults in style and syntax. Not professing at any time to be an English scholar, I became increasingly depressed at this continuing criticism, and felt the need to seek help to restore my confidence through rectifying any errors. I turned to Muriel Yates-Mercer for assistance, a friend from childhood days at St Paul's Church, who had risen to become head of English at the Grey Coat School for Girls, the well-known independent school in London. My worst fears of ineptitude were not confirmed, although I am sure my style improved with her expert tuition, which took place before the copy was dispatched to its next destination. The recipient was the chairman of the BDA Council, who read the leader, to ensure that I did not conflict with stated BDA policy, although at no time was I told that the *Journal* had to be the mouthpiece of the Association, rather of British dentistry. Over the years I was fortunate to benefit from the wise counsel of Gil Daley, Bryan Gillard, and Geoff Garnett, who had unrivalled knowledge of the political scene, and who, thankfully, were staunch supporters of the *Journal*, and gave liberally of their encouragement to achieve our aim.

'Now look what you have done! Professor Cohen has just phoned and wants you sacked,' exclaimed Ronnie Allen as he entered my office, courteously extinguishing his cigarette. At the end of a day, I would know how many times Ronnie had called, by counting the stubs in the office ashtray. He was an excellent communicator and hands-on manager, and always made it his business to see and be seen around the departments. So what was the misdemeanour which had invoked such a demand? My first thought was that perhaps there was anger at the recently published readability scores for the *BDJ*, which I had received from Andy Blinkhorn, a senior lecturer in preventative dentistry at that time, at the Edinburgh Dental School. His research had shown that the 'reading age' of the old *BDJ* was 16–18 years, and the score for the new-look *Journal*, at 12–13 years, was hailed as a great improvement. However, this was not the issue at stake and Ronnie, with a twinkle in his eye, said, 'I have also had many dentists on the phone, commenting that it was the best thing the *BDJ* had ever done, so leave it to me to sort out.' He then returned to his office to keep his word.

So what was the fuss about? Unusually, the publication date in 1980 was 1 April, and I had decided to run an article written by Barry Scheer, about 'Dental Disease in Brunus Edwardii' (Teddy Bears). Gradually, it had dawned on observant readers that it was a harmless 'April Fool's Day' prank, not a view shared by the Professor. Amazingly, the subsequent correspondence columns bulged with letters on this single topic, many picking a humorous theme. 'One can only thank Mr Scheer for his article which has opened our eyes to the vast new field of zoopaedodontia . . . And I am now wondering if Peter Rabbit would be in line for orthodontic treatment?', penned R. Selby from Oldham. Absolution was complete when I received the ultimate request for permission from the *American Journal of Irreproducible Results* to include the article in their journal. Sadly, or maybe fortunately, for the remainder of my term the date of publication did not again coincide with April Fool's Day!

With an increase in staff and *Journal* activities, we rapidly outgrew the cramped office space on the ground floor at the front of the BDA building and were fortunate to be relocated to a comfortable suite of offices, vacated by the Dentists' Provident Society, at the rear of the HQ building. No journal is ever in its final form, as it has to adapt to changes in style and content to keep up to date. As a result, on average every five years, there was a readership survey and then a relaunch which brought a renewal of interest from readers, subscribers and advertisers. In fact, the *BDJ* was then so attractive that Ray Barker from Macmillans approached me with an interesting business proposition. However, the delicious lunch at Rules Restaurant in Covent Gardens strengthened my resolve to resist. It made me realise that our improving publication was being viewed with commercial interest by the big players in the publishing field. It is worth recording that a couple of decades later, under my successor, Mike Grace, Macmillan achieved their ambition.

Nevertheless, despite the upturn in the fortunes of the *BDJ*, I decided to cast my net wider. I wanted to discover new ways to raise funds for the *Journal*, funds which I could claim and spend as my own, to enhance the *BDJ* for the readers.

So, just what initiatives had I in mind to achieve this altruistic aim?

Chapter 12

Journal initiatives

'DON'T LET THEM STOP YOU going to the FDI; it's important for the *BDJ* editor to be there,' was a further piece of wise advice given to me by Archie Donaldson.

At that time, the membership of the Federation Dentaire Internationale (FDI) comprised nearly ninety national dental associations from around the world and, each year, a world dental congress was hosted by one of the member associations. So, emboldened by my predecessor's comment, I indicated that I had every intention of attending, especially as the congress in 1979 was to be held in a captivating city, which I had always dreamed of visiting: Paris.

I stayed for the week at the Hotel Chateau Frontenac, situated between the famous Champs-Elysées and the magnificent Avenue George V, with the BDA delegation, Geoffrey Howe and Ronnie Allen. These seasoned FDI attendees ensured that I became fully conversant with the fascinating political meetings held alongside the scientific programme, as well as accompanying me to the extravagant social events, many convened in prestigious venues. The closing banquet was in the Versailles palace, with a display of dancing fountains on the terrace to the strains of classical music specially activated for guests of the FDI. There was an air of opulence amongst the FDI dentists, most running exclusive dental practices in their country, with, for example, Harley Street and Wimpole Street being well represented by the English dentists.

My previous experience of attending a British Dental Association annual conference, with six or seven hundred participants, did not prepare me for the gigantic size of an international congress. Here, I was faced with thousands of delegates from all parts of the world (how I wish I had studied harder at foreign languages at school!), an enormous trade exhibition with literally hundreds of stands straddling several halls, and a lecture programme providing parallel sessions, with some offering simultaneous translation into English from French, German, Spanish, and Japanese. But, for me, the overriding excitement was the discovery of the diversity and consistent quality of the presentations, given by internationally-renowned speakers, all aimed towards busy general dental practitioners – the target audience of the *BDJ*. I will never forget listening awe-struck to Peter Kurer and his brother Hans explaining their revolutionary invention for restoring a missing tooth. To me, their description of the 'Kurer Anchor System' was exactly the type of practical and clinical article that I desperately needed for publication in my *Journal*. So, I tracked down the inventors, who were fortunately from the

UK, and floated with them the idea of not only preparing a series of papers for the *Journal*, but also sharing their methods and talking about alternative techniques for restoring endodontically treated (root treated) teeth, at a specially convened postgraduate study day organised by the *BDJ*. Further, I suggested that the course notes could be a series of articles, first published in the *Journal*, and then reproduced as a glossy A5 booklet, a more stylish accompaniment than the usual sheaf of loose A4 papers. Peter and Hans Kurer embraced this new concept with what I was to learn was their characteristic enthusiasm, and so the '*BDJ* Teach-In' was born!

I enlisted Barry Scheer's help as course organiser, and he (the well-known author of the now infamous 'Teddy Bear' article) recommended the Tower Hotel, next to Tower Bridge, where he organised several meetings in his role as postgraduate tutor at the London Hospital Dental School. I was fortunate to have ready access to my *Journal* pages for free publicity, and soon an editorial item in the 'News and Notes' column appeared: '"Success Hangs on a Thread", the first *BDJ* Teach-In to be held on Saturday, 27 September 1980 from 10 a.m. to 5 p.m. at the Tower Hotel.' The Jeremiahs at the BDA lamented the choice of a Saturday for a full day course, and the exorbitant price for a place, £30, although this included coffee on arrival, a sit-down three-course luncheon, and a refreshing cup of tea on departure, added to which there was available in each delegate's pack a copy of the booklet. With great relief I found I was inundated with applications and the ninety available places were taken within the first week. Obviously, there was an appetite for a postgraduate meeting with a difference. My family were roped in to help my secretary, Marjorie Gillate, with the registration of the delegates. However, it never failed to amaze me how dentists, who have a reputation of being prudent with money, would purchase a ticket in advance and then decide to do something else on the day, without making any effort to notify us of their intentions, or even request a refund. This pattern of 'non-showing' became known to disappointed late applicants, who would risk making the journey to London early on the Saturday morning to see if they could secure entry – which they usually did. The success of the first teach-in was endorsed by a generous gift from the Kurers of an ornately enamelled Chinese plate. This was displayed in the *BDJ* office on the inscribed stand as a permanent reminder of an initiative, which was destined to become a fixture in the *Journal* calendar for nearly ten years, as well as an enterprise providing a very much needed injection of funds into the *BDJ* budget.

It is interesting to read the names inscribed on the splendid glass vase donated to mark the tenth *BDJ* teach-in, for many later became much sought-after speakers in their own field of interest. So, although the *Journal* could not pay a lucrative fee or ensure sizeable royalties from book sales, the greatest prize was to offer exposure to approximately twenty thousand readers around the world, to men and women working their way up the career ladder.

An early ten-part series of articles for the *BDJ* was on 'Occlusion and Restorative Dentistry for the general dental practitioner' by Michael Wise, who also proved to be a very popular speaker at the third teach-in. However, due to the insatiable demand for places, the venue was moved to the Cumberland Hotel in central London and was held there on a regular basis, that is, on the same Saturday in September. Professor Michael Wise today has a highly-acclaimed private practice in Wimpole Street and is a much sought-after lecturer internationally, as well as being the author of beautifully illustrated and definitive texts on occlusion. Little had I imagined when he spoke for me at the inauguration of the Enfield and District section of the BDA that his career and mine would be so inextricably linked through a *BDJ* initiative.

It is impossible to refer to all the teach-in speakers, although I owe them a debt of gratitude for making the new method of postgraduate study days a success. However, I will mention Philip Wander who, on making his first nervous attempts to lecture on dental photography, recalls: 'I remember being "spotted" and then coerced by you to give a lecture to candidates sitting the membership in general dental surgery.' I was aware that an important part of this examination involved the preparation by the dentist of a logbook, featuring photographic details of several clinical cases from the start to the finish of treatment. For many dentists the taking of good quality close-up photographs of the teeth and restorations proved to be an insurmountable task and could lead to failure in the examinations. Surely the *BDJ* could come to the rescue? Soon, I had commissioned a practical series of articles, co-written by Philip Wander and Peter Gordon. This was quickly followed by a lavishly coloured and illustrated book, again doubling as course notes, for a sell-out teach-in, held in London and also in Sheffield due to the demand from practitioners. Later, Philip commented, 'Thanks to your help, dental photography is now firmly established on the dental scene: there is even a NHS fee for it!'

Their book, *Dental Photography in Practice* had an unexpected boost to its sales when I presented a copy 'hot off the press' to Edwina Currie, MP. This was in October 1987 when she agreed to give an exclusive interview for the *BDJ*, discussing her responsibility for dentistry as the Parliamentary Secretary of State for Health. I well recall excitedly making my way to the Department of Health, which was then in Alexander Fleming's House (and referred to by Edwina Currie 'as that dreadful dump') with my notepad, tape recorder and trusty Canon 'sure-shot' camera tucked safely inside my most presentable briefcase, poised ready to interview the Minister. However, on arrival, I was greeted with the news that Mrs Currie was marooned in her office, owing to severe flooding on the ground floor, so access by stairs and lifts was impossible, but she was waiting to see me in her office. I was therefore directed to wind my way through the corridors of an adjacent building, and after negotiating an emergency fire escape, was greeted by a delightfully cheery and composed Minister, who spoke enthusiastically about having dentistry in her portfolio. 'I like dentists,' she enthused, 'They are thoroughly sensible and articulate, but also seem to have a lot of fun – and nice food at their dinners!' she added, drawing on her experience of a recent visit to a members' dinner at the General Dental Council. On that occasion she had implanted a new word into our vocabulary: 'Edwinaism' which, she explained, meant 'Don't get on a bandwagon unless it's rolling.' This was perhaps a phrase that came back to haunt her when, in December 1988, the 'Salmonella in eggs' crisis caused her honourably to resign from the Thatcher government. Nevertheless, the interview, published in the 7 November issue of the *BDJ*, remains an excellent record of the thinking of the Government at that time, which was reflected in the White Paper 'Promoting Better Health', published a couple of weeks later. Edwina Currie claimed it to be 'one of the most significant documents on health care that has been produced this half-century' and, she added, 'I hope dentists will like it!'

When the interview was ended, and after a photograph of Edwina Currie holding the latest *BDJ* book was secured, she intimated that she would like to visit a dental school and could I arrange it? This, of course, I was delighted to undertake, and it was to my Alma Mater that I turned. She had already become aware of the difficulties facing women dentists in trying to re-enter the workforce after a career break, often for child-rearing reasons. She further quizzed me on this topic during her visit to the dental school and I shared with her my desire to organise a dedicated course to help women return to practise dentistry, but was hampered by the cost of initiating such a project. Her reaction was immediate; in front of the 'great and the good' of the dental world, she offered me funding to run a pilot 'Getting Back to Practice' course at the London Hospital. There was considerable dismay from the assembled postgraduate dental deans at this ministerial diktat, because, in effect, she was directing a 'top slice' for me off their already perilously stretched budget. Undeterred and heartened by this *coup*, I enlisted Alan Lawrence, who shared my interest, and with tremendous help from the staff at The London, we mounted the first of what was to become replicated around the country, 'Getting Back to Practice' course. The issue of women returners was then acknowledged as an important area to focus on and allowances were made in the postgraduate budget around the country. From this personal encounter it became clear to me that Ministers in government do have real power and can make things happen: the onus is on us to put the case for the reasons why.

It soon became apparent from consumer demand that a *BDJ* book did not have to be confined to appearing first as a series of articles in the *Journal*. So, when the time came to appoint a new deputy editor, I enlisted one who had considerable experience with a book publishing house. Chris Adamson energetically set about his task of organising a stylish new livery for all the book titles and, in 1985, we enjoyed a unique and profitable year with four new publications published within three months.

Professor Crispian Scully's *Hospital Dental Surgeons Guide* was an early title that was not first serialised in the *BDJ*. It was designed for recent graduates who were in need of assistance in applying practically the academic knowledge which they had soaked up during the previous five years of study. This deservedly became an indispensable aide-memoire, not only for the newly-qualified, but also for the busy general dental practitioner. Later, in 1990, when we were fortunate to publish Crispian's *Patient Care*, it proved an acclaimed entrant for the 'Glaxo prize for medical writing and illustration'. Such success enhanced the popularity and reputation of our publishing initiatives, and also provided extra income when sales were enhanced through displays at trade exhibitions, conferences, and even at one of the Saturday meetings of the representative board at the BDA headquarters. Notable was the time in 1992 when most of the hundred or so members of the board present returned home with a *BDJ* purchase.

But not all the books were targeted at dentists. When I attended the course at the London College of Printing, I became friendly with a fellow student, Jacqui Hine, who had graduated as a home economist and was training as a cookery journalist with the *Family Circle* magazine. We had kept in contact and, flushed with the success of my publishing venture, I suggested to her that she might like to write a series of recipe articles on low-sugar cooking, covering every stage of development from toddlers to teenagers. Each article was limited to one page and then assembled in a folder, with an inside pocket to provide a suitable receptacle for storing other low-sugar recipes which might be discovered. The folders were instantly popular as useful literature to have in waiting rooms and for community dental officers to distribute through welfare centres and community clinics.

Throughout my time as editor, I was oblivious to the impact that my approach might have, especially on authors who I considered portrayed an aura of unflappability. Statistics proved to be a challenging topic for *Journal* readers and an area where many authors stumbled when they submitted their articles for refereeing. Perhaps, I thought, it was time to commission a series on this topic. Thus I turned to John Bulman whom I had known since my student days at The London, and to whom I was everlastingly grateful for discovering the spare set of keys for my infamous car, the Triumph Herald, secreted in the most unlikely place: inside the offside rear light. John had become an acknowledged expert on statistics, through his extensive epidemiological studies on the adult dental health surveys and had worked closely with a professional statistician, John Osborne. So, I approached the two Johns about my desire that they write 'easy to understand' articles on statistics for readers of the *BDJ*. John Bulman tells me that their initial reaction was 'blind panic. We couldn't have agreed to do that!' He further recalls that, 'after months of floundering, the first tentative drafts were so well received that our morale rocketed and the remainder was plain sailing.' The resulting book was a winner and continues to remain popular, having passed through several reprints and new editions.

Normally, authors would take the rejection of their submitted article with good grace, while others contrived more unusual approaches in order to get me to change my decision. 'How would you like to come down one Sunday to my farm for lunch? We could then discuss what I have to do to get my paper published.' This rather thrusting, and not so young, dentist, assuming that his chance of acceptance was high, enclosed an ordnance survey map of his location, in the depths of the English countryside. It will be of no surprise to learn that I refused this intriguing offer, and lunched at home with my family, as was our custom.

A different approach was engineered by John Mew, who was an orthodontist known to both Gordon and myself, and a person who propounded treatment methods contrary to the collectively accepted wisdom of the orthodontic fraternity. He believed he was being wronged when his articles, submitted to the *BDJ*, invariably fell at the refereeing hurdle. Determined to discover if there was any question of bias, he phoned my secretary, Sue Hayman, who had succeeded Marjorie Gillate when she retired, to arrange a lunch date on a Wednesday. Sue explained that I was heavily booked for weeks ahead. 'I only need one hour and will wait until a date is free.' After repeated phone calls from John, we decided to accede to his request in order to put him and us out of our misery. The appointed day came round and Sheila Langley, the BDA receptionist, phoned to alert us that John Mew had arrived wearing a brightly coloured and striped blazer, more suited to Henley, and a panama hat, and was carrying a long rolled umbrella, despite it being a sweltering summer's day. 'Get the editor to come quickly,' Sheila pleaded. 'He has a taxi running outside in the middle of Wimpole Street.' Behind the office net curtains, rows of eyes belonging to my editorial team watched as I clambered into the cab and sped in a northerly direction down Wimpole Street. Soon we reached the outer circle of Regent's Park and I wondered which venue he had in mind. Suddenly, he called out to the taxi driver to stop, and out we clambered. He then guided me via the York Bridge into the park alongside the tributary of the lake, with swans and geese paddling around and countless workers from the nearby offices sitting or lying on the grass enjoying their lunch break. 'This will do fine – let's sit here,' he said, pointing to an unoccupied wooden seat alongside the path. He carefully placed his briefcase between us and extracted two fluted glasses and a bottle of champagne, heavily lagged in a dripping wet towel. Finally, he produced a packet of cheese sandwiches, 'the best of British Rail that I could find at Waterloo!' Then, with great gusto, and accompanied by the greatest bang, he removed the cork from the well-travelled and shaken bottle, causing numerous reclining sunbathers to shoot bolt upright, thinking someone was on the rampage with a gun in Regent's Park. By now, most of the hour had been expended but sufficient remained for me to explain the kind of scrutiny applied to papers for scientific journals, and I encouraged him instead to share his ideas through a letter for the correspondence columns, or write an 'In my opinion' article for the *BDJ*.

To circumvent any more of these imaginative approaches, it was suggested that I should hold a day long workshop, 'How to get published'. Professor John Murray, assistant scientific editor, agreed to take part and so did Sue Silver, our talented assistant editor whose role was to prepare the scientific papers for publication. It was salutary also for those of us taking part, let alone the participants, to provide information on the refereeing process; what happens to a manuscript once accepted; the continuing responsibilities of the author until it appears in print, and the ethical dilemmas associated with the distressing emergence of plagiarism and 'salami' submissions, multiple articles on the same theme. Learning about the processes and the hidden secrets 'behind the scenes' turned out to be a popular initiative, in no little measure due to the infectious enthusiasm of Professor John Murray and also to one of my honorary scientific advisers, Professor Colin Smith, when, due to demand, the workshop was rerun in Sheffield. For me it had the desired effect: no more unsolicited lunch invitations to get their paper published!

One day, as was customary, my secretary Sue brought in the morning post to my room, all neatly opened and ordered. 'I think you will find the top letter interesting,' she tantalisingly remarked. And she was right! The letter from a Gordon Burnett began, 'Can I introduce my company, Interchange, to you, as we organise study tours abroad for groups of health care workers, nurses, pharmacists and doctors. I was wondering if dentists might be interested?' The timing of this approach in the summer of 1986 was perfect because I was aware of the waning popularity of the *BDJ* teach-in, owing to the growth of commercially organised postgraduate courses now in attractive venues, and so I was on the lookout for a new initiative for the *Journal*. I was even more excited about the study tour when, on continuing to read the letter, I discovered that a free place was on offer for the tour leader, and that the company would contribute £25 per person to organisers, the *BDJ*. Certainly the idea seemed worth pursuing and when we met, Gordon suggested Russia where changes were slowly taking place through glasnost and perestroika. I was overwhelmed by the response to the first announcement of a trip to this country which, in the mid 1980s, was something of an enigma and was rarely visited. Four groups, each of around 25 in number, travelled in 1987, followed by another four groups in 1988 as the demand for places seemed insatiable. But, above all, this was not just a travel club of dentists; there was a serious purpose. It was an opportunity for dentists to exchange ideas, about dental practice and daily life, with colleagues in countries not normally perceived as a tourist venue for individuals.

Briefing sessions were held at BDA headquarters, to meet the tour leader and English-speaking interpreter to hear about the formalities we would have to cope with, to learn about the more unusual food on offer, and to get to know one's travelling companions. But this proved scant preparation for the trip to Russia. We all returned wiser and deeply moved. It was after one of these trips that

Bernard Caplan and Peter Lowndes wrote a 'Travelogue' for the *BDJ* in which they commented, 'The emergence of the *BDJ* Study Tour has been among the happier developments in the dental world, and an increasing number of practitioners have taken the opportunity to combine an alternative view of the profession, with a visit that exceeds the usual tourist experience.' Obviously, when the study tours expanded into China, Iceland, Hungary, Kenya, South Africa and Malta, it was impossible to lead all the tours myself, so I was grateful for assistance from members of the BDA staff, Linda Wallace and Pat Paterson, and senior executives of other organisations: David and Anne Phillips, Elizabeth Elliott, and Bryan Gillard, at the time the president designate of the BDA.

Clearly it would be impossible, and potentially boring, to recount in detail the individual people we met or happenings in each country that we visited during a period of seven years. Rather, I will briefly dwell on two of the countries which engendered much to ponder.

I was completely unprepared for the sights and sounds of Moscow in March 1987. I was also apprehensive about taking the first group abroad and so decided to take my own aide, a Russian teacher from The Latymer School, Mr (Mac) McNeil, whom we knew as a friend and who was fortunately on his school Easter holiday at the same time. It was reassuring to have such expert back-up but, in the event, I should not have not been concerned because all the guides provided by Interchange were superb.

Moscow was a city of contrasts: rows and rows of dull and dowdy apartment blocks, and equally drab streets, with few cars, and any pedestrians going quietly about their business while old women cleared the side-walks of snow. Everywhere there were queues, and the longest was outside the bakery as food was scarce. Happier queues were spotted outside the florist shops. This was because we were there on International Women's Day, when it was customary for men to give the ladies red carnations. The Soviets' pride in their first astronaut, Yuri Gugarin, was evident, as was the homage given to Lenin, his Mausoleum situated by the Kremlin in Red Square. Facing it, on the other side of the square, was the famous department store, GUM, which seemed appropriate for a group of dentists to visit. However, there was great disappointment, as no luxury or attractive clothing was on offer, only displays of lisle stockings, sold individually. Incongruously, St Basil's Cathedral, with its Byzantine 'onion' domes, brought colour to the drab landscape, although the story that Ivan the Terrible, who commissioned it, ordered the architect's eyes to be gouged out so that he could not repeat the design anywhere else, served as a reminder of the harshness of previous regimes.

Our Russian guide, Tanya, was truly glamorous, tall and elegant and speaking impeccable English. She had also worked hard, when hearing of her assignment, to learn dental terms and phrases, which were invaluable when we visited the stomatological polyclinic in Kalin, a town straddling the upper reaches of the

Volga. Here the children waiting for dental treatment were thrilled to get surprise gifts of toothbrushes, which were in extremely short supply and, a complete novelty, oral health stickers. There was a preponderance of women in the dental profession and they all wore uniform clothing, a white hat and gown. Nevertheless, it was also notable, as in other countries where women were in the majority, that the professors and directors were men. Lack of funding was clearly evident and although there was a desire to achieve good standards and learn about new advances in techniques, any progress was hampered by the equipment, which was outdated when measured against our standards. Cotton wool rolls were fashioned by hand, suction was unavailable so the spittoons were not plumbed in, and local anaesthetics were reserved for patients having teeth extracted. We had been forewarned that dental materials and hand-held instruments were in short supply, and so our UK intrepid travellers had filled every spare corner of their suitcases with various unused items from their surgery stock-cupboards, as well as *BDJ* books and journals, and the universally popular biro pens.

At the end of the group's visit to the polyclinic, I presented the director, Professor Naumove, with a semi-adjustable anatomical articulator for use when constructing dentures or similar oral appliances. 'Thank you,' he said in halting English and, with tears running down his cheeks, he continued, 'This is the only one in the whole of Russia.' We were very moved and humbled to witness the joy that this modest present had brought to our dental colleagues. Throughout our stay when talking with dentists or students, either at the clinic or in the evening at our hotels, there was an intense desire to see perestroika work and a voracious appetite for information about British education, culture, and way of life.

After Kalin, it was an eight-hour train journey to the 'Venice of the North', still called Leningrad (later renamed St Petersburg). We were all excited, as we were looking forward to viewing the exquisite collections of paintings, sculptures and artefacts in the Hermitage, the former Winter Palace of the Czars, and attending a performance of a Tchaikovsky opera, in the beautifully restored opera house, and a traditional Russian Circus with performing animals.

As was customary throughout the Study Tour, the location of our hotel was a closely guarded secret. Imagine our delight when our coach stopped in front of the splendidly restored nineteenth century building, the Europoskaya Hotel, situated just off the famous Nevsky Prospect in Leningrad. We stood expectantly waiting in the entrance hall with our luggage and, as Tanya went forward to the reception desk to collect our room keys, she was handed a letter. As she read it, the colour drained from her cheeks and she was visibly shaken. She returned to inform us that she had been ordered to return to Moscow immediately. This was no family crisis; it was that she had been observed as too friendly with the group. We were subdued as we said our sad farewells and could only hope that on her return to Moscow the authorities were not too harsh with her. We had been aware of 'bugging' in our rooms and being closely watched by a stern lady, positioned on each floor alongside the famous urn of hot water – the KGB activity was thinly disguised. However, it was especially poignant because Tanya had worked assiduously to put into action the trumpeted claims that the Soviet society was changing. Sadly, it was clear that the changes were not universally embraced by her political masters.

A couple of years later, when I made my second visit, I shared a bedroom with the English interpreter who opened up for most of us a rich and beautiful new world associated with the treasured Russian icons. The evening before our departure from Moscow she confided in me that this would be her last opportunity to see a friend who lived on the other side of the city. She warned me not to get worried, and certainly not to tell anyone, if she was not back in time to go to bed. 'If I am delayed,' she said, 'I promise I will be with you in time for our departure after breakfast.' Unsurprisingly, I did not sleep well and realised as dawn broke that I was still alone in the room. When breakfast was finished, the cases were loaded onto the coach and I began to panic as I wondered what I should do if my interpreter failed to appear. I need not have worried because as we began to clamber onto the coach, miraculously, she appeared. Explanations were neither sought, nor given: a surge of great relief sufficed. It was to be nearly a decade later before I discovered the purpose of her errand to the other side of Moscow. I was shocked to learn that with forbidden literature in her possession, she had exposed herself to grave danger as she traversed the capital that night. She was carrying Holy Bibles. It was an extraordinary coincidence, or was it providence, how I made this discovery. One Sunday afternoon, I was invited for tea at the home of a friend, Jill Northam, in Hadley Wood, who, knowing I had visited Russia, thought I would be interested to meet the guest visitor to our local church, a Russian orthodox priest who was attending a course at the nearby Oak Hill Theological College in North London. Imagine my disbelief when he began to explain how he had managed to procure bibles during the time of prohibition of religious literature. Yes, our interpreter had been a reliable source each time she had gone to Russia. The risks both had taken to deliver and receive the banned word of God left a deep impression on me. Comfortably cocooned in the UK, it is so easy to take the gifts of freedom of speech and the written word for granted.

In April 1989, when I landed at Beijing airport with the first *BDJ* Study Tour to China, it coincided with the death, on the previous day, of Hu Yaobang, the former general secretary of the communist party and student hero. The impact of this event was immediate and as we made our way the next day to Tiananmen Square, students surged forward to encircle the *BDJ* visitors and split the thirty strong group into clusters of two or three people. The amazingly good-natured and polite students were anxious to explain, in excellent and self-taught English, their desire for reform of the political system, the introduction of a free press, and emphasised the need for a young leader, not the ruling 'old man', to bring about the necessary changes. Although we did not feel threatened, our Chinese guide decided we should cut short our visit to the square and we returned to the coach through a myriad of underground passages uncharted on tourist maps. As the tragic events associated with the people's revolution unfolded during the following months, it was moving to realise that the UK dentists had witnessed the first flicker of the campaign for democracy which had unleashed the deep frustrations of the educated elite throughout the whole of China. By the time we had completed the obligatory tourist climb of the Great Wall, visited the Norman Bethune International Peace Hospital in Shijiazhuang to learn about the art and practice of Chinese medicine as applied to dentistry, and visited a couple of dental clinics in Shanghai, the quiet protest had changed to a massive display of angry defiance against the government, with the resultant imposition of martial law and hunger strikes by impatient youths yearning for a new social order. As the uprising escalated, we could only watch with horror on the televisions in our homes as we saw the tanks rolling onto the streets in Beijing to quell the protest. The image of the lone student's unsuccessful stand against the might of the advancing tank remains a vivid and sickening reminder of the sacrifice that occurred throughout the cities, towns and villages in their struggle for democracy

As a great advocate of team dentistry, I was increasingly concerned about the poor provision of educational material for crucial members of the dental team, particularly the dental surgery assistant (dental nurse). Some relied on receiving training from the dentist in the practice, but many found that their time for tuition was limited and insufficient to gain formal qualifications through the nationally run examinations. Those who were highly motivated would often enrol, at their own expense, on courses which were run by local technical colleges. This normally meant studying in the evenings or at weekends as it was difficult to leave the dental practice during the day.

With this knowledge I immediately recognised the potential when Brian Mouatt, the acting chief dental officer at the Department of Health in England, contacted me to enquire whether the *BDJ* could devise and produce a distance-learning programme to enable the busy dental practitioner to train his staff on the premises, with funding provided by the government. This method was, as yet, untried in the dental field and I could see it as an exciting new initiative for the *Journal*. But where to start? It was obvious that I needed someone with expertise and flair in designing training programmes. I approached Lynn Maris who had worked with me at the BDA before leaving a short time before to set up her own company. Also excited by the challenge, she agreed to act as programme coordinator. The next key appointment was a person who could advise and ensure that the material being produced was relevant for the target training group, dental surgery assistants. I was assured by Diana Wincott, senior tutor at Guy's, and her colleague Sue Adams, that they knew the exact person and would bring her along to the *Journal* office to meet me. Duly they arrived with Sue Goodwin, a trained tutor of dental surgery assistants but currently not working. With the four of us seated around the large office table I enquired of Sue, 'What are you doing for the next six months? How about running Teamwork for me?' There was a lengthy pause and Sue recalls that she was firmly kicked under the table by her two 'escorts' and spluttered her reply, 'What – uh – me? – Ye – yes, I think so.' An unorthodox mode of appointment maybe, but an inspired one, as Sue excelled in her role as executive secretary to the project, eventually becoming the national Teamwork coordinator.

Equally pressing was to appoint scientific advisers to assist in selecting the appropriate topics for the programme. Recruited were Professors Peter Rothwell and Gordon Seward, Martyn Amsel as a general practitioner, and Roslyn Walters, a general practitioner but also a senior member of the national examining board for dental surgery assistants. Everyone was excited and anxious to help, as such an initiative was long overdue. It was further essential to assemble an advisory panel, to assist with the preparation, reading and refereeing of the modules produced: the more people involved the better, for a couple of good reasons. Not only would it help us to complete the project in an exceedingly tight timescale of six months, but also ensure that information about the new distance-learning initiative was widely disseminated. For me, secrecy is never a sound policy. The more people in the 'tent', the greater is the chance of success. So, in order to achieve my goal, my initial panel was wide-ranging: Ken Eaton represented the Department of Health, as sponsors of the project, Vivienne Lister, David Radford, Charles Scola as specialist general practitioners, Penny Whitehead from the BDA, Karen Dalton from the GDC, and Professor Andy Grieve representing the Dental Surgery Assistants Standards and Training Advisory Board. So there were plenty of people to discuss the logo design, which proved to be as tortuous an exercise as designing the *BDJ* tie! After discarding many sketches, a symbolic logo was adopted, depicting three team members holding hands, dressed in green uniforms against a white background. This logo was synonymous with Teamwork and became instantly recognisable when it appeared on the manual and other subsequent products encompassing newsletters, T-shirts and mugs.

Amazingly, the timescale was met so that on 9 March 1991 the first of twenty-four successive supplements were enclosed with the *BDJ* for members, or mailed separately to non-members. The entire programme was carefully structured to provide a core foundation for the dental surgery assistants (DSAs) who wanted to take the certificate of the national examining board, although there was no compulsion to do so. Indeed, for many, the manual provided a welcome refresher course, especially for those returning after a career break. It also encouraged team members to check that they were up-to-date because at the end of each article there was a challenging self-assessment and further reading sections so that Teamwork combined all the best of the tried and tested distance-learning techniques.

There was a tremendous response from dentists to register their DSAs on the programme. In return they received a handbook to explain the learning material available, a smart ring binder complete with logo in which to file the twenty-four supplements, and an attractive 'Practice Participation Certificate' to display, encouraging interest amongst patients as well as team members. But not all dentists were enthusiastic and some even rejected the offer of free learning material. Members of staff were appalled when a husband phoned to ask if he could purchase a manual for his wife who was so upset because her dentist refused to apply for one. We were delighted to forward a copy with our compliments and I often wonder how long she remained working in that practice.

The pressure on the *BDJ* editorial team was enormous as this was extra work fitted around the relentless production of a twice-monthly publication. With great grace and professionalism they rose superbly to the challenge and the material produced was acclaimed in the dental press as of the highest quality and relevance. As I commented in my forward 'Introducing Teamwork', for the first edition in March 1991, 'I hope that you will find the programme useful in your practices and that you enjoy using it as much as we have enjoyed producing it for you. In reality, it truly has been an exercise in Teamwork.'

Suddenly everyone was talking teamwork. Stocks ran out so a reprint of the manual was undertaken six months later, in September. Then there was clamour for a second volume to extend team members' knowledge of techniques and working practices, including preparation for examinations in specialised areas. The Department of Health of England, now joined by those of Scotland, Northern Ireland and Wales, continued to provide financial support as we diversified, producing a video, 'Spot it with Teamwork', to help candidates in the national examination to identify a variety of instruments which seemed to be a stumbling block to some of the most gifted candidates when a practice was limited, for example, to orthodontics.

Also, in 1991, a landmark report on general anaesthesia, sedation and resuscitation was authored by Professor David Poswillo. We were encouraged to produce a video to feature the dental surgery assistant (dental nurse) in a 'real-life' situation. 'IV sedation – get it right with Teamwork' was screened, with Sue Goodwin playing the role of patient, although it came as a shock when she had to comply with providing her vein for a real-life enactment of venepuncture. Her consolation was the popularity of the video, which was also recognised as an important teaching tool with the award of a prestigious Certificate of Achievement.

Internationally there was also great interest and Laura Wiles and I were invited to run two three-hour sessions for the dental nurses in Hong Kong, followed by another exciting visit at the invitation of Clive Ross to take part in the Asian Pacific Regional Conference in Auckland. Sue Goodwin accompanied me on this tour and dentists were encouraged to bring their dental nurses with them to

Teach-In Teamwork courses organised in Dunedin through invitation from the New Zealand dental association and encouragement from Professor Angela Pack at the dental school. This country took the programme to its heart, designating it as compulsory reading for their qualifying examination.

Within a busy dental practice there is not always time available to provide extra support for dental nurses enrolled on the programme, so we hit upon the solution, which was to appoint Teamwork coordinators in various regions of the country. A good idea maybe, but the enthusiasm of the coordinators was insufficient: funding was needed. This time the visionary sales manager, Jacqui Garcia of Stafford Miller, came to the rescue because, as a former dental nurse, she understood the true potential of this distance-learning package. Soon there was a network in place and the selected dental nurses provided important back-up for dental nurses on the programme. Instigated by Jacqui, we brought these Teamwork coordinators together for two training days each year, which not only provided support for them in the field, but also provided us with ideas for future volumes or initiatives. Teamwork had exploded onto the dental scene. People were hungry for more information and this was disseminated through a newssheet '*Teamwork News*' and competitions were held to discover the best Teamwork Training Practice, giving them recognition with a gold award and a Practice prize. The initiatives were rolling off the drawing board: Teamwork had become a self-promoting business venture – there seemed to be no stopping the popular bandwagon.

Unannounced, Bryan Gillard, now president designate of the BDA, arrived in my office to debrief me on his visit to Russia in his role as Study Tour Leader. He then proceeded to outline his plans for his forthcoming presidency of the Association and quipped, 'Won't be long until your branch nominates you.' This I just took as a friendly comment because, unlike Bryan, who had been an officer of the BDA as Chairman of Council for six years, I was an employee and the divide between an honorary officer and employee had never been bridged. However, Bryan's words turned out to be prophetic: my name was put forward by the Middlesex and Hertfordshire Branch and, to my amazement and great pride, I was elected to serve as President of the BDA in 1993, and so became the second woman to hold this position after forty-seven years, Lilian Lindsay, the first woman to qualify in 1895 as a dentist, assuming office in 1946.

Once the euphoria had settled, I tendered my resignation as Editor of the *BDJ*, a post I was contracted to work in until my 60th birthday. Both the secretary, Norman Whitehouse, and the then Chairman of Council, Geoffrey Garnett, were supportive in facilitating my early departure to assume the role of President-elect. So, on 10 June 1992, my staff conceived the most memorable leaving party for me. More than one hundred friends and colleagues, who had been involved with the *Journal* during my thirteen years as editor, were invited to join the festivities. 'Come and join MHS *Enterprise* and watch the lift-off – to boldly go where no editor has gone before' they wrote, and inscribed these sentiments on the most decorated and imaginatively-designed leaving cake ever seen. BDA Council spoilt me with a delicious dinner and presentation of glassware and the inevitable speeches: were they really speaking about me? I responded with a farewell lunch for the BDA and *Journal* staff and, as my conference was to be held at a seaside venue, we had fish and chips and ice-cream dispensed from gaily decorated stalls, constructed by the handy members of staff. After lunch we retired to the open atrium, where a paddling pool had been strategically placed and even proved a challenge to Mark Paulson (a senior staff member) who had gamely donned his flippers for the occasion!

A wonderful camaraderie was in evidence and indeed at all times. I was always blessed with members of staff who had a great sense of fun, tolerated my jokey sense of humour but, above all, were prepared to go the extra mile to get a job done to a pressing, and at times ridiculous, deadline. For me the reward has been to see many of them progress in their careers and attain top jobs: Sue Silver head-hunted from the USA to launch a new environmental Journal; Laura Wiles transferring the Teamwork skills into producing *Pathways in Practice*, the first distance-learning manual for the Faculty of General Dental Practice UK, and simulating the Teamwork coordinators, establishing a network of divisional advisers throughout the country, and Sue Goodwin continuing to be involved with Teamwork and its publications from its new base in Sheffield overseen by Professor Rothwell.

I can, as if it were as yesterday, remember emerging on my last day from Oxford Street tube station where that initial, almost clandestine, rendezvous with Archie Donaldson took place, skirting round All Souls Church in Langham Place, crossing Devonshire and Harley Street, to arrive at No 64 Wimpole Street barely fifteen minutes later. Now, I was destined to join the ranks of the retired. Just how was I going to occupy myself for the next twelve months as President-in-Waiting?

Chapter 13

The presidential year

As it turned out, I need not have worried about not having enough to do. In 1992, there was only one full-time member of staff, Helen Mackay, responsible for organising the annual conference. While other staff members shouldered additional roles at conference time, a great deal of work was taken on by the Conference Organising Committee under its energetic and supportive chairman, John Phipps. If the president-elect wished to get involved then this was encouraged and I certainly was delighted to be able to share my ideas gleaned from attendance over the years at international meetings.

It was customary to hold the annual meeting or conference in the president's branch, so in my case this would mean a venue somewhere in Hertfordshire or Middlesex. Central London was prohibitive as far as the cost of accommodation and travelling, apart from the hire of facilities catering for nearly two thousand people. Ken Swiss, the previous president from our branch in 1982 had chosen Brighton, so I decided to check out another south coast venue. Many of our happy seaside holidays with the family had been spent along the Dorset Hampshire borders, starting at Mudeford and migrating west to Studland and Swanage, the now Jurassic Coast, a prized heritage site. Within this region, Bournemouth boasted a purpose-built conference centre and there were plans for extension, thus increasing the already attractive facilities. 'The powers that be' seemed to warm to the idea of a seaside conference at the beginning of July after a run of capital cities throughout the UK. It was clearly given the seal of approval by the chairman when very early on one Saturday morning John Phipps arrived, after a busy week in his practice, to inspect the facilities; or was it to enjoy the great sizzling English breakfast served in the café at the end of the pier, a venue for one of our social events after a boat trip round the bay.

There also seemed to be a surfeit of meetings for me to attend to help pass the time, not only with the organising committee but also with representatives from the national associations of the members of the dental team: dental nurses, dental hygienists, dental therapists and dental technicians. I was thrilled that they had agreed to reschedule their own annual meetings to coincide with the BDA in Bournemouth. Thus the conference logo was designed to reflect the team approach, five seagulls each representing the team members, as obviously the dentist was added to the four auxiliary groups. This new initiative was reflected in the choice of an overall theme for the conference, 'The New Generation'. Indeed, with repeated use the logo became instantly recognisable as it appeared on the full range of conference stationery, on promotional material such as triangular three-colour highlighter pens, table coasters, stickers and T-shirts and was incorporated into the president-elect's Christmas card to advertise the event, a design by my former editorial staff member, Katie O'Malley.

I was keen to include new faces into the programme, especially from overseas, and with whom I had been particularly impressed when attending meetings abroad. However, I was only too aware that to realise this ambition, especially with the cost of air travel, was impossible from the modest annual conference BDA budget. So I re-honed my sponsorship skills and set about getting companies to underwrite a three-hour session. I remember well spotting Keith Taylor in the reception area on a visit to the secretariat in Wimpole Street. 'Keith, after your meeting can you pop over to the BDA office?' From time to time Keith wrote articles for me on Personal Pension Planning and NHS Superannuation Schemes, and obviously believed I had another assignment for him. Instead, he was completely taken by surprise when I broke the news to him of a new idea – would he like to have the privilege of sponsoring a three-hour session at Bournemouth? Without too much persuasion he agreed that MADRAS, the Medical and Dental Retirement Advisory Service, would sponsor a session and that he would take part himself. He then retorted, 'That was the most expensive visit I have ever made to your office!' Emboldened by his aquiescence to the suggestion, I contacted other companies with whom I had enjoyed close working relationships during my term as editor. Surely it was time to call in favours. In no time at all, especially once they knew a competitor was taking part, I had a further six sessions underwritten: Colgate, Procter and Gamble, The Wrigley Company, Stafford Miller, Gibbs Mentadent P, and Regent International. In fact, all were delighted to be more involved than just through a trade stand with the prime BDA meeting of the year.

Now I was on my way, able to invite speakers of international calibre: Dr Marjorie Jeffcoat, a leading periodontist from the USA, who later became the first woman editor of the *Journal of the American Dental Association*, Dr Jan Pameijer, the crown and bridge guru from the Netherlands, Ivar Mjör, caries researcher from Norway, Leo Screeby the 'saliva king' from the USA, Angela Pack, a leading periodontist in the dental school in Dunedin, New Zealand, and Jennifer St Georges, from the States who continues as a popular speaker on 'Keeping Staff – and Spouses – Happy'. Combined with the UK talent, there was, unusually, a total of one hundred speakers on the programme and Colgate spoiled them all with an inscribed fluffy white bathrobe to mark the occasion.

Innovative parallel sessions for team members were arranged and four three-hour forums were hosted by the BDA Groups and the Commonwealth Dental Association, who also held their meeting at the same time, centred on one of the local hotels. My teach-in speakers were brought back into action and over a two-day period they ran fifteen clinical table demonstrations. And not to be forgotten, a workshop for the Teamwork Coordinators was organised which, despite all the other activities, caught the imagination of the reporter from the *Bournemouth Daily Echo* with the somewhat unoriginal headline: 'Dentists brush up on their skills'. Overall there was commendable local, national radio and newspaper interest, as this side had been left in the capable hands of my former *BDJ* staff.

There was also great enjoyment provided on the stretch of golden sand below the conference centre, where Polly Munday, a dental educator from Lambeth, Southwark and Lewisham Community Dental Services, set up a dental health puppet show. The children screamed with delight and shouted loudly when the dual began between the 'goodies', Sammy Molar, and the 'baddies', Jimmy Germ, Stanley Sugar, and Percy Plaque. We were concerned that we might offend the local Punch and Judy man, but he very kindly offered to move his pitch nearer the pier so as not to detract from our shows with an oral health message.

For three days, Thursday 1 July to Saturday 3 July, the sun shone strongly on Bournemouth, which greatly assisted the successful discharge of the social events, during the day for those accompanying the delegates to Beaulieu and the Hardy Country, and in the evening, boat trips and barbecues. During the preceding months we had caught the imagination and generosity of the dentists, when they were encouraged to adopt a duck, at one pound a time, in an effort to raise money for the BDA Benevolent Fund which supports all dentists and their dependants in time of need. So, early on the Saturday morning, with the local Council's permission, we amazed passers-by, who witnessed sack loads of numbered yellow ducks of the plastic variety, being tipped from the bridge into the River Bourne in the Lower Winter Gardens. Even more startling was the sight of a very respectable local general dental practitioner, Sandy Williams overseeing the proceedings and wading gallantly in the stream to rescue the wayward ducks before they disappeared through the sluice gates into the sea. An amazing amount of money was raised for a very good cause but the intense competition amongst the BDA staff to be chosen to wear the duck outfit resulted in shared responsibilities, with Bryan Harvey on the opening evening to promote the race and Paul Rothwell on the day of the race. It was hailed as the first BDA duck race, but we are still waiting for the second race to be organised – perhaps there is a shortage of the human variety of ducks.

The Wessex branch, whose territory we had invaded, gave us tremendous support and provided the local 'know-how'. The Middlesex and Hertfordshire branch ensured a record attendance amongst their number and the branch president, Edgar Gordon, who had deliberately delayed his presidency so as to support me during my year, splashed out with a party on his boat *Routine* moored alongside *Enigma*, the boat of a former president, Alan Bergman, in the Poole Town Marina, colourfully decked out for the special occasion.

For me the grand climax was a stupendous presidential dinner and dance in the Pavilion Ballroom, graced by the attendance of presidents from many international organisations and national associations overseas: the USA, Iceland, Ireland, Malta, the Netherlands and the FDI. Even the most reluctant feet found their way onto the dance floor when Lord Colwyn's orchestra began to play. Our only hereditary dental peer, in great demand at Society Balls, was a delight to watch and hear as he oscillated between performing on the trumpet and the triangle. The dinner speeches were unusually entertaining, especially that of the principal guest, Sheriff Irvine Smith, QC, who inflicted bruised ribs on many of his audience with the non-stop laughter that he invoked. It was also a particular honour to have not only the American Dental Association's president, Jack Harris and his wife Mary Ellen, but also their previous president, Gerry Morrow, the first woman to hold that office in an association of around one hundred and fifty thousand members, who accepted the invitation to propose the Toast to the BDA.

The conference format had been completely reconfigured and some changes caused eyebrows to be raised, although it is interesting to see that with the passage of time some customs have returned. For example, as we were at the seaside it seemed to me highly inappropriate to put on academic dress and so we dispensed with this attire for the branch presidents and BDA officers who formed the platform party. 'Loss of dignity' was the claim, so it was reintroduced the following year but thankfully this unnecessary 'stuffiness' has disappeared from more recent annual conferences.

Again, as at the seaside and taking a lead from the American Dental Association opening ceremony, a light entertainment was organised with sponsorship from SmithKline and Beecham. The popular singer Vince Hill entertained with songs and acts entitled 'Magic of the Musicals', after the customary valedictory and presidential addresses. As the conference was targeted at the dental team, all the presidents of the auxiliary associations, nurses, hygienists, therapists and technicians were introduced to me as the new president.

That first evening concluded with a seaside supper, with delegates and friends mingling around the trade stands in the exhibition hall opened for the first time during the evening. Here another surprise was in store for me, planned by Jacqui Garcia and my former editorial staff. As I approached the Stafford-Miller stand, I was confronted by King Neptune (a heavily disguised Roy Higson liberally covered in green greasepaint) complete with his entourage, the most attractive mermaids I have ever seen. Then I was presented with a framed caricature depicting my favourite pastimes, cooking, walking and my prized 'Jag', and prominently displayed was my first mobile phone – heavy, with large batteries needing constant recharging. It had been an imaginative leaving gift from Jacqui and, in 1992, was the envy of many.

During the daytime at the conference, alumni lunches were organised by my own Alma Mater, the London Hospital Dental Club, the European Section of the International College of Dentistry and Women in Dentistry, and the first past BDA presidents' lunch was masterminded by Bryan Gillard the immediate past president. There is no doubt that all these associated activities for disparate groups of people resulted in breaking the two thousand barrier, with a total record attendance of two thousand two hundred people and seventy-six exhibitors at the trade show.

My family and personal friends have had to put up with the demands of my career, so I was at long last able to repay some hospitality to 'the gang' from my halcyon days way back at St Paul's Church in Enfield in the 1960s. They were invited to join us for the dinner dance and then it was entirely appropriate that they came on the Sunday morning to the first service held as part of the conference at St Peter's Parish Church by the kind invitation of the Rector and Rural Dean of Bournemouth, Canon Dick Jones. The Christian Dental Fellowship members were also in the congregation and as the church had bells, I wondered about the possibility of ringing a peal or quarter peal to celebrate this special event. I then discovered that a Guild of Medical Ringers existed and they formed, through consultation with the Ringing Master, dentist Peter Cranfield, the first dental band – eight dentists, including John Pidgeon from my student days, who climbed the tower following the end of the service, and after forty-nine minutes and executing one thousand two hundred and sixty plain bob triples, they completed their mission with much energy and sweat expended, gained a certificate, and a notable write-up in *Ringers' World* magazine.

Interviewing me before the conference for an article in the *BDJ*, my successor, Mike Grace, asked me what I would like to achieve with the Bournemouth Conference. In reply I told him, 'My challenge is to reverse the falling number of delegates to the annual conference over recent years and this can only be done with a great deal of marketing and PR.' As it turned out, I was thrilled beyond all expectations that we had alighted on a winning formula, only possible through the tremendous hard work and commitment to the enterprise by all involved. I was also fortunate that contacts and friends made through my editorship, rallied round to make it, for me, a conference to remember. After the longest and most physically demanding party of my life, I was now launched into the serious business of discharging the responsibilities of president: the highest honour that the Association can bestow. As the first woman president for forty-seven years, and only the second in the one hundred and twelve years' history of the BDA, I was determined not to let them down. It was a coincidence that the first woman president, Lilian Lindsay, gave her valedictory address at the annual conference in 1947 held in Bournemouth.

A good communicator, I believe, is a person who knows how to listen and I was determined to excel in this role. The president has an ambassadorial role and must remain apolitical. However, that does not mean that he or she should refrain from encouraging energetic and full debate leading to positive decision making. In 1993, dentists were still reeling from the effects of a draconian 7 per cent cut in their fees and from the consequent inquiry, 'The Bloomfield Review', which put forward a series of options rather than recommendations as to state financing of dentistry. As if that was not sufficient to occupy dentists' concerns as to the long-term commitment of government to dentistry in the NHS, there was the publication of the 'Nuffield Inquiry into the Training and Education of Personnel Auxiliary to Dentistry' (the dental team members) just two months into my presidency, proposing new and extended roles for them. These events made dentists apprehensive and there was a need for a 'talking shop' to permit debate and share concerns. I decided to fill the vacuum by holding 'sound-bite sessions' in ten locations around the country; focus groups had not burst upon the scene at that time. The formula was to invite eight people to dine with me in a private room in an upmarket hotel. Then, after the coffee was served, we embarked on a full and frank discussion, but all conducted without notes or tape recorders whirring. I chose as participants people reflecting the age, sex, and sphere of practice, a list assembled through consultation with local dignitaries. It was amazing how themes and topics resurfaced around the country but, above all, participants valued the opportunity for someone from the centre to listen to them. This, as far as I was concerned, proved to be money well spent and I was again grateful to Stafford Miller for sponsorship so that it was not a drain on the BDA's finances which, after all, represent members' subscriptions.

It was an exciting year visiting branches, sections and groups of the Association, mainly for their annual dinners. I believe I did my bit dining for dentistry. I was also called upon to make speeches, draw raffle tickets for the Benevolent Fund and unveil numerous plaques. To reach many of the venues, which were not accessible by public transport, Gordon and I travelled many miles, the length and breadth of the country, in the comfort of my trusted Jaguar Sovereign car – B975 YPP. On one evening, I was to open new premises after dinner, during which time Gordon was placed next to the top man of the parent company who had just flown in from Europe. Unaware of my husband's identity, he confided in Gordon as the meal progressed that they wanted a top rugby player as the guest celebrity to open the laboratory but 'we have settled for the BDA president. It's cheaper.'

When you are having fun, the time passes all too quickly, with rarely a free weekend to spend at home. I was also fortunate to be invited to attend other dental associations' annual conferences and visited Ireland, Australia and New Zealand. These visits had to be fitted in around the monthly BDA council meetings and the meetings of the Representative Board three times a year, when it was encouraged that the president should present a short report on his or her activities on behalf of the Association.

During this time I remained a member of the General Dental Council and continued sitting on the Professional Conduct Committee (PCC), which heard cases of alleged complaints of serious professional misconduct by dentists. The hearings could last for a week to ten days and the PCC was convened in session following the full-day session of Council. Members of the panel (functioning as a jury) were expected to stay within the vicinity of the GDC in Wimpole Street, where the hearings were held, so as to avoid any delay from traffic disruption or cancellation of services. Failure to turn up could result in lengthy and costly interruption or even cancellation of the hearing.

During the second week in November, and with the PCC in full swing, I returned to my hotel room to find a message waiting for me from my husband. 'Margaret, there is a letter here in the post today from the Prime Minister, marked urgent and personal. Perhaps you should come home and open it.' With my curiosity well and truly aroused and with the clock approaching six p.m., I was confident that if I departed immediately, I could make Hadley Wood and back on the train before bedtime, which is exactly what I did.

So, what was in that envelope in November 1993? On opening the letter, I read that the Prime Minister 'has it in mind to submit your name to the Queen with a recommendation that Her Majesty may be graciously pleased to approve that you be appointed Commander of the Order of the British Empire.' The urgent element was to know whether I would accept the honour if offered. How I wondered could anyone refuse? I viewed it as an honour for the whole profession, especially occurring within my year as president – I was just the fortunate person to receive it. To confirm my acceptance I was invited to place a tick in the appropriate box in the reply card and then trust that the Royal Mail would deliver the very special acceptance letter because there is no confirmation or further correspondence before the New Year's Honours (and likewise for Birthday Honours) lists are published in the national or local press.

The most important caveat in the letter is that the approach is in strict confidence, underlining that the outcome must not be taken as a foregone conclusion and the contents of the letter must not be discussed with anyone. This was the ultimate test of keeping a confidence, and not betraying a trust, when my natural inclination was to shout the wonderful, extraordinary news from the rooftops. At times it felt as though 31 December would never arrive. Then, at last, there we were in at the newsagents at six a.m., the first customers buying a selection of different newspapers and opening the pages in a frenzy to check if my name was safely on the list under CBE: 'Mrs Margaret Helen Elizabeth Seward, for services to dentistry.' I had made it and it clinched a special double for the family, as Gordon had been awarded the CBE in the June 1990 Queen's Birthday Honours.

The handover to the next president, a special friend of mine, Professor Harold Jones, at the conference at the Barbican in London, was only a few months away. My involvement was limited to preparing my valedictory address and then, as my final act, investing the incoming president with the jewel of office. Throughout the year I had worn with pride the gold president's badge which depicted, in embossed profile, the head and shoulders of the first and founding president of the Association in 1880, Sir John Tomes. But I looked like 'the poor relation' when attending evening functions in the company of masters of livery companies, presidents and deans of Royal Colleges and Faculties, as well as civic dignitaries who were all adorned with beautifully designed and fabricated chains which displayed their badge or jewel to perfection. In token of my appreciation for an outstandingly memorable and happy year, I enquired whether I could rectify this state of affairs and present a chain worthy of the dignity of the office, while still retaining the maroon ribbon which held significance alongside the blue ribbon for branch presidents and yellow for vice-presidents. The offer was graciously accepted and soon my spare time was filled with arranging visits to Fattorini, the supplier of gold and silver insignia in Birmingham, to discuss appropriate designs and materials, as well as making a closer examination of chains in use in other professional organisations. With great relief, it was completed in time and I was delighted to observe how well it looked in ceremonial use by Harold.

Over the years, a recurring question that I have been asked is, 'Did you have a plan for your career path?' The short, and truthful, answer is 'No'. So far, you will have discovered that my two top posts at the BDA have arisen due to being in the right place at the right time. Naturally, I have been disappointed along the way and in particular in 1989 when I was strongly encouraged to stand for election as the president of the General Dental Council. I considered I had a good chance as, after thirteen years' service on the council, I was now a senior member and had a wide experience of different committees. More surprisingly, the editor of the *Probe Journal*, who had called for my resignation after my election to the GDC in 1976, now wrote, 'The support for Margaret Seward among elected members of the GDC is growing. But will the academics be generous and add their backing?' The reason for this comment was that there was an opinion that the presidency should alternate between nominated (academics) and elected members, and the retiring president was Sir Frank Lawton, former Dean of Liverpool Dental School. To my mind this was an arbitrary division, as surely any election to a top post should be on merit and not influenced by how the member had arrived at the GDC, either through election, or nomination.

In the event, there were five candidates, four professors and myself. The voting took place in a secret ballot held at the half-yearly council meeting in May. I made it through to the third ballot, when two of my supporters deserted me and there was then a straight vote between the two remaining candidates in the fourth ballot, resulting in Professor David Mason, CBE, Dean of Glasgow Dental School, being elected as president.

In the aftermath, people were very kind, but if all the people who said they had voted for me in the secret ballot had done so, I should have won by a landslide! However, I was surprised to have unexpected expression of disappointment from the rival professional organisation, the General Dental Practitioners' Association. The General Secretary, Michael Watson, writing in its Journal commented: 'I would like to have seen an elected member and it is time a woman had the top job. Margaret would have shaken the place up; perhaps that's what worried the Council.'

Now, five years later, as my tenure of office at the BDA was finishing, the five-year term of office of Sir David Mason was also coming to a close. He was eligible to stand for re-election and follow the precedent of the previous president, Sir Frank Lawton, in holding office for two five-year terms.

Again I was being encouraged to allow my name to go forward as a candidate. However, I did not favour my chances against an incumbent candidate. Likewise, if I did not stand this time, a wait of a further five years could be too long. After all, Gordon had already notched up four years of retirement and was thoroughly enjoying joys outside dentistry, so perhaps I should call it a day and join him. Gordon was confident that I should try again. Was I brave enough to risk defeat for a second time? It was decision time.

CHAPTER 14

Interests and intrigues

THIS WOULD SEEM AN OPPORTUNE moment to rewind, to the commencement of my tenure as editor of the *British Dental Journal*, and recount certain events which ran parallel with my paid employment. Undoubtedly, as you will discover, these shaped my character and beliefs and greatly influenced how I took decisions in my professional and private life.

My great mentor, Dr Gerry Leatherman, the former executive-director of the International Dental Federation, the FDI, encouraged me to pursue interests outside the dental association and was a staunch advocate for the work of the faculty of dental surgery. Its home was located within the Royal College of Surgeons of England, an imposing building in grandiose style which graced the east side of Lincoln's Inn Fields. I, too, was attracted to the ideals of this independent professional organisation, founded in 1947, whose *raison d'être* was to promote and maintain the highest quality and standards of dental care for patients. This was accomplished through providing advice on the training requirements of specialists, holding postgraduate examinations, granting higher diplomas and ensuring representatives of the faculty were members of panels convened to appoint consultants to vacant hospital posts.

Holders of the fellowship in dental surgery, known as fellows, were entitled to stand for election to the ruling body of the faculty, known as the Board. In 1974, it comprised eighteen members, including the dean and vice-dean, all of whom were Caucasian males. I considered that, with the increasing proportion of women in the dental profession, this fact should be reflected in the membership of the Board. So, I floated my concern with colleagues, who encouraged me to declare myself as a candidate at the next election. It is outrageous to think I had the nerve to put myself forward as a contender when I now read the credentials that I listed on the voting paper: 'sessional dental officer in the Hertford County Council, honorary secretary of the south-east group of the British Paedodontic Society'. Listed as special interests were 'children's and public health dentistry'. This was a meagre pen-profile compared to the sixteen high-flying male colleagues, nearly all of consultant rank, who were also candidates for the four vacant seats on the Board. Nevertheless, owing, I am sure, to the novelty of a woman's name appearing on the voting paper, I was placed at the top of the 'not-elected' list. My attempt to breach a male bastion had been noticed; the near-miss result made me more determined to try again if the opportunity arose.

Three years later, there was great excitement in the Seward household, when Gordon, now Dean of Dental Studies at the London Hospital Dental Institute, was elected to the Board. Inevitably, my interest in the work of the faculty was heightened, so that when in 1980, six years after my first attempt, it was announced that five vacancies were to be filled, I decided to throw my hat into the ring for a second time. Now, I believed, my credentials had substance. I was editor of the *British Dental Journal* and a member of the General Dental Council. I was thrilled to succeed handsomely, gaining second place amongst a field of twenty-four male candidates. However, my arrival as the first female member of the Board did have unexpected repercussions. After each faculty Board meeting, it was customary to conclude with a splendid dinner, held in the magnificently oak-panelled college Council room, the venue for the meeting during the day. By night, it was transformed into an elegant dining room with white starched linen tablecloths adorned by candelabra and exquisite pieces of silver, many presented to the Board by fellows on completion of fourteen years of dedicated service. Members were encouraged to bring guests to the dinner, perhaps a colleague at the hospital or the senior registrar who could be carrying extra duties for his boss, while on faculty business in London. I began to give some thought as to whom I might take as my guest to the dinner, when I was politely, but firmly, told to remember that only a male guest was permitted. I was not amused by this, to me, illogical edict, but concluded that as a 'new girl' I would initially abide by this ruling, so I rustled up male colleagues and relations. After attending three dinners, I thought I might run out of suitable men to accompany me, remembering that I was not only a married woman, but also that my husband, as a member of the Board, watched with interest my choice of dining companions. Finally, I decided to challenge this nonsensical rule and asked that an item, 'dinner guests', should be placed on the agenda for the next Board meeting. In the event, I had completely miscalculated the strength of feeling against the proposal. 'If we admit women it will spoil the dining club ambience which we enjoy,' uttered one fellow with great feeling. 'I don't know of any woman I would want to bring to the dinner,' opined another fellow. Following a heated debate, a vote was taken and to my great relief it was agreed that I could bring a woman as my guest to the dinner. I still smile when I recall that barely a couple of months elapsed before male members took advantage of this change in the rules.

Gordon was greatly admired as a knowledgeable and gifted member of the Board who was respected for his wise counsel and measured contributions to debate. When he spoke, people listened. With his detailed understanding over a wide range of topics, coupled with his well-honed eye for detail, it was not a surprise when he was elected dean of the faculty in 1986. During his three years in office, one day stands out as exceptional: Friday, 18 June, 1988. On this day, Her Royal Highness, the Princess of Wales, was made an honorary fellow of the faculty of dental surgery. As the only woman on the Board, I was assigned the delightful task of escorting Princess Diana and her lady-in-waiting, Viscountess Campden, to the robing room prior to the ceremony. As the three of us entered the room, Princess Diana spotted three black mortarboards with gigantic tassels, thoughtfully laid out on a small table so that she could decide which size would fit best. Giggles ensued, as she tried on each in turn, in front of the mirror, quipping: 'Oh, what fun – let's play schools.' Suddenly, her infectious exuberance evaporated, when I unzipped the protective cover over the gown she was to wear for the ceremony, revealing a black gown trimmed with a brilliant peony pink silk. 'That clashes with my scarlet dress, shoes and handbag,' she exclaimed in dismay and immediately disposed of one scarlet item by passing her handbag to her lady-in-waiting, first retrieving its contents: a handkerchief and her speech. Studying the numerous photographs taken on that day there was ample evidence that she need not have worried: she herself was nothing other than truly stunning.

In fact, the Princess of Wales made history as the first member of the Royal Family to be appointed an honorary fellow in dental surgery of the Royal College of Surgeons. Her dazzling smile captivated the packed audience of parents and friends and the one hundred and twenty dentists who were sufficiently fortunate to be receiving their diplomas on the same day.

In his address, the dean reported that 'the faculty had considered very carefully the curriculum vitae and attributes of potential new members of our profession.' Gordon, as dean, continued, 'Your charming smile, friendly manner and deep interest in children and the disadvantaged impressed us as representative of the ideal image of the dental practitioner.' In thanking the fellows for the award, the Princess explained that, 'I was taught the importance of good dental health as a small child. Now that I have children of my own, I am of course passing on that message.' Spontaneous laughter followed her humorous concluding remarks: 'Thankfully, this is one of the first times that I have not been asked to unveil a plaque.'

At the close of the ceremony, a gold brooch depicting the College emblem and studded with three sparkling rubies was presented to a delighted Princess of Wales, who then endeared herself to everyone present as she walked amongst the new diplomates. She chatted with them as, with family and friends, they enjoyed the fork buffet and noticeably she made a beeline for those unable to advance on their own, whether they were in wheelchairs or were small children in the arms of their parents. On leaving the college, Princess Diana expressed a wish that she would like to return to take dinner with the Board members after one of their meetings, a promise which she kept to the delight of everyone. I often wonder how the Board would have reacted to this request, if the old rules had been in force. 'Sorry, Ma'am, we only have male guests.'

As I have mentioned, the duration of office as a member of the Board could be a lengthy one, an initial period of service for eight years and then, if successfully re-elected for a further six years, the total could be fourteen years. As a consequence it was possible to rise through the committee structure and with seniority become a chairman. This happened to me and I was delighted to be appointed chairman of the postgraduate education committee which had the responsibility of organising programmes for study days. Running concurrently was my appointment as Bradlaw Adviser, whose role was to provide advice and support to dentists who failed on a recurring basis the hurdle of the fellowship examination. Later, when a new dean, Derek Seel, a distinguished orthodontist, was appointed, he reconfigured the committee structure and to good effect. He created a fellows and members committee, inviting me to be joint chairman with Edgar Gordon, a close friend of mine who was one of the first Members in General Dental Surgery and a gifted contributor to the dental press. The aim was to improve relations, not only with the public, but also with our own fellows and members. This was a communication challenge which I relished.

It was also during Derek's deanship that I was elected vice-dean, by which time Gordon had finished his term of service on the Board. Inevitably, colleagues thought it great fun to provide me with the nickname, 'Mrs Vice', which I took in good part, hoping it was meant as a form of endearment for the first woman to reach this position. There came to fruition during this period the initial stirrings which had taken place during Gordon's deanship regarding the desire by general dental practitioners to form their own advisory board. In February 1986, Peter Harvey, the chairman of the committee on General Dental Surgery which had been convened by the faculty five years previously, wrote to nearly six thousand dentists who held a diploma awarded by the Royal College of Surgeons of England conveying groundbreaking news. 'An Advisory Board in General Dental Practice: A Collegiate Home' was to be formed. General practitioners had become increasingly frustrated because, although they had four representatives who attended the faculty Board meetings, most of the business of the Board revolved around the problems faced in a hospital or academic environment, and not in their specialist area of general dental practice. Recognising that I was in empathy with general dental practitioners through my editorship of the *BDJ*, I was appointed to the Advisory Board, as the representative from the long-established faculty of dental surgery. It was an exciting time to be involved and, due to the enormous commitment of its founding members, the Advisory Board evolved in 1992 into a free-standing faculty of General Dental Practitioners of the Royal College of Surgeons of England. The new faculty was also unique in that it encompassed the four countries, England, Scotland, Wales and Northern Ireland, and this was signalled by the diploma FGDP (UK). For so many it was the fulfilment of a dream to establish an academic home for the 90 per cent of dentists who practised in primary care, so maintaining and advancing standards to ensure the highest quality of patient care. Several years later I was honoured by the faculty with the award of its fellowship. I know my father would have approved: at last, I could claim to be a general dental practitioner, albeit an honorary one.

However, I did not forget my early days working as a community dental officer at the Cheshunt dental clinic when I was all too aware that my clinical colleagues lacked any opportunity to acquire a higher qualification in their chosen speciality. During the intervening years, representations by senior members of the British Paedodontic Society to the faculty of dental surgery had been made on several occasions for a diploma in children's dentistry or child dental health, only to be met by rejection. Now, from within the organisation, surely it should be possible for me to persuade members of the Board of the need for a higher qualification to be available for clinicians working in the community dental service, not only to enhance their own self-esteem, but also to improve their standard of care for a very deserving group of patients. Learning from previous mistakes, I took time to prepare the ground thoroughly and was relieved when the Board agreed to introduce the membership in clinical community dentistry. I was appointed chairman of examiners and, to everyone's surprise, we were overwhelmed by the number of candidates wishing to take this new examination. There was added interest, especially as the dental faculty at the Royal College of Physicians and Surgeons of Glasgow was also developing a diploma for dentists working in the community. The Convenor of the examinations committee, Professor David McGowan, worked tirelessly to ensure that, when Glasgow introduced its diploma, reciprocity would be established with the English College. Thus, for the first time for any College examination, there was introduced flexibility which enabled a candidate to sit, for example, Part I in Scotland and Part II in England, a great advance in cooperation across the borders.

In some of the Royal Colleges, when a new examination is introduced, it is recognised that the initial panel of examiners is excluded from taking the examination and so the longheld custom is to present them with the diploma. So, with minimal effort, seven more letters were appended to my name: MCCD RCS.

In the early eighties, I was fascinated by the burgeoning computer technology and did everything to facilitate those wishing to be involved. However, my technical skills did not match those of the younger generation, and in particular, of our son Colin, who at 15 years of age, was proficient on any new computer model which appeared; Video Genie, Sinclair's ZX-80, ZX-81 and ZX Spectrum. This proved to be fortuitous. In 1981, Gordon had been installed as President of the British Association of Oral Surgeons and followed the tradition to hold the spring meeting in his home town. Near Hadley Wood was Trent Park, famous in March for its drifts of yellow daffodils, and crowds came from throughout Hertfordshire to view the display. As a venue it seemed most appropriate, as its splendid Mansion House in the centre of the Park was linked with health care, because King George III gave it as a gift to Sir Richard Jepson for saving the life of his brother at Trent in the Tyrol. Not too many health care professionals receive such generous gifts from grateful patients or relatives.

Colin watched askance as his father each evening checked delegates' registration forms by hand. As often as not, the total of the costs of the various items did not tally with the oral surgeon's submitted cheque: adding up was clearly not their strong point. Colin suggested using our home computer and in no time at all had devised a computer program for preparing a budget and for entering the registration data of delegates. Much to everyone's delight, the participants' conference bags bulged with computer print-out lists of delegates and accompanying persons. As a result of the success of this venture there were numerous requests for detailed information about the computer program. So Colin and Gordon decided to write a paper 'Why not run your next conference on a computer?' and submitted it to the editor for possible publication in the *British Dental Journal*. The editor (alias mother) sent it, following the normal procedure, to referees for comments and, for an additional computer expert opinion, to Professor Fred Smales. What a thrill it was for me to be able to send off the letter of acceptance, a thrill which was shared by all, as the names of father and son appeared together as authors when the article was published in the March issue of the *BDJ* in 1983. From that experience I realised it is so easy to overlook our children's expertise and forget to harness their special talents to help us in our work. Thank goodness Colin had seen the potential to assist his father with what was proving to be a time-consuming chore.

However, while Gordon was president, I assumed a new role – the president's wife. It was my responsibility to organise an entertainment programme during the day for the ladies attending the conference, who were mainly spouses of the Council members. For the two-day programme, I decided to turn my back on visits to nearby stately homes and try something different. Firstly, I organised a cordon bleu cookery demonstration at Middleton House in nearby Theobald's Park, and followed this, on the second day, with a fashion show in our home, Tudor House. A great friend, Joyce Lockhart, who lived a couple of hundred yards up from us in Beech Hill Avenue and who had worked as a buyer for top fashion houses, was enthusiastic about the idea and offered to help. So, early one cold March morning and before it was fully light, Joyce and her husband Jim gingerly pushed down the road a very heavily laden clothes rail. This was then dismantled in our hallway and reassembled upstairs in the large front bedroom. The garments, a selection of the latest eye-catching fashions in dresses, jackets, trousers and coats, were then rehung. I had enlisted a few friends in the group to be models and my dear friend Brenda Hipkin found herself in charge of the hot water urn, ready to dispense tea and coffee to the guests. So the scene was set for the arrival of a 48-seater coach conveying the ladies from Trent Park to Tudor House, much to the amazement of our neighbours in a normally sedate residential tree-lined road.

With coffee well underway, the models appeared in their pre-assigned garments and Norma Rayne, a tall, dark-haired, elegant lady, provoked the loudest applause when she appeared in the newest look in the fashion scene: black leather hot-pants. As we approached the end of the show I brought in a tray of glasses brimming with sherry. Joyce announced that if anyone would like to try on the garments they were welcome to do so and that most were available for purchase at competitive prices. The sherry was forgotten: it was a stampede as the ladies elbowed their way upstairs to try on their 'favoured little number'. Gales of laughter drifted to a few of us downstairs and every room with a mirror was commandeered for use. Immediately a garment was discarded it was quickly seized upon by another eager 'would-be purchaser'. Eventually, the coach sped back to Trent Park and, due to the unexpected volume of transactions completed, it was well behind schedule. A group of worried husbands watched in horror as their wives clambered down from the coach clutching large fashion bags bulging with their purchases. One lady, with her face wreathed in smiles, announced to her husband that she had found the exact coat for her son's wedding and how much she had saved. The husband appeared unimpressed. 'It's how much you spent, not what you saved that matters.'

Still in use at dinner parties at our home is the thoughtful gift from these ladies at the end of the day's activities, a beautiful Wedgwood Kutani Crane cheeseboard. I never cease to relive the fun we had over the two days. It was an unexpected privilege to be the president's wife.

Having enjoyed my foray into computer technology, I began to wonder if it could be harnessed to encourage children to look after their teeth. When I shared my idea with Patricia Whitehead, who had responsibility for dental health education at the General Dental Council, she was very supportive and soon I found myself chairing a working party. The idea was to organise a national schools' competition, embracing computing and dental health and so we coined the title 'Computadent'. Support of the district dental officers was enlisted to distribute details of the competition to the secondary schools in their area. Contained in the information was a request to let the GDC know by 1 November 1983 if they intended to enter the competition for which we had publicised the closing date for entries as 30 March 1984. Tantalisingly on offer were generous prizes. There was the opportunity to win a computer, not only one for individual use, but also for the school. These prizes had been donated by Acorn, Apple, Atari, Commodore, and Sinclair, and also included were printers and other computer accessories. However, we had completely underestimated the response. More than one thousand schools contacted the GDC for details and ninety-five completed entries were submitted by the closing date. Perhaps the knowledge that Chris Searle, the popular TV presenter of a series of programmes on the computer, was to present the prizes also encouraged the positive response.

The judging panel, chaired by the president, Sir Frank Lawton, supported by technology advisers, had the unenviable task of selecting the winners. Chosen as the outright winner was a 15-year old schoolboy from Belfast. The program was considered so outstanding that it was subsequently professionally produced and marketed as 'Teeth and Dental Care' for use on a BBC computer. Through the use of the program, children especially above the age of ten learnt the types of teeth, their structure, the importance of diet and the prevention of decay and gum disease. Animated graphics and sound effects increased the program's appeal, as did the final quiz.

There was so much interest in the project that it was entered for the 1985 Domestos Health Education Awards. Again, Colin volunteered to produce in colour a transcript of the program and print out the graphics. I had to submit three copies and the deadline for entry was fast approaching. On the final evening I went to bed leaving Colin working at his computer. When I went downstairs to breakfast, the three copies were neatly stacked on the table. On the fourth copy was a message in Colin's neat handwriting: '2.05 a.m. This is the original set. Please do not give in to the competition.' I didn't, and I still proudly possess it.

At the beginning of 1983, Ronnie Allen announced that he would take early retirement. Naturally, I was concerned about who might be appointed to succeed him as secretary of the association for I had been fortunate for five years to enjoy his friendship and to have his active support in defending the *BDJ* against unwarranted criticism. The prospect of change was unsettling for all the staff at headquarters, but I had plenty to keep myself occupied. One task, which I was thoroughly enjoying, was attending the debates in the House of Lords on the Dentists Bill in order that I could report the proceedings in the *Journal*. This was a significant time for the profession as it awaited the long overdue Dentists Act, which would allow the introduction of important new powers for the General Dental Council, including the establishment of a health committee which was for the enhanced protection of patients and provided vital support to sick dentists.

I was fascinated when watching the intricacies and procedures of debate and observing the departmental team of civil servants, including the chief dental officer and his staff responding to requests from the government minister, Lord Trefgarne, for information during the numerous sittings of the committee. On one occasion, during the debate in the House of Lords, Baroness (Trixie) Gardner of Parkes, herself a dentist in practice with her husband, moved an amendment which she hoped would permit dentists to use the courtesy title 'doctor'. I was taken aback while sitting in the public gallery to hear my name mentioned. 'I am rather pleased,' said Baroness Gardner, 'that the editor of the *BDJ* is attending the debate today, so I am sure she will report the minister's remarks on this matter.' I did indeed publish the debate in the 5 March issue of the 1983 volume of the *BDJ*, but disappointingly the amendment was withdrawn and the legal use of the courtesy title 'doctor' is an issue that remains unresolved.

Inspired by my frequent visits to the Palace of Westminster, I was captivated by the workings of Parliament. Therefore, when a couple of weeks later, in the same month, an advertisement appeared in the *BDJ* for the post of chief dental officer in the Department of Health and Social Security in England, due to the retirement of George Gibb, I decided to apply for the post. If Ronnie was departing, then perhaps my fears about his successor could be allayed if I moved on. He gave me his full support to apply, acting as a referee; the other was Sir Frank Lawton at the GDC. I was called for interview on 14 June 1983. It was a sweltering hot day and the interview by the Civil Service Commission was scheduled for 3 p.m. in the Management and Personnel Office in the old, airless Admiralty Buildings in Whitehall. Contrasting with my interview for editor of the *Journal*, there was not a suggestion or a question about how I would cope as a 'working mum'. I certainly did not feel confident with my performance and was not at all surprised to learn that Dr Martin Downer, the current chief dental officer to the Scottish Home and Health Department, had been appointed. Naturally, disappointed at the outcome, my spirits were raised when I received a letter from the dean at the faculty of dental surgery, Professor Paul Bramley. 'This is not a letter of consolation,' he wrote, 'but one of congratulation and encouragement. When you first spoke to me about applying, I expressed surprise that you wanted to put your head into this particular noose – rather, you should crack a bottle of champagne, and even persuade Gordon to have a glass, and be thankful you haven't been successful.'

I am not alone within the profession in having received, from Sir Paul as he was later to become, a note of encouragement at a low point or when ambitions are thwarted. Throughout my career I have tried to follow his thoughtful action, although I have never been able to replicate his bold and distinctive handwriting accomplished with a fountain pen.

Pam Clarke, secretary to the faculty, also expressed her delight on hearing the outcome of the interview. 'I am also glad that there will still be a lady on the Board – the men have had it too much their own way!'

This brought me up with a jolt. I had failed to work through the consequences of my appointment as chief dental officer. It would have been obligatory to relinquish my hard-fought seats, not only on the faculty but also on the GDC. In addition I would not have been able to continue as a member of Council and of the Dental Advisory Board of the Medical Protection Society, a professional indemnity organisation for doctors and dentists. On reflection, Professor Bramley was right. I put the champagne on ice: I had just had a lucky escape.

On 11 June 1983, three days before my interview for the chief dental officer's post, there was a meeting of the Representative Board of the BDA at which they approved the unanimous recommendation from the appointments committee that Keith Johnson should be the next secretary of the association. 'Keith who?' was the universal reaction to the announcement. Ralph Followell, the popular chairman of the BDA Council, and formerly chairman of the General Dental Services Committee, had been strongly tipped to be appointed. He had acted scrupulously in immediately resigning as chairman when he declared his intention of submitting his name for the top job at the BDA and he was also all too aware that if unsuccessful he could not reclaim his position because Bryan Gillard, his vice-chairman, had been confirmed as acting chairman of the Council. As it transpired, following the announcement, Ralph had to begin the unenviable task of rebuilding his general practice: he paid a high price for entering the race to be secretary.

So who was Keith Johnson who succeeded in convincing, so spectacularly, the experienced and senior members of the profession who comprised the appointments committee? Keith, at 45 years of age, was a successful dentist, running on his own a busy general practice in Beeston, in Nottinghamshire. At one time, assistants worked for him and the last one was at the time a newly qualified dentist, Bill Allen, who became chairman of the Council of the BDA many years later. Keith was involved at local level in BDA affairs and was known as a very conscientious honorary secretary of the East Midlands Branch and, through this position, held a seat on the Representative Board for four years. I commissioned Colin Davis to conduct an interview with Keith for publication in the *Journal*. Colin commented, 'We have tried to reveal him as a doer and singularly well-fitted to his new assignment – but he is quite capable of talking as well.' In his exchanges with Colin Davis, Keith had emphasised his affection for his Alma Mater Liverpool, where he had graduated with honours, and paid tribute to his mentors, Professor Frank Lawton, Geoffrey Slack, Ronnie Hartles and Roy Storer. The latter he singled out as possessing that rare gift of remembering names and taking a keen interest in the personal progress of each student.

At that time, it was customary for the President of the BDA to write a New Year Message to the membership. Thus in the first issue of 1984, Richard Miller Yardley commented on the fact that the new year began with a new secretary of the association and a new chief dental officer and echoed everyone's thoughts. 'It is my conviction that, with goodwill and intelligent cooperation among all concerned, difficulties can be overcome and the future of the profession will be bright.' This was a statesmanlike message, full of positive optimism at a time of unprecedented political interference which threatened the closure of two dental schools and the merger of the Royal Dental Hospital with Guy's Hospital Dental School.

So, on 1 January 1984, Keith Johnson was thrown in at the deep end to learn the management skills for running a professional trade union and to deal with the intense anger and frustration amongst dentists provoked by relentless and devastating media attacks. Initially there was the *Daily Express* investigation of dentists' earnings in Coventry. There followed in May Esther Rantzen's trial by television during her highly popular '*That's Life*' programme, which unearthed the complexities for patients of the existing complaints' procedure against dentists regarding treatment. Then, a month later, on 25 June, there was screened a highly damaging programme on Granada's '*World in Action*' with the emotive title, 'Drilling for Gold'. This brought the problem of over-prescription of treatment into the sitting rooms of the nation, and, most disturbingly, portrayed dentists as uncaring high earners, enjoying a luxurious lifestyle. Further embarrassment was caused due to disparate opinions given by members of the profession on TV and radio. To the public it was clear that the profession did not speak with one voice, so where was the truth?

As a result, in the summer of 1984, when normally there was a lull in political activity, there was the urgent need for strong leadership to mount the biggest public relations exercise ever tackled by the BDA. In a courageous, if not expensive, step, a public relations company, Shandwick, was hired to improve the image of the profession.

Also during the summer, in fact in August, it was time for Keith Johnson to attend his first World Dental Congress scheduled in Helsinki in his role as secretary and thus a member of the association's delegation. We all choose to approach our involvement in different ways, but Keith, although aware of the work of the international dental federation, was completely unprepared, as I had been several years previously, for the sheer size and complexity of the congress and the importance of the business meetings which ran concurrently for the members of the BDA delegation. His decision to absent himself from these political meetings for more attractive daytime excursions, albeit in the company of another national association secretary, was frowned upon by his colleagues.

Once returned from Finland, the relentless autumn schedule of BDA committee meetings recommenced, and as a member of staff I became aware of mutterings and misgivings amongst some of the elected officers about the manner in which the secretary was handling his responsibilities. However, I was completely unprepared for the statement, agreed by solicitors on behalf of the association and the secretary, which I was asked to publish in the 10 November issue of the *Journal*. It read: 'As a result of recurrent fundamental disputes between the Principal Officers of the Council of the Association and Mr Johnson over the role of Secretary, with mutual agreement Mr Johnson has resigned from his post as Secretary of the Association and suitable financial arrangements (negotiated entirely on legal advice) have been agreed.'

On 20 October, the Representative Board of just over one hundred members received this bombshell, but were also told that they were all legally bound to secrecy about the matter. But such a hope was short-lived. On 2 November in the satirical magazine *Private Eye* revelations appeared. 'The official explanation of Johnson's premature departure from his job is that he failed to prevent the Government from raising dental charges. But no BDA Secretary has ever had the slightest influence over such political decisions.' More worryingly for the rank and file members was the news in the magazine that, '1,500 subscriptions have been written off this year in paying Keith Johnson £112,500 to keep his mouth shut and go quietly.'

Then the anonymous author continued, 'Many dentists believe Johnson's difficulties with the executive (a six-man team elected by the Board) have arisen from his objection to the high expenses they – quite legitimately – claim for BDA work . . . Many feel the whole question of compensation and expenses should be re-evaluated.'

It will not take much imagination to realise that, as editor, I was quickly embroiled in the fall-out from this very explosive piece of journalism from the pen of someone with inside information. My postbag was full to overflowing with numerous letters for publication, written by concerned and bewildered members of the association. As so often occurs in these shock events, the correspondents base their opinions on rumours and supposition, demanding scapegoats and offering advice on how the resignation should have been handled, and querying whether there should have been one at all. The true sequence of events was confined to a very small inner circle – the executive and lawyers.

The extent of the tragedy and damage to the association was obvious for all of us to witness as we travelled about our normal business and met with practitioners. Kevin Lewis, writing in his highly regarded leader column in the *Dental Practice* magazine reported, 'I had six lecturing engagements all over the UK within three weeks of the announcement and the disquiet and unrest was not shrouded in any such veil of mystery; it was there for all to see and hear.'

The entire episode troubled me deeply. I recalled that a frequent question put to me when visiting the branches and sections, when referring to the independence of the *BDJ*, was whether, if necessary, I would write a leader critical of the association's thinking. My reply was unequivocal, for what I considered a hypothetical enquiry. 'Yes, I would, but of course within legal constraints.' Now, I was right in the throes of such a situation, which from my editor's chair would need strong and decisive handling, aware of the legal constraints and yet seen to be even-handed to all parties.

People look for inspiration in taking decisions in different ways. I favour going for a walk, alone, to think through the 'pros and cons' and consequence of a preferred action. If I am fortunate enough to be at the coast, my ideal is to pick a path along the wet sand at the very margin of the breaking waves upon the shore. As I was pondering what to do with my bulging postbag on the issue, I was on my way to speak in the West Country and was booked in at a hotel in Exmouth. I took my solitary walk along the sand and within minutes believed that I had alighted on the solution and quickly returned to the hotel to put pen to paper. So what had I decided? Firstly, I would not publish any letters on the topic in the *Journal*. Second, I would shed the customary anonymity of the editor's chair and write a leader on the tragic situation of the secretary's departure, explaining that, as few were privy to the full course of events, I did not intend to publish the letters. So, for the first time in the hundred years' history of the *BDJ*, the leader in the issue of 24 November 1984 was signed by the editor. I expressed disquiet that an informed debate could not be based on the truth of the events. I then added my own serious misgivings about the handling of the situation. 'None must seriously believe that members of a professional association can be denied the right to hold informed debate at any stage on a matter of fundamental importance as well as financial implications.'

In the final paragraph, I wrote 'Now we must refrain from embarking on a suicidal witch-hunt in our own publication. We must concentrate on the future. A new Representative Board will elect our officers on 10 January: we shall eventually appoint a new secretary. The membership of the BDA will look to them to work together in such a way as to command our total confidence and restore lustre to our temporarily tarnished image.'

However, emerging from the shadows unleashed another avalanche of mail, and not all complimentary.

'Your editorial was sanctimonious and patronising and has made me even more angry about the incident,' wrote Trevor Barnes.

Fraser McDonald observed, 'There is no doubt in my mind that there are two sides to every story. But from your leader it appears that the sides of the stories are not to be known.'

Ken Brown, the editor of the magazine *The Probe*, sympathised with my dilemma regarding publication of letters on the topic of the resignation. 'Like you, I would go a long way to avoid a writ – so I did not publish the letters sent to me as I did not want to interfere.'

Another editor came to my aid. Kevin Lewis included in his Christmas Column in *Dental Practice*, 'I have just read the leader in the 24 November issue of the *BDJ*. In a quite impossible position, not only as editor of the *Journal*, but also a member of the GDC, she has done the profession great credit in so admirably refusing to sweep the problems under the carpet. I trust that our readers will recognise and appreciate the courageous stand she has taken.'

I began to ponder if these unsolicited expressions of support would engender mistrust, even jealousy, amongst those in authority. However, in my own mind, and for the credibility of BDA of which I was a member, as well as an employee, I had to speak out and be prepared to shoulder the consequences. With perfect timing, reassurance came again from Paul Bramley. 'I really have no idea what it's all about – "To thine own self be true" – Shakespeare. Keep taking the tablets.' Truly magical words.

Following publication of the leader, I received a letter from Keith Johnson. 'I found the whole recent experience quite shattering,' and the depth of his anguish did not abate with time. Each Christmas he would write to me a three- or four-page letter, and would, amongst other items, comment, 'I still have depressed times when reflecting on my experiences as BDA Secretary, but remember the good times when Council meetings seemed to coincide with matches at Twickenham.'

Howard Carrington, a member of the Representative Board commented in his letter to me for the *BDJ*, 'What about the appalling personal trauma inflicted on Keith Johnson?' His insight as to future events proved true. Because of the intrusive media coverage, Keith found it impossible to re-establish himself in practice in his home town of Beeston and his marriage also disintegrated. The 'suitable financial arrangements' did not ease the situation or heal the scars, as he embarked on a round of locum jobs. Twenty-two years later his annual Christmas letter did not arrive. His second wife, Sally, phoned to say that Keith had been crushed to death by an articulated lorry while towing his caravan in France. Conveying this sad news to younger BDA members, the response was chilling, an echo of former times – 'Keith who?'

So closed an unglamorous chapter of BDA history.

I learnt many lessons from this episode and the turmoil it created in Wimpole Street. Foremost is my distaste of firing staff. Gurus of management write: 'A good manager has to be a good butcher.' Certainly there are times when it is the correct course of action for effective teamwork or stability of the organisation, but the aftermath has to be worked through.

Each Christmas, when I received Keith's epistle, I continued to wonder if I had taken a strong enough stance, or if I had allowed myself too much comfort by remaining rooted on the sidelines.

One morning, just after arriving at work, Mary Barker, the executive secretary at the FDI, came into my office. 'Margaret, do you think Pamela would like to come to the congress this summer in Helsinki, and act as secretary to the communications committee and the world dental editors meeting?' I could not wait to share this tantalising offer with our daughter, fully aware that she enjoyed a long summer vacation as she was studying natural sciences at Cambridge University. This was a fantastic opportunity to stand in for a member of staff on maternity leave and to travel, with expenses paid, to a country not regularly on the tourist map, Finland. As predicted, the idea was met with great excitement and, as Gordon and I had planned to have a short holiday afterwards in Lapland, we included Pamela in our plans.

Before departing for the Congress, the family spent a few days at our flat in Troon in Ayrshire which had passed to me after being in the Mitchell family for three generations. Holidays there were real relaxation and we spent happy times cycling through Fullerton Woods, scrambling over the rocks and hunting in the pools on Ballast Bank or sailing on the romantic paddle steamer, SS *Waverley*, to the nearby Isle of Arran. As with any property, there were always plenty of DIY jobs waiting attention, and on this visit Gordon's allotted task was to refix the bathroom tiles, which was neatly accomplished with the aid of a very pungent adhesive. At breakfast the following morning, Gordon complained of feeling shivery and definitely 'out of sorts'. Later, he asked me if I thought he was jaundiced. He tells me that I briskly dismissed this suggestion, and as he began to feel better we agreed that he must have flu. When we drove home to Hadley Wood at the end of the week, the episode was all but forgotten as lawns were mowed, cases packed and we were soon on our way to Finland.

Arriving in Helsinki was a memorable and exciting experience. We fell in love with the stunning architectural buildings and especially the acoustically superior Finlandia Hall, built in 1971, where we enjoyed an organised concert to celebrate the congress and to absorb the wonderful music of their national hero Sibelius. His is the oddest monument in a park that I have ever seen, consisting of steel pipes resembling a huge organ, although strangely he never played the instrument. In the market square, the stalls were groaning under a huge selection of berries, many unknown to me – red arctic bramberries, blueberries, and yellow lingonberries or cloud berries. From these were made delicious jams and sauces, a popular accompaniment to ice-cream and, for an extra special treat, doused with Finlandia vodka, or the even stronger Koskenkorva.

It was a joy to have Pamela looking after the chairman of the communications committee (me) so efficiently and she endeared herself to the world dental editors as she organised the daily briefings with great humour and used her artistic skills for designing eye-catching posters, so ensuring record attendances at the various press events. At the end of the conference, we started our journey to Lapland, a country which endures continuous days, as well as nights, of darkness during the winter months. Even as early as August, the time of our visit, there had been a substantial snowfall and the temperature dropped dramatically at night. In mid winter it could be nearly −40°; no wonder it was common for houses and hotels to have windows with quadruple glazing. We visited Father Christmas's special house in Luosto but he was so busy answering the letters sent by boys and girls from around the world that, sadly, we didn't manage to meet him. Perhaps another time.

Just before we left Helsinki, Gordon was beginning to feel unwell. By the end of the trip to Lapland he was experiencing severe back pain and general discomfort. Thus, on our return home, I drove him straight to the London Hospital to be seen by his medical colleagues. The diagnosis was swift and devastating: hepatitis B. As a surgeon this meant that Gordon could not operate on patients because they could be at risk of catching the disease, so he had to rest at home. The diagnosis also had repercussions on family life. I had to be protected with a large dose of gamma globulin, which was not a comfortable experience. General use of household utensils, linen and towels had to be curtailed: Gordon had to keep his own items isolated, so that the risk of contamination with saliva and thus infection for the rest of the family was minimised. Gordon's condition deteriorated and, as a result, he was admitted to the London Hospital for full bed rest. We all remained positive that the necessary hepatitis B antigen would soon appear in his blood. Until that happened, he was not allowed to return to be in contact with patients.

The New Year came and went, and depressingly with no improvement. Gordon was given the opportunity to be treated with a new drug, interferon. This entailed hospitalisation at the Royal Free Hospital in London, the only centre undertaking this drug trial at that time. It proved to be a cruel regime. Following the first dose, Gordon produced a rigor of such intensity that the bed literally shook violently. The reassuring expectation from other people's experiences was that, as the dose increased, the rigors would decrease, but this did not occur for Gordon. The course lasted twelve weeks, and injections were administered on a Monday, Wednesday and Friday. As a consequence, Tuesdays, Thursdays and Saturdays were very bad days, accompanied by backache, shivering and sweating, the worst of flu-like symptoms. The toll on family life was considerable, especially as Gordon changed from a fit and active husband and father, to a man short of breath, unable to climb the stairs, with marked loss of appetite and weight, and balding as his hair began to fall out in noticeable amounts. Colin, in the middle of A levels and still at home, became an expert with the lawnmower and other male domestic tasks. It was a sombre time for us all because we had been informed that if antibodies failed to appear, the prognosis was bleak: cancer of the liver.

Here I learned the strain from the intrusion of kindly-meaning colleagues and friends. 'How is Gordon?' It can be so depressing to have to reply 'No progress' or 'worse'. The ceaseless phone calls, expecting a response, had to be fitted in after returning from hospital visits, or my own speaking commitments for the *BDJ*. I found that a little note, or card, is worth a hundred phone calls. Pamela, sensing my frustration, again put her artistic talents to use and designed a badge for me to wear, depicting a happy smiling face which if turned through 180° then presented a sad face. I certainly found pointing to this a great way to deal with enquiries, and it was also guaranteed to bring forth a smile, irrespective of the message, so making us all feel better.

On reaching the twelfth week, the antibodies failed to materialise and the physician advised a further two weeks of injections. But worse was to come as they advised yet another two weeks and six more injections. Gordon's stoicism and fortitude all but departed him and so we pleaded with the physician to allow us a short break from the regime to recoup some strength. This was readily granted and so almost one year from the initial onset of the illness, we motored, on a bright Sunday at the end of July, to Hove near Brighton which boasts long flat stretches of promenade, with conveniently placed shelters along its length, providing a perfect stopping place for a short rest. Changing for dinner on Thursday evening, Gordon recalls that I exclaimed with excitement, 'Welcome back.' His demeanour had dramatically changed: it was as though a thick fog had dispersed. We hardly dared to hope that there had been a miracle, but four days later the phone call came from the hospital reporting the results of the last blood test before we went on holiday. 'Professor, you have A and E antibodies.' He was no longer a risk to his patients or himself. Our prayers, our friends' prayers, had been answered and thankfully Gordon was well on the road to full recovery. Such events, involving the health and well-being of family, refocus your mind as to your priorities in life. Top jobs and riches come a very poor second.

Gordon enjoyed a well-deserved reputation as a meticulous surgeon and he had been fastidious in taking all known precautions when operating on patients, especially on those arriving from war-torn zones abroad, because the risk of these people being carriers of disease was recognised. 'If it could happen to Gordon, it could happen to any of us' was the universal cry from a shocked dental profession. As a consequence, there was prompt action by the Department of Health to include dentists in the vaccination regime which, until that time, was available only to doctors and general nurses. In due course the vaccine against hepatitis B was extended to all members of the dental team, who now enjoy full protection from an occupational disease with devastating consequences.

When experiencing testing times, it is wise to indulge in an extravagance – new clothes, new furniture, or for me a luxury item, a car. I fancied the new Rover saloon, with a sliding roof, convinced that this would raise my spirits. My Saturday shopping trip into Barnet took me past the Hadley Green Garage showroom, full of glistening new and second-hand cars. Rolls Royce, Daimler, and Jaguar featured prominently. These were certainly outwith my price bracket. Then my eye caught the price tag of a second-hand black Daimler with a gorgeous ivory leather interior, walnut clad dashboard, a sliding sun roof and a low mileage. I realised with amazement that its price was less than for the brand new car which I was contemplating buying. I convinced myself that, while a test drive would not commit me to a purchase, it would provide me with the opportunity to drive a luxury car.

Gordon was very supportive of the idea and anything to lift my spirits during his injection regime he backed wholeheartedly. So a time was fixed for the test drive and soon we were travelling away from Barnet towards South Mimms. Then the sales manager pulled over into a lay-by, got out of the driving seat, walked round to the front passenger seat and as he opened the door, pronounced, 'Mrs Seward, your turn now.' Confidence drained. Perhaps it had been a bad idea to book a test drive; this was a big car to handle. However, Gordon in the rear seat seemed unperturbed as I settled myself into the driving seat. The car purred smoothly along, and handling my first car with power-assisted steering and an enormous engine was more of a challenge to keep below the speed limit of 30 mph. I had no hesitation in coming to a decision so a trade-in price for my Vauxhall car and a delivery date of the Daimler were arranged. I am confident that this will remain the only time in my life when a car, new to me, is delivered to my home with a bottle of superior 'bubbly' wedged in the compartment between the front seats. Draped along the entire length of the rear seats was the most beautiful and gigantic bouquet of flowers. I truly loved to drive my Daimler and increased its mileage by leaps and bounds as I drove to my various BDA engagements throughout the length and breadth of the country, until I had to pension it off in the interests of safety. Succeeding 'Jags' gave reliable service, but nothing subsequently gave me the thrill and uplift so much needed in some of my darkest days.

You will recall that earlier I described the survey of women dentists which I undertook in 1975 and which resulted in the introduction of a dentists' retainer scheme and other initiatives to assist dentists to return to work after a career break. Ten years on, in 1984, it seemed to me to be a good time to review progress, through using the same questionnaire and methodology in a repeat survey.

I turned to the Department of Health for funding and found the new chief dental officer, Martin Downer, sympathetic to my request as he appreciated the value of up-to-date information on feminisation in the profession, especially in relation to workforce planning. However, this time, due to my full-time commitment as editor of the *BDJ*, I needed someone to undertake the day-to-day conduct of the project. I was fortunate to discover that Elizabeth (Pippi) McEwen, the author of the survey amongst women who had studied at Scottish Dental Schools in 1976, now lived in Islington, North London, and was willing to be appointed Research Fellow. Soon a meeting was arranged, including Dr Don Neal, the same statistician from Reading University, who was also excited about the opportunity to undertake a ten-year review. The official operating address was, as before, the London Hospital Dental Institute, but this time our office was located in one of the turn of the twentieth century terrace houses, originally attractive, but now completely dysfunctional and awaiting demolition to make way for the development of modern teaching facilities.

The resultant and pleasing response rate of 76 per cent to the 1984 postal study enabled meaningful comparisons of the work pattern and commitment to career of women dentists to be made with the data acquired ten years previously. Immediately apparent was the continuing upward trend, not only of the number of women on the dentists' register, but also of women working in general dental practice. Also confirmed was the moderate success of the dentists' retainer scheme and so a re-branding of the initiative into a Keeping in Touch Scheme (KITS) and Getting back to Practice Scheme was launched. However, there still remained disturbing instances of discrimination. A reported scenario was that on one occasion, when a woman phoned in response to a vacancy advertised in the *Journal*, she was politely told, 'Sorry, it's been filled.' Yet later on the same day when a male dentist phoned, the reply was at variance. 'Delighted to have your call – when can you come for interview?'

The findings from the survey 'The provision of dental care by women dentists in England and Wales in 1985: a ten-year review' was presented by Pippi McEwen at the first full-day symposium, 'The Working Lives of Women Dentists', held at the Royal Society of Medicine on 30 May 1987, by the newly-formed Women in Dentistry Group. I was delighted to be invited to chair the meeting and among the speakers were three women dentists: Shelagh Farrell, Dorothy Geddes and Pamela Usher, talking about how they tackled their careers and coped with attendant problems. Professor Peter Rothwell, the postgraduate dean at Sheffield University, described his imaginative scheme to assist women returning to work after a break for rearing children or other domestic commitments. Over the years his support to women in dentistry has been invaluable and undoubtedly his early experience in general dental practice was an enormous advantage.

The need for a network group for women dentists was first recognised by Marie Kosloff when in 1965 she undertook a survey on the need for support during career breaks for women dentists who wanted to have children. Marie was a great support to me as I undertook the 1975 survey and together we made our case to the Representative Board for it to set up a women's committee within the BDA. Marie, an elegantly dressed, softly spoken and gracious lady, was shouted down. 'What next! You'll be asking for a special representative group for left-handed dentists.' Grudgingly, a couple of working parties were set up by the BDA but were half-hearted in their deliberations, hoping that the issue would go away.

The impetus for founding Women in Dentistry came from a cause célèbre in the 1980s when Jennifer Pinder took a major insurance company to court on sex discrimination charges. So a group of women dentists, in November 1985, under Jenny Pinder's leadership, set up the independent organisation Women in Dentistry and outside the BDA. Shock, horror was the response. 'It's bound to fail.' But the issues set out to be tackled resonated with many women, and within a couple of months the membership was nudging 500. The initial objectives were clear and unequivocal: acquire maternity pay for dentists, eliminate the disadvantages which existed for women in the NHS Pension Scheme and the difficulties experienced by women when approaching banks for financial assistance when purchasing premises to set up dental practices. Significantly, the Department of Health were delighted that at long last there was a well-informed and motivated group with whom they could negotiate. Despite their initial rebuffs from the BDA for women's concerns to be taken seriously, the association agreed to cooperate on addressing obvious anomalies that did exist and an early success was the acquisition of maternity pay for women dentists.

As a BDA employee it was obviously not appropriate for me to be involved in the running of the new organisation, but I gave my wholehearted moral support. Later, once the success of the group was observed, the association was content when I was made an honorary member and later, to my great delight, I was appointed honorary president in succession to the founding honorary president, Baroness (Trixie) Gardner, herself a practising dentist.

The glittering setting for the first Women in Dentistry (WiD) dinner was in the Peers' dining room in the House of Lords, in November 1986. As the host, in her opening speech Baroness Gardner entreated, 'Women must have high expectations and choose their own lives.' She then added, 'When attending interviews they must set their sights high and not gratefully accept the first mediocre offer.' Katherine Whitehorn, the guest speaker, known for her wit and provocative remarks, commented, 'If women took Baroness Gardner's advice on refusing mediocre offers, many men would never get married.'

At a subsequent annual dinner, Betty Boothroyd, deputy speaker at the House of Commons, and the first female in a man's world, told us that she had to determine her title in the classic phrase, 'Call me Madam' and then to devise her own robes of office: breeches were singularly inappropriate. Referring to some of the other forms of address during debates in the House, she shared with WiD members that she would rather be called a 'young pup' than an 'old witch', telling us that the former expression is unparliamentary – whereas the latter is not.

It is worth noting that I was succeeded by Dorothy Geddes as honorary president. She had recently become the first female professor in the UK and later was the first distinguished and most successful dean and convenor of the Dental Council of the Royal College of Surgeons in Edinburgh. Women were truly on the march to the top jobs. In 2006 the chair, Penny Joseph, wrote in the *BDJ*, 'We are celebrating success and confident that WiD has fulfilled its remit.' How refreshing to wind up an organisation mission completed: a brave decision for others to follow.

So now, I return to the decision which I had to make at the end of my year as President of the British Dental Association. Was I going to stand as a candidate in the 1994 election for President of the General Dental Council'?

Professor (now Sir) David Mason, had decided not to seek a second five-year term of office, so I agreed to be nominated for one of the most important jobs in dentistry in the UK. At the closing date for nominations, on 13 April 1994, Norman Davies, the registrar, wrote to all members of the GDC that he had received two names; Ian Gainsford, proposed by Professor Basker and seconded by Professor Smales, and Margaret Seward, proposed by Professor Laird and seconded by Miss Pinder. It was a straight contest (unlike in 1989 when there were five candidates) – Ian Gainsford, an appointed member of the University of London and a most successful chairman of the influential education committee, and myself, an elected member. Ian was also a good friend of mine and was a demonstrator at the London Hospital Dental School when I was a senior student. He taught us new techniques, which he learnt during a stay in the USA but, more importantly, he cured my excruciating toothache which even continued unabated while watching in the cinema the newly released film featuring Cliff Richard's popular song, 'We're all going on a summer holiday'. Ian was the solitary practitioner, amongst the great and the good at The London, who made the correct diagnosis: a cracked tooth. At that time it was an unnamed syndrome, which today is well recognised and documented. Ian was highly regarded in the academic world, was dean at King's College dental school, had a most successful general practice in the Sloane Square area of London, and was one of my very supportive *BDJ* scientific advisers. I did not underestimate the strength of the competition.

Election fever was running high on the evening before the vote took place on Tuesday 10 May 1994. The proposer and seconder from both camps were making their last-minute entreaties and tallying up the promised votes. Alan Fearn, a formidable debater and long-standing member of the GDC, notoriously ran a book for all important dental elections. He wrote to me on 22 February telling me that the result in the Presidential Stakes was too close to call. 'Honest Al, the dentists' pal,' he said, 'is offering Gainsford and Seward both at 6-5 on,' and then encouragingly, he shortened the odds to 4-6, a month later.

Many of the Council members regularly stayed overnight in the Domus Medicus at the Royal Society of Medicine, at the Oxford Street end of Wimpole Street, when on GDC business and this occasion was no exception. Fiona Simpson, the elected member for Northern Ireland, came to my room late in the evening to lend me her lucky St Christopher, and there were numerous messages wishing me success in the election.

The GDC met in public session at 10.30 a.m. on the Tuesday morning and the first item of business was the election of the President-elect, a position held for six months before assuming the presidency. The Council Chamber was crammed to capacity, the press gallery was bulging with eagle-eyed reporters and joined by as many staff as room or business would permit, because they were also anxious to see who would be in the 'driving seat' for the next five years. The public gallery was also full to capacity with many interested parties from the dental field, but none so important as Gordon, for a successful outcome would certainly impinge on his peaceful existence in the ranks of the retired.

As decreed by the GDC rules for the election of President, there were no speeches from candidates, proposers, or seconders. The ballot was conducted swiftly and silently amongst the forty-four members and the voting papers were collected and handed to the Registrar to be counted. The President from the chair announced the result to an eager and attentive Council, no member more apprehensive and attentive than Ian and myself. Ian Derek Gainsford seventeen votes; Margaret Helen Elizabeth Seward thirty votes.

Instantly, loud and prolonged applause broke out, people leaned forward to congratulate me, and I somehow managed to coax my jelly-like legs to work and I rose to thank the Council for its confidence and the privilege to be their president. Life was destined to change greatly during the next five years, as I crossed Wimpole Street to take up the reins at Number 37.

Chapter 15

My GDC years

I had barely six months to get myself organised before assuming the mantle of president on 1 October 1994. Most pressing was how to cope with the impending change in my personal life, which meant not only frequent trips from Hadley Wood to London for meetings, but also how to put to good use the president's flat situated on the top, fourth, floor of the GDC premises. As this meant I literally had a base in London 'over the shop' for the necessary overnight business stays, it seemed an opportune time to put into action our long held dream, like countless other married couples whose offspring have fled the family home, to downsize and move to the south coast. Previous family holidays in Mudeford and Swanage, providing easy access to beautiful walks along the Purbecks, were firm favourites, and of more recent exploration, when we were in Bournemouth for the BDA Conference, the magnificent New Forest area and attractive villages. The Thomas Hardy country was not far away.

Within a couple of weeks the Hadley Wood house was on the market and 'house-hunting' in the Bournemouth area began. We were advised by our estate agent in Hadley Wood of an agent in Canford Cliffs and he turned out to be a true gem. Gordon christened him the Mr Jeeves of estate agents, picking us up each morning in his car from our hotel and escorting us to view a host of attractive properties, in tree-lined avenues, with gardens, orchards and swimming pools and, although we could afford to make a purchase, they were more extensive than Tudor House and we were endeavouring to downsize. After a second day of viewing we felt despondent at the lack of progress, so decided to unearth from our file details of our 'discarded properties' in case we had been too hasty in our decision to reject them.

First, with a different estate agent, was a three-bedroom property, built in 1971, in a delightful cul-de-sac, backing onto Meyrick Park and surrounded by beautiful tall and gently swaying pine trees, with camellia and rhododendron shrubs growing healthily in the sandy soil. Most importantly, it was within walking distance of the mainline station for the fast trains to Waterloo, to the shops in the centre of Bournemouth, the lush Winter Gardens and the Pier. The sea was within reach: so was the purchase of the house. It had been unloved, due to a succession of short-term owners, and so we had the opportunity to refurbish to our tastes and Gordon, now into his fifth year of retirement, was delighted to have a new project to utilise his considerable 'handyman skills'. The contracts were signed before we left for Vancouver at the end of September where I was attending the International

Dental Congress in my role as editor of the *International Dental Journal*, the FDI's scientific publication. When we conveyed our decision to move to Number 1, Wychwood Drive to 'Mr Jeeves' he responded with a wry grin. 'You have purchased a house which differs in every respect from the instructions you gave me – but I wish you well.' I gather the variance of dream to reality in house-hunting and buying is not an uncommon occurrence, but we genuinely felt a pang of conscience that we had not been able to clinch a deal with him.

I enjoyed a civilised six-month run-in period as president-elect before the formal handover, and was invited to attend a multitude of committees, which when president, I would either chair or attend in an ex-officio capacity. I was also shown the interior of the president's flat by the registrar, Norman Davies, who indicated that it would be freshened up with a coat of paint. I was completely unprepared for the size of the flat: it would be an insult to call it a bed-sit. However, it had great potential, despite its limited space, because to have dedicated accommodation and the use of a lock-up garage strategically accessed from Wimpole Mews, the rear entrance of the GDC, was a true perk of the unpaid job. Much to the astonishment of the registrar, I intimated that I had no intention of taking up residence until the flat was modernised. The existing bed was a heavy iron fold-up structure, which I was not prepared to heave in and out. The cooking facility was, I grant, ingenious, as a previous president, an advocate of caravanning, had installed a similar sort of cooking and washing arrangement. Again, the bathroom and shower facility left much to be desired. The interior of the president's flat had been sacrosanct and few members had been invited inside, so I now shared my dilemma with colleagues who, thankfully, all supported the need for its refurbishment. Certainly, it was cheaper for the Council to have a president resident on site, rather than in an expensive neighbouring hotel, especially where there was not the privacy available for the many confidential papers that were destined to become, throughout my five-year-term, essential bedtime reading.

Apart from sorting out accommodation, there were other personal commitments to be considered. For the last thirteen years I had been chairman of governors of the Latymer School and it was clear that because of the time involved and my impending move away from the catchment area, I would have to relinquish this post. I will refer more to my experiences and friendships over those years in a later chapter, for they greatly influenced my modus operandi during my subsequent career assignments. Another resignation on the cards was from the Medical Protection Society, an indemnity organisation for doctors and dentists, where, as a director, I was a member of the Council and of the Dental Advisory Committee. This society provided legal and moral support to dentists and, especially, to those few who were destined to appear before the disciplinary or health committees of the GDC. As the president chaired these two committees it was wholly appropriate to sever all links and avoid any charge of conflict of interests. The same, I considered, applied to other dental organisations: the Medical and Dental Retirement Advisory Service, and Denplan, a provider of private dental health insurance. As an aside, it is interesting to note that I had slipped into Professor David Mason's seat on Denplan's Board when he became President of the GDC, and now, as I vacated Denplan, David Mason, having relinquished the presidency, took up the place again, a dental musical chairs. However, after advice, I continued as associate director of the Barnet Health Authority because it was agreed that this did not interfere with my statutory role. Personally, I was relieved, as I did not wish to sever all links with the NHS, an organisation in which the vast majority of the 30,000 dentists on the GDC Register worked as self-employed practitioners.

Then on 21 June, barely a month into my tenure as president-elect, I received a letter from the chairman of the Regional Health Authority, Sir William Staveley. I had met him on the occasion of his visit to the Barnet Health Authority, when we rapidly established a rapport as we discovered his link with my Alma Mater: he was wearing a London Hospital tie. 'Dear Mrs Seward,' the letter began, 'You must be well aware of the difficulties at Barnet Health Authority and the challenges that must flow following Alan Jacob's, the chairman's, resignation. I would be very grateful if you would be prepared to come and see me to have a discussion as to what, if any, part you would wish to play in the restructured authority.' He then concluded, 'I can't keep away from old Londoners!' I have always found it hard to resist a tantalising letter; just what information did he want from me? Under Alan Jacob's leadership we had produced a five-year strategy document, which had also included the highly controversial closure of a well-loved local hospital, the Edgware General Hospital.

It was a hot, sunny, Friday afternoon when I arrived at the North Thames Regional Health Authority offices in Eastbourne Terrace opposite Paddington Railway Station. I was ushered into Sir William's office suite and after exchanging pleasantries he put his cards on the table. 'I want you to be chairman of the Barnet Health Authority.' I was completely unprepared for this forthright approach, but as he was a retired Admiral of the Fleet, it was not surprising that he conveyed his message in this direct way and without finesse. I hastened to explain that as I was to become president of the GDC in October, his suggestion was impracticable and I knew my husband would agree. Unaccustomed, I suspect, to people not jumping to his instructions, he added, 'Do I have to send you home with a bottle of best claret to persuade your husband to let you do the job?' I left without the wine but promised that I would talk to the chief executive of the Barnet Health Authority and the chairman of the neighbouring authority to determine the commitment needed to discharge the role effectively, especially in view of the press interest surrounding the resignation of Alan Jacob, cited for personal reasons after less than a year in the job.

Within the week I had conveyed my decision to Sir William not to accept this particular role. While it was flattering to be asked, I knew that I would need all my energies and to be single focused as president of the GDC, which indeed proved to be the case. So on 6 July 1994, I concluded my letter of rejection with the words, 'I am really sorry that an Old Londoner has to say No.' It is an irony of fate that in life you can be offered two exciting opportunities at the same time. The gamble is to make the right decision and time has proved that I did.

Later, that same year, I met Sir William again at an oral health conference at the Queen Elizabeth II Conference Hall in Westminster. 'Are you still sure you don't want to be involved?' he teased, 'Remember, I am still seeking someone to fill the chair at Wellhouse.' 'No,' I countered, 'but I know someone who would be worthy of serious consideration: David Phillips.' I had worked closely with David in his role as Dental Director of the Medical Protection Society and I had seen how he inspired people and had witnessed his managerial skills at first hand. This suggestion did not fall on deaf ears and David was appointed chairman of the Wellhouse Trust, which comprised the Edgware and Barnet General Hospitals. He discharged his role superbly, restoring morale amongst a totally disenchanted staff, pushing through urgent new building and modernisation projects, introducing imaginative art schemes to improve the ambience for patients and staff, but above all restoring financial stability. As I have witnessed with great sadness, there are casualties in successive and much flaunted reorganisations of the health services. In this instance a few years later, just as Barnet General Hospital was fast becoming a flagship enterprise, two adjacent local trusts merged and a new chairman was appointed from outside the area; David's proven talents were lost to the NHS.

On 1 October, my first day as president, I was attending a meeting of the communications committee of the FDI thousands of miles away in Vancouver. My successor as editor of the *BDJ*, Mike Grace, arrived bearing an envelope addressed to me. Inside was a card, which read: 'Margaret, with very warm wishes for a satisfying, rewarding and happy term of office as president. We are here to try to ensure this!' Signed: Norman and Penny. This was an example of many thoughtful and kind acts and discharge of appropriate courtesies by the registrar Norman Davies and his wife Penny, which eased tremendously my tentative steps in a demanding role.

On my return from the Vancouver conference, Norman Davies phoned me to discover when I intended to come to the office. I indicated my time of arrival, dependent on the trains running to schedule, and thought no more about it as I ambled nonchalantly down Wimpole Street from Oxford Circus, passing my former habitat of thirteen years at No. 64 en route to my new offices at 37 Wimpole Street. Just as I began to climb the steps, suddenly from behind a pillar gracing the portico style entrance to the GDC appeared the registrar to welcome me to the Council premises. He then escorted me to the elegantly furnished president's room, and there on the Queen Anne mahogany table was a neat pile of documents for the attention of the president, with an accompanying top summary sheet explaining the matters commanding my attention. As if on cue, the door opened and Wendy Davidson, the housekeeper, appeared, carrying a gigantic silver tray with my tea-time refreshments – much needed and greatly enjoyed. I felt I could soon get accustomed to this level of sophistication because I was more familiar with a mug of tea, and often self-brewed.

At the onset of a five-year term of office, it is easy to be lulled into thinking that one has plenty of time, but if you are really intent on making a difference this can only be achieved with a strategic plan. There is no doubt that an organisation which has evolved very slowly since its establishment in 1956 can be resistant to change, especially when long-serving members of staff are comfortable with the current working practices.

Early on in my career I had learnt that if you want to institute change it is essential to ensure that the people involved understand the reasons for the change and the objectives to be achieved. Central to success is that those involved have ownership of the proposed changes through a collective decision-making process. To achieve this aim I have discovered that it is an excellent idea to take the key players away to a location where they can be free from interruption or conflicting pressures, preferably including an overnight stay. I had become a staunch advocate of the method of holding a retreat when I was first involved as a participant when I was director at the Medical Protection Society and we were seeking to appoint a new chief executive. Also of importance is the choice of the facilitator and, as I had been impressed on the previous occasion with Philip Hetherington in this role, I enlisted him to assist me with the first GDC retreat. Initially, my suggestion of such an exercise was construed that I had a criticism of the registrar and his staff, which was farthest from the truth because a more hardworking, dedicated and courteous group of nearly forty people you would be hard pressed to find. Furthermore, the exceptional standard of Council reports and documents, written in exemplary style and with minute attention to grammar, was the envy of many organisations within and outside the profession and I was determined that this worthy reputation should be protected. Thankfully, once it was realised that the aim was to indulge in blue-sky thinking, formulate our strategic plan and decide our priorities for action, with the Council members and staff discussing it together, the initiative won whole-hearted support.

So, barely six months after taking office I took the entire Council of forty-four members, the registrar and seven senior members of staff, to the Stakis Country House Hotel in Braunston, Leicestershire, for a twenty-four hour break from lunch-time Friday to the same time on Saturday. The location was ideal as it was situated in the middle of intersecting motorways and not only did it provide a challenge to find, it also did not encourage escape!

In preparation, during the preceding weeks, Philip spoke with a cross section of the Council: dentists elected by the profession, dentists nominated by dental authorities including universities, elected auxiliary members and lay representatives nominated by Her Majesty on advice of the Privy Council. He was then able to produce initial papers for discussion, identifying areas of concern and themes needing further exploration. The first evening concluded with an informal dinner and a challenging speaker from the Consumers Association, Derek Prentice, who it is interesting to note became a valued lay member of the GDC and Chairman of the much heralded Private Patients Complaints Scheme launched in May 2006. Personal dynamics is as interesting as it is illuminating. There are those who frequent the bar, those who chat in discreet groups, and those who retire early to bed. Of particular interest was the respectable number who responded to the president's invitation to join her for an early morning swim in the hotel's fabulous leisure centre. 'Got to keep in with president' was a muttering overheard as alarm clocks were set to rise before breakfast. An immeasurable bonus from the coming together of members and staff on neutral territory was the depth of understanding and appreciation acquired not only of the complexity of the business of the GDC, but also of the talents and aspirations of individuals. 'Bonding' may be a glib term but it is the one essential ingredient to ensure delivery of a programme of radical change in a sedate organisation. A unanimous decision from the retreat was to strengthen the core functions of the GDC – registration, education, conduct and health. We developed a Mission Statement to inform the profession and public: 'The GDC is the regulatory body of the dental profession. It protects the public by means of its statutory responsibilities for dental education, registration, professional conduct and health. It supports dentists and dental auxiliaries in the practice of dentistry and encourages their continuing professional development.' But our image with the profession remained to be enhanced as they viewed us as the 'Orwellian Big Brother' organisation, intent purely on collecting the annual fee in return for issuing a dentist with a licence to practise dentistry, or making contact if they had transgressed. I was convinced that the only way to improve matters was to strengthen our communication with the profession through issuing our own positive press releases to counter the negative comments frequently appearing, especially in the dental journals.

It was not difficult to identify within the dental ranks an enormously popular dentist, well-known for his writing and speaking: Stephen Hancocks. I sounded him out over lunch in an Italian eatery on the corner of Devonshire Street to see if, at our forthcoming Retreat, when hopefully the decision to appoint a Communications Manager was taken, he would be interested in applying for the post. It seemed to me unwise to float the idea if there was likely to be a dearth of candidates. However, I was encouraged by Stephen's enthusiastic response and also with his innovative ideas in discharging the duties of this radical new position. As it transpired at the Retreat there was unanimous support for the employment of a dentist to help the Council coordinate its various public relations activities and so it was agreed to advertise the new post as a matter of urgency. There was a good field of candidates and, following interviews, Stephen Hancocks was appointed to take up the post from July 1995. 'It is a unique and fascinating opportunity to help shape the future,' commented Stephen in the June issue of the *GDC Gazette*. Seemingly the only person unhappy was the executive director of the FDI, Per Åke Zillen for whom Stephen worked. 'It is a disaster for the FDI,' he exclaimed when I contacted him for a reference, 'but it is a good day for the GDC.'

This it certainly proved to be. With Stephen's input, the frequency of the *Gazette*, sent to all registered dentists and enrolled dental auxiliaries, was increased and the format and content redesigned and enlarged. Already we had a series of GDC Roadshows held in various regions of the country at which the president and registrar gave presentations, followed by lively discussion and debate so that we were able to listen to 'grass roots' problems and ideas for the future. Our new Communications Manager was invaluable in sharing the increased workload as the roadshows were extended further afield in the UK. Council members also assisted as we took stands for the first time at professional and trade exhibitions in an effort to improve the accessibility of the Council to the profession. To continue to enhance the professional contact, events catering for up to seventy people were held at the GDC premises, targeting different groups. For example, the influential local dental committees located throughout the country, were invited to send representatives and the response was so overwhelming that instead of the one planned seminar three were held. In addition, by popular demand we extended the invitations to other specialist groups. The format for each seminar was similar, commencing with a number of talks explaining the business of the GDC and the development of current initiatives, which included setting up Review Groups to look at specific areas of activity within the profession. I considered this was the only method to widen the participation in GDC business as only members could serve on the Council committees under current legislation. Most importantly, once it had produced its report a Review Group could be disbanded, a much more efficient way of examining a problem area. I have always had a loathing for Committees which just keep going, despite having completed their task.

A tour of the building was also included in the programme and, after refreshments, there was the opportunity for a frank exchange of opinions under the provocative title 'Your expectations of the GDC'. The effusive response from participants was unexpected: 'This is the first time in my thirty years of practice that I have been inside this building. Now, we understand more clearly why we need to pay increased annual fees. Thank you for opening the doors – more please.' Such activity did generate extra work for an already overburdened staff and so an assistant communications manager was recruited to deal with the increasing number of enquiries from national newspapers, TV and radio stations, many requesting interviews or comments from the president. Even the GDC stationery did not escape a 'face-lift' and on it was emblazoned the byline:

'Protecting patients, supporting dentists'. Free information leaflets were produced in a new smart mauve-coloured livery for dentists to distribute to their patients: 'The GDC – What it is and what it does'. The GDC was certainly raising its profile in a positive way.

As I have mentioned, a tour of the premises was an integral part of the seminar programme, purposely so that dentists could understand why and how their increased dues were being spent on a refurbishment programme. Following my discovery of the state of the president's flat, I decided to take a closer look at the entire building and again it was more than a 'coat of paint' that was required. I recommended to the registrar an architect, John Harvey, with whom I had worked closely on refurbishment schemes in my role as Chairman of Governors at The Latymer School.

At the first meeting with the architect on 27 March 1995, the extent of the proposed work was discussed; 'fire-fighting' to ensure the safety of the premises, with urgent attention to the tank, boiler and flat roofs, and identification and controlled removal of any asbestos lagging; installation of improved security arrangements and increased office space, preparing for the expansion in the number of staff needed when other members of the dental team, for example dental nurses and dental technicians, were registered with the GDC; and modernisation of all the existing accommodation which included improvements to the waiting room areas for lawyers and witnesses during conduct hearings, the kitchens, heating, lighting and furnishings throughout the premises. This was a mammoth programme by any standards, not only costing substantial sums of money, but also causing massive disruption to the working environment of the staff.

I was especially relieved to learn that the tank, reported as sprouting barnacles, was to be removed as soon as possible because it was strategically positioned over my bed in the flat and I did not fancy its contents being emptied onto me in the middle of the night. Similarly, I was relieved when Tony Davidson, the premises manager who lived on site with his wife Wendy, returned from John Lewis's with a bag of smoke detectors to fit throughout the building, because I did not wish to be fried in bed.

Within two months, John Harvey presented initial plans and options to the President's Committee, the senior members of the Council, Professors David McGowan, vice-chairman of Executive and in effect deputy president, Ronnie Laird, treasurer Alan Fearn, the longest serving elected member, and Joan Harbison, a lay member. In the meantime we had been taken to view offices in central London, renovated by the architect, in order to garner further ideas of how to adapt large floor spaces, such as the Council's grand dining room, used infrequently, into the much needed varying sizes of meeting rooms through the judicious use of soundproof partitioning.

The Council members appreciated the heritage of the building, especially as the original architect was Sir Hugh Casson and it was hailed in the early sixties to be at the forefront of modern design with the antegallery wall adorned with a gigantic colourful mural painting and furnishings of super quality, although the dark wood panelling in the entrance hall projected an aura of dark foreboding. However, we were completely unprepared for the reservations expressed by some long-serving staff to the proposals:

'Wholesale destruction of features such as entrance hall panelling or dining room ceiling would be widely regretted. What seemed to be put forward was an architect's view of a modern office interior, equally at home in W1, EC2 or Swindon. The large open-plan areas might meet the needs of clerks in large office complexes but not appropriate for those who had to draft papers and write letters where accuracy was paramount.'

I had admiration for their defence and indeed the genuine affection which they showed for a building which was showing signs of age and desperately in need of a face-lift. Here I was dealing, not with a culture change in the working environment, but with a culture shock. Consultations with the staff continued and the eventual building work took place in planned phases, floor by floor, giving staff 'breathing space' between the inevitable noise, dust and disruption that resulted, as many were decanted two or three times from their working stations.

It took four years to reach the stage at which we could invite HRH Princess Alexandra to open the premises. A truly gracious lady, she charmed everyone as she toured the building and took tea with members of staff and the Council and unveiled the plaque marking her visit. At the conclusion of her visit, I escorted her to the front door when she suddenly cried out, 'Can I take that for you?' and bounded down the steps of the GDC, deftly skirted round the rear of her waiting limousine and began extracting a large tube from under the armpit of a cyclist who had just dismounted. 'Don't worry,' said the detective, sensing our alarm. 'It's her husband, Angus Ogilvy. He cycles everywhere and she will take the parcel home in her car.'

The conduct of the business of the GDC followed a well-established routine. All the Council committees met on two occasions each year during the third week in March and September. The recommendations from these meetings formed the basis of the reports presented formally by the chairmen of the committees to the Council for approval. The president chaired the full Council meeting on the second Tuesday in May and November and its formal proceedings were open to the public and journalists, who watched from two designated galleries, one for the public and the other for members of the press. Reminiscent of our schooldays, the first item of business on the agenda was the roll call of members conducted by the registrar. He would stand and call out the names in alphabetical order. Listening to the response was always entertaining. Initially members called would respond with a brisk 'Here' and then for an unknown reason, a member broke rank and called out 'Present' and this could eventually be followed by 'Yes' or 'Sir', each occurring in different order each time. If there was failure to elicit a response, the registrar repeated the name so underlining that a person was missing and for which there had to be a cast-iron reason. Some years previously, when I was editor of the *Journal*, the dates of the May Council meeting and the BDA's annual conference clashed and as an employee of the Association I was obliged to attend. In fact, on one occasion, five of the Council members found their allegiance stronger to the BDA Conference and as a result we were all publicly admonished for shirking our GDC responsibilities. We revelled in our new-found rebel status. Although at the start of my presidency the verbal roll call was conducted, I eventually had it replaced by the less obtrusive, but just as effective, method of signing an attendance sheet on arrival.

The second item on the Council's agenda was the president's address. This was a comprehensive review of the work completed, the decisions to be taken, and the achievements and awards secured by members of the profession. Subsequently, the address was published as the leading article in the *BDJ* so that not only would the 20,000 or so members of the BDA know about the work of its regulatory body, but also it would provide an invaluable future resource for dental historians.

After a full day's meeting, with sometimes heated differences of opinions forcibly made and resolutions won or lost on the narrowest of margins, there was the opportunity to end the day on a convivial note with a dinner on the Council premises for members and guests, which at the May dinner embraced husbands, wives and partners, all dressed in formal attire: black tie, kilts or colourful evening dresses. These splendid affairs were well supported and the reputation of the GDC as one of the best dining clubs in London ensured that there was no shortage of guests to accept an invitation. Tributes to Norman Davies on his retirement in 1996 emphasised how we as Council members indulged in the fruits of his gastronomic expertise. Sir Colin Berry, a member of the GDC through his membership of the sister regulatory body, the General Medical Council, spoke fulsomely at the November Council meeting. 'The hospitality shown by the Council is legendary and the quality (and quantity) of its board and cellar are widely known and admired. Council dinners are a special experience: the elegance of the table, its floral decoration by Penny and the delightful custom of small gifts when partners are present, are something not to be missed.'

Looking back over the guest lists to the dinners reads like entries in *Who's Who*. We were fortunate to be able to attract the current Secretary of State for Health, so over time we entertained Rt. Hons. William Waldegrave, Virginia Bottomley, Frank Dobson, and Alan Milburn, as well as Ministers for Health who held the dental portfolio. When Parliament was sitting, politicians had to obtain permission of the Government Whips to attend the dinner, even although the GDC premises were considered to be within the boundary set for the 'division' bell, which sounded when a vote was to be taken. It was far less stressful for all concerned if the MP could be 'paired' with a fellow MP of the opposite party who had been granted leave of absence. Occasionally, if the vote was anticipated to be very close, the Minister would speak before the meal, negating the intended relaxed ambience of the evening. These logistical problems did not arise when we were entertaining presidents of other professional self-regulatory bodies, deans of Royal Colleges, chief medical and nursing officers and other academic and civil dignitaries.

A long-established custom was that members of Council contributed to the cost of the incumbent president's portrait as a gift. The president, again by custom, then immediately returned the gift, so allowing it to hang in the Council's premises. The final and thoughtful touch was that a framed photograph of the portrait was presented to the president and two smaller editions given for the siblings.

Norman Davies had steered his two former presidents, Sir Frank Lawton and Sir David Mason, through this process with pleasing results so I was keen that the registrar should do likewise for me before his retirement. Although normally the portrait was painted in the penultimate year of office, the procedure began with the search to identify a suitable painter and at an affordable price. I was entering unknown territory and so was grateful to be advised to go to the National Portrait Gallery, the Royal Academy and special art exhibitions to familiarise myself with styles, media and artists. As a result it did crystallise my idea of where I wished to be painted and that was in the long antegallery in Wimpole Street, sitting against the magnificent backdrop of the most bold and colourful full length mural of boats on the Regent's Canal, Little Venice being just a ten-minute walk from the GDC.

One of the members, Douglas Pike, who was very knowledgeable about the art world, suggested a talented young artist, Victoria Saumarez, and after I met her and perused her impressive portfolio, she was commissioned to paint my half-length portrait. This was an inspired choice as we established an immediate rapport, which was as well because it took seven sittings and five months to complete the portrait. There were decisions to be made at every stage – what to wear, and even although the seasons came and went as the portrait progressed, strict adherence to the chosen outfit was demanded; no casual change of glasses or hairstyle: the list is endless. However, I am led to believe that for men it is even more challenging. Their chosen favourite tie must be preserved in pristine condition throughout the painting period. The position of my chair had also to be faithfully replicated for each sitting and so it was placed with great care on the four taped crosses on the carpet and cleaners were instructed not to be over zealous and remove them.

The first sitting of just under two hours passed swiftly as Victoria took countless photographs and recorded measurements of every aspect of my countenance with the assistance of her plumb line. Then with easel and canvas also positioned in the same place on each occasion, the sittings continued as I took my place in the agreed pose. Work was also undertaken away from Wimpole Street in Victoria's studio in Fletching, East Sussex, and I marvelled as the sittings progressed to see recognisable features emerge.

At the penultimate sitting, I was able to share the unfinished portrait with Mrs Jane Gordon, now appointed to the new post of deputy registrar, who had a wide appreciation of fine paintings, and I was relieved at her positive reaction to the nearly completed commission. Soon it was the final touches, the application of varnish, the choice of frame and the inscription. Then the big day arrived. The portrait was unveiled in front of the benefactors, the Council members attending the May Council dinner with their guests, including the artist, Victoria. Amongst the 'oohs' and 'ahhs', Shelagh Farrell, a great friend and elected member of the GDC, was heard to remark, 'Margaret, you will grow into it,' which in a way was flattering to think I looked younger in real life than portrayed. The major problem for viewers was that I was cast in a stern pose. 'Where has your characteristic smile gone?' was a frequent query. Early on during the sittings I had also questioned the absence of my smile and teeth. I learnt for the first time from Victoria that it would be impossible for the facial muscles to maintain such a stationary pose for the lengthy period needed. For me to sit still in one position for long is a challenge: to also maintain a grin I conceded would have been impossible. Subsequently, I have assiduously studied portraits for a smile showing teeth: I am still looking. In spite of these comments there was general approbation for Victoria's painting and this was confirmed when the Faculty of General Dental Practitioners commissioned Victoria to paint the portrait of its first dean, Dr Stephen Rear, OBE, which now hangs in the Faculty offices at the Royal College of Surgeons in Lincoln's Inn Fields in London. Eventually, my portrait was hung in the newly refurbished committee room on the first floor, named as 'The Seward Room'. I understand from staff and Council members it was somewhat unnerving to have the past president keeping an eye on them at work. Nevertheless I still do consider it a privilege to have had my portrait painted, although it took nearly ten years to possess the courage to display the presented framed copy in our living room at home. Perhaps, subconsciously, I felt I had at last grown into it.

As the months passed, there was an increase in my commitments as I intended to be a 'hands-on' president. Thus, I became more informed about the day-to-day business taking place at the GDC and, through instituting an open-door policy for colleagues from home and abroad, I could explore different issues of mutual interest or concern and share ideas or seek advice for future initiatives. In addition my diary was soon crammed with invitations: to give talks about the work and future vision of the GDC; to deliver eponymous lectures named after distinguished people; to present awards, or to give the keynote address at degree ceremonies and prize days, and to attend conferences and represent the Council at official dinners. 'Dine for dentistry' was again a truism and my long-held practice of shunning taxis in London's West End and choosing instead to change into comfortable walking shoes had benefits as I battled with the unaccustomed assault on my girth.

However, on one occasion, on 20 November 1997, I was dispatched in style from the GDC, into a chauffeur-driven limousine, after I had negotiated the guard of honour arranged on the Council steps by the waitresses of Whitehouse Catering in their crisp uniforms and aprons, who were preparing to serve lunch to Council members sitting in session on the Conduct Committee. The business had been rearranged so that I could be relieved of chairing the session because I had received a very special invitation. It was to attend a luncheon, to celebrate the golden wedding of Queen Elizabeth II and Prince Philip, which was being held in the Banqueting House in Whitehall. This fine Palladian-style building had been designed by Inigo Jones in 1619, and while famous for its exquisite Rubens painted ceiling, it was equally notorious for the gruesome historical fact that, in 1649, Charles I stepped out of one of its windows and onto the scaffold erected on the balcony.

Three of the ten health professionals invited foregathered at the GDC: Professor John Murray, Professor Elizabeth Russell (my cousin) and myself. Although the event had been dubbed in the press as the 'Ordinary People's Luncheon', it was soon apparent that this was an understatement and, as crowds began to fill Whitehall, it was cordoned off by the police to traffic, and we completed the last couple of hundred yards on foot. The guest list was awesome: how lucky we were to be included. Every living Prime Minister was present as well as all the current members of the Cabinet, with Mo Mowlem's immense popularity evident for everyone to see. I was given a sisterly bear-hug by Shirley Bassey, although it was our first encounter, such was the spirit of camaraderie amongst the highly select guests. Prince Philip thanked people for coming ('My wife and I . . .') and Tony Blair, just a few months into his premiership, proposed a toast to the happy couple. It was an extraordinary occasion and as we emerged into the wintry sunlight, a microphone was thrust towards me asking for comment, but John and Elizabeth thought it preferable to steer me into a waiting taxi and recover from the excitement over a welcome pot of tea. So we hastened to my club, The Lansdowne off Berkeley Square, where we regaled each other with our experiences, as we had been seated at different tables of ten. Whether the gently dozing recipients of an early lunch at the club were appreciative of our exuberant mood was difficult to discern, but it certainly proved to be a sensible course of action rather than return to the GDC in a hyperactive state.

The venue for the GDC lunches, before refurbishment, is also worthy of mention. Guests were always encouraged to shun the lift and to climb the stairs to the dining room situated on the fourth floor. This enabled them to stop halfway and look out across Wimpole Mews to see the house frequented by the extremely attractive and charismatic nineteen-year-old Christine Keeler, whose affair with the Minister, John Profumo, in 1961 brought down the Macmillan Government, a stop which sparked speculation as to whether, forty years on, the affair would have resulted in such drastic consequences. This top-floor dining area was also used to provide lunches for members of the Health Committee, which had been established through the introduction of the new 1984 Dentists Act during Sir Frank Lawton's presidency. I was a member from its inception and it was there not only to protect the public, but also to strive to facilitate the rehabilitation of dental colleagues who had alcohol and drug dependency problems. For too long, many of us had failed to understand the extent of the problem and the fact that addiction is a serious disease. The alarming statistic confirmed this when we were told that 7 to 10 per cent of dentists are affected in the UK, and without treatment this disease is progressive and fatal. As a member, and later as chairman of this committee, when president, I was moved greatly, time and time again, when listening to the poignant personal testimonies of those afflicted and led to question how, as members of a caring profession, we could allow dentists to descend to such depths of despair through addiction and encounter family and professional tragedy of mammoth proportions. Hearings were held in private and the Committee was advised by psychiatrists specialising in substance misuse.

Rarely was there a dry eye amongst the panel members when two or three years later, a dentist initially deprived of practising dentistry to protect the public, and who had often to resort to menial labouring jobs to earn money, appeared smiling and smartly dressed with glowing medical reports to confirm recovery. 'Thank you,' one addressed the panel, 'I will never forget; you gave me my life back.' Granted it was a team achievement as so many individuals and dedicated agencies provided support, but I believe the GDC can be proud of its role in the rehabilitation process.

However, I became increasingly uneasy chairing these hearings and then adjourning for an excellent lunch with a glass or two of delicious claret from the GDC's cellar. As Douglas Pike recalls, 'Subtly and without anyone being aware who made the decision, we were all eating lighter and healthier lunches and alcohol was enthusiastically embraced, not during, but deservedly after, a hard day's work.' My recollection is that the mood was not as 'enthusiastic' as Douglas made out. 'Margaret is behaving like a Matron; we know how much we can drink at lunch-time.' 'Margaret, the wine snatcher' recalling the days when Margaret Thatcher was dubbed as the milk snatcher, when she abolished the free one-third of a pint of milk for primary school children. Fortunately, I was given moral support from an unexpected source, Norman Whitehouse, chief executive of the BDA, who had also decided committee work and alcohol did not mix and withheld it from lunch if the business of the BDA committee was unfinished.

My undiminished admiration of the courage and tenacity of those who fought back to regain their self-esteem after drug and alcohol problems was replaced by anger and deep disappointment when a very small number of dentists resorted to criminal acts or negligence and so destroyed the highly regarded reputation of the profession and the trust normally enjoyed by dentists and other health care professionals. Conduct cases covered, for example, incidents of theft, false accounting and attempting to pervert the course of justice; indecent behaviour to female patients; cheating in professional examinations; failing to maintain surgery premises in suitable hygienic conditions; driving while disqualified and without insurance; failure to provide satisfactory treatment; use of inappropriate materials and the death of a patient under general anaesthesia.

The president chaired the Professional Conduct Committee which heard these cases in public and which normally lasted for the fortnight following the May and November Council Meeting. Legal teams were present in the Council Chamber acting on behalf of the Council and the defendant and witnesses were called by both parties and evidence was taken on oath. The committee was advised, as required, by a legal assessor, who was a senior lawyer, normally a QC. Predictably, the GDC disciplinary procedures attracted national media interest and the press gallery could be full if a hearing involved a high profile case. Even on leaving the premises at the end of the day, or when the judgment was announced, reporters would be anxious for more than the official statement, so that an exit through the rear door into the Wimpole Mews could be preferable, to avoid the reporters and cameramen camping outside the front of the GDC in Wimpole Street. I never failed to be impressed by the ability of lawyers to master a brief and describe complicated clinical procedures with aplomb using dental terminology. One could be forgiven for thinking that they were registered dentists.

It was satisfying to witness the gradual modernisation of the conduct of the Council's business, the mode of communication with the profession and the refurbishment of the Council premises. However, this could be viewed as 'tinkering around the edges', when compared with the need for modernisation of the legislation under which the GDC was operating. On becoming president, I was extremely fortunate that the Chief Dental Officer (CDO) for England was Brian Mouatt, who was acutely aware of the constraints of the Dentists Act 1984 hampering the many forward-looking changes I wanted to take place in the profession and in the self-regulatory body. Through Brian's influence, Gerald Malone, the Minister for Health with responsibility for dentistry, and MP for Winchester, accepted our invitation to lunch on Thursday 22 February 1996. Because the builders were at work converting the main dining hall into multifunctional rooms, we had to use the smaller dining room on the fourth floor and to restrict the guest list mainly to the chairman of the various Council committees and senior staff. The Minister was impressed with the desire for change. This was translated into positive action, as within a week I received a phone call asking the GDC to undertake preliminary work in the areas which we would wish to include in a draft Dentists Bill, the precursor to a new Dentists Act. The only downside was that due to the strict cordon of confidentiality imposed by officials at the Department of Health, I was not even permitted to share this favourable outcome with members of the GDC legislation committee who, thankfully, under the able chairmanship of Professor Andy Grieve from Dundee, kept in readiness the amendments required to the Act, with a list of priority items. These provided a sound starting point for commencing work with, on our side, the Council's solicitor, Paul Honigman, and Jane Gordon, who had been intimately involved with the constitutional aspects of the working of the GDC for many years. This small team, in addition to their daily commitments, worked tirelessly during the next few months exchanging drafts of the sought after amendments with officials in the Dental Division, Ken Eaton, David Gort and Heather Rodgers, and the department's lawyer Paula Cohen: copies of all correspondence were shared with me for information and comment. Suddenly, with only a couple of days warning, a message was received at the GDC: 'The Minister for Health will make an important announcement on Wednesday 12 June in the House of Commons after Prime Minister's Question Time; can the President be there?' This was just the phone call we had all been longing for and I was marooned in Italy at an International College of Dentistry meeting. Fortunately, I was scheduled to return home early on that Wednesday morning, although my anxiety levels began to rise when the homeward flight was repeatedly delayed. Surely I was not going to miss this important milestone in our dental history? To my great relief, I was soon making my way from the airport direct to the CDO's office in Richmond House in Whitehall, with barely time to change into appropriate attire before being issued with the security pass to enter through St Stephen's Gate into the House of Commons and then escorted up the stairs to take my place alongside other key staff from the GDC in the Distinguished Strangers Gallery.

Almost immediately, as if on cue, I watched the Minister rise to announce, 'It is the Government's intention to seek an opportunity to introduce a draft Dentists Bill for consultation and possibly as early as in the autumn. The draft Bill,' the Minister told his fellow MPs, 'would provide an opportunity to take forward the GDC's proposals which it had outlined in its consultation papers circulated to the entire profession. These proposals included setting up pilots for new classes of dental auxiliaries, a statutory career redevelopment scheme, a complaints scheme for non-NHS patients and conditional registration in disciplinary cases.' The Minister's statement also referred to the future role of clinical dental technicians, replacing denturists, many of whom were working illegally in the UK and from premises in the High Street, not conforming to the routine health and safety inspections which existed for dental practices. The Minister finished his statement about the reforms for the GDC by emphasising the need for updating the legislation which would allow us to increase the lay membership, a move welcomed throughout the profession.

The Minister then turned to other proposals announcing, 'We intend to pilot and evaluate a system of local contracting for primary care dentists in several areas around the UK,' and further reporting, 'The Chairman of the General Dental Services Committee has stated that they will work with us constructively.'

For me this was a momentous announcement by the Minister for Health. However, dentistry fails to claim the interest of MPs and the majority had left the chamber before Gerald Malone rose to make his statement. Among the handful remaining was Dennis Skinner, a colourful character, who is described in *Who's Who* as 'of good working-class mining stock' and representing a Derbyshire constituency, who proceeded to give an energetic demonstration of how to remove one's own tooth, much to the mirth of his fellow MPs.

Normally, the summer months were a welcome respite for the president and staff, free from committee work and attendant preparation of papers. However, as a result of the Minister's announcement, the GDC became a hive of activity, as the fine detail of each amendment had to be drafted, submitted to the Department of Health's lawyers and then reworked in light of their searching questions. Drafts upon drafts were exchanged by fax or courier: e-mail had not yet arrived on the scene. The deadlines were demanding: a fax of twenty pages received at the GDC at 10 a.m. could have a cover sheet from the Dental Services Branch at the Department of Health marked 'Very Urgent. Please look at this section – let me have the GDC's comments – my deadline is midday.'

The intense activity was not confined to Wimpole Street. Weighty faxes followed me at home, on holiday and, during August when I was guest of the New Zealand Dental Council, to Wellington. I remember being disturbed on several consecutive nights by an over enthusiastic porter trying to push the bulging envelope containing the fax from the GDC under my bedroom door at an hour which, of course, for the Council, was the productive daytime.

During the first week of September, I was on the move again, this time to Edinburgh where I had been invited by Professor Alan Brook to welcome delegates from around the world attending the 13th Congress of the International Association of Dentistry for the Handicapped on behalf of the dental profession in the UK and to give a lecture on Teamwork in the scientific programme. As it turned out, apart from these two contributions, I spent most of the three-day event outside the Conference Centre at the Heriot Watt University on my mobile phone giving clearance to the final version of the instructions on the amendments to the Dentists Act. We were all greatly encouraged to learn that the necessary changes were going to be attached to the Primary Care NHS Bill designated as Part III: this was substantial as there were thirty-five A4 pages encompassing ninety-one paragraphs. Throughout, I was full of admiration for the legal team with whom we worked; they turned ideas into draft laws, compiled the memorandum of instruction and, even more amazing, this elite group of experienced barristers and solicitors, employed as civil servants, and known as parliamentary counsel, converted the instructions into a draft Bill. No wonder there is always intense pressure to get dentistry into any legislative programme when competing with the volume of Government business.

Concurrently with working on the Dentists Bill there had been significant changes taking place at the GDC. At the end of May 1996, the extremely popular registrar, Norman Davies, retired after fifteen years in post and his successor, Ros Hepplewhite, was appointed and designated as Chief Executive and Registrar, a term which I believed more accurately reflected the emerging new responsibilities of the job. I remain of the view that the Council was fortunate at that time to have someone who, as a former civil servant, had understanding of the workings of national Government, particularly during her period as the first Director of the Child Support Agency, and with a knowledge of modern management and technology, both attributes needed for the GDC to realise its full potential.

Finally, came the news we had been waiting for: the Government's White Paper 'Choice and Opportunity' would be published on 15 October. I was eager to receive my advance copy and to see all our dreams for the modernisation of the GDC in print. Panic, horror, disbelief overcame me as I began to read the White Paper. Scouring the pages I found the proposals to pilot and evaluate a system of local flexibility in NHS dentistry as announced by Gerald Malone in the House of Commons on 12 June were included, but absolutely nothing about the proposals to amend the Dentists Act. It did little to raise my spirits when I received, on the same day, a personal letter from the Secretary of State for Health, the Rt. Hon. Stephen Dorrell. 'Dear Mrs Seward . . . In his statement to Parliament on dentistry on 12 June, Gerald Malone said that we hoped to publish draft legislation. You will be aware that we stand by this commitment and intend to issue a consultation document in due course. We are most grateful to you and your staff for the hard and sustained effort that has enabled us to do this.' These placatory words were of little consolation. The profession was disappointed and I personally took it hard and felt that I had let everyone down.

However, the wise mandarins at the Department of Health took these setbacks in their stride, as they happened regularly, so encouraged us to make use of the delay constructively and consider if we wished to add to our list of proposed amendments. This advice we acted on, so at the GDC we were ready when the following March we received a letter from the Department of Health enclosing a copy of drafting instructions and advising us, 'We await an indication of the likely timetable for drafting the Bill from Parliamentary Counsel.'

We were back in business but the euphoria was to be short-lived. In June, a General Election was called and John Major's Government was dissolved. I naively thought that all our hard work on the Bill over the previous years would not be in vain. However, I was informed to the contrary; unfinished legislative business dies with the end of an administration. National politics is a hard task master.

The 1997 General Election swept Tony Blair's Labour Government to power with an unassailable majority and as they had been in the opposition wilderness for twenty years, they set an enormous legislative programme in motion and, not surprisingly, it did not include a Dentists Bill. Writing in the summer issue of the GDC *Gazette*, I stated, 'The profession will need to work collectively to ensure our voice is heard, not just narrowly on the Dentists Bill, but on all issues related to dentistry.' This indeed proved to be the case and, fortunately, the newly appointed Chief Dental Officer, Robin Wild, who succeeded Brian Mouatt on his retirement on 1 January 1997, was strongly committed to an updated Dentists Bill.

Thus began again the round of meetings with politicians to convince them of the urgent need for modern legislation in order to run the dental profession effectively. First I met with Frank Dobson, MP for Holborn and St Pancras since 1981, who was obviously delighted with his appointment as Secretary of State for Health. On entering his sizeable office in Richmond House in Whitehall, I was beckoned to join him on the sofa. No pomp or ceremony here, rather an affable chat about the governance of dentistry. It was reassuring to see well deserved promotion for MPs who had served so long and loyally in opposition, but sadly there were casualties. I was so disappointed when I learnt that (Lord) Ted Graham, former MP for Edmonton and a great supporter of Latymer School, had not been given a post in Government. He was a most effective and popular opposition Chief Whip since 1990 and appointment to the definitive post was anticipated. However, it transpired that age was a criterion for appointment and, as he was 72 years old at the election, this did not act in his favour.

My next appointment was to meet the Minister for Health, Alan Milburn, MP for Darlington, who held the brief for dentistry. On this occasion, I took with me Professor John Murray, a nominated member, and Mrs Joan Harbison, a lay member of the GDC. Coincidentally, the Minister had just returned from answering questions in the House of Commons on the accessibility of NHS dentistry, but we were not to be diverted from our mission. That was to describe the statutory role of the GDC and to raise our concerns that without up-to-date legislation, we could not deliver our modernisation agenda. As a bright and articulate young minister, he immediately grasped our problems. This was confirmed when in his speech at the BDA Conference he stated particularly, 'We are fully persuaded that the proposed changes would enhance the regulatory role of the General Dental Council' but to us it was still unclear how this was going to be achieved. But Alan Milburn's tenure at the department was to be brief. He commenced his meteoric rise by becoming Chief Secretary to HM Treasury in 1998, before returning a year later to replace Frank Dobson as Secretary of State for Health.

However, the GDC was not alone amongst the regulatory bodies endeavouring to get the ear of the new administration to change its legislative modus operandi. The Government's response was to introduce in 1999 a Health Bill which contained a provision for an Order-Making Power. My unequivocal enthusiasm was not shared by other statutory regulatory bodies, most of whom did not have the straitjacket of primary legislation, which prohibited us ever to change the composition of membership of the Council. Nevertheless, I did appreciate their concerns at the wide and unlimited scope of the Order-Making Power which, if misused, could threaten the future of the GDC. Thus, eventually I did lend the Council's support for amendments to the Bill proposed by Lord Walton, a former President of the General Medical Council, during the second reading of the Bill in the House of Lords. I attended this debate and it was rewarding to hear the Parliamentary Under-Secretary of State, Baroness Hayman, when responding to various points raised, mention that the Order-Making Power could change the Dentists Act in such a way as to allow the Council to amend its constitution to bring in more lay members. This progress, as well as the introduction of safeguards and limitations on the Order-Making Power, was conveyed to members at a special meeting of the Council, which I convened on 23 February 1999. It was also explained to them that the new power contained in the Bill provided our long desired opportunity for the GDC to achieve essential and overdue reforms without the need to update the 1984 Dentists Act. This has proved to be true and the Order-Making Power continues a decade later to be used to effect change. Naturally, after all the hard work over the years, I would have much preferred to leave behind a brand new 1999 Dentists Act. But you can't win them all.

The year 1999 started in momentous fashion. '*Bournemouth Echo* here' a cheerful voice announced at the end of the phone. 'We've got an advance copy of the Honours List and we see you are to be made a Dame. Can we come round for a photo?' The most difficult secret to keep was now out. Six weeks previously I had received a letter from 10 Downing Street which began: 'Mrs Seward, the Prime Minister has asked me to inform you, in strict confidence, that he has it in mind on the occasion of the forthcoming list of New Year's Honours, to submit your name to the Queen with a recommendation that her Majesty may be graciously pleased to approve that you be appointed a Dame Commander of the Order of the British Empire. Before doing so, the Prime Minister would be glad to be assured that this would be agreeable to you?' What an amazing question: of course, it would be very agreeable to me. I viewed it as an accolade for the dental profession and what a wonderful way to end my career by receiving the first damehood in dentistry. I was more than aware that I was fortunate to have been in the leading role as president of the GDC for five action-packed years, surrounded by a dedicated and energetic team of people: nothing can ever be achieved in isolation.

Ros Hepplewhite speedily researched from Debrett's the correct form of address. I was to be known as 'Dame Margaret Seward' which is used immediately on announcement of the award, not waiting until the time of the investiture. More importantly, when abbreviated, it should be 'Dame Margaret' and not 'Dame Seward'. It is up to the recipient as to how much or when they wish to use the title: certainly it is a help when attempting to book a good table in a restaurant! 'So is there a title for Gordon?' many enquired, aware that the wife of a 'Sir' becomes a 'Lady'. Sad to report, neither the husband of a Dame, nor of a Baroness, receives a title. My response to the enquiry was always the same: 'It is unfair, but I will call Gordon my Prince Charming.'

In quick succession I received two summonses. First I had to return the insignia of the CBE to St James's Palace, which I had been awarded in 1994, because I had been promoted in the same Order, the Order of the British Empire. However, I was permitted to retain the initials and these appear, following the DBE, after my name. My second summons was to attend an Investiture at Buckingham Palace on Tuesday 9 March, when I was to receive from the Queen the insignia or decoration of the Dame Commander, a stunning chest-worn pink-bowed ribbon with a badge and a star. The latter, which sparkles beautifully, is sharply pointed on its four corners and carries a thick and lethal pin designed for a gentleman receiving the KBE, to secure the decoration to the breast pocket of his dinner jacket, and not conducive to wearing on a fashionable and flimsy evening dress. Indeed, now with tightened airport security, the star is classed as a weapon.

Recipients were allowed to take three guests to the Investiture and on this occasion I took Gordon, our son Colin and his fiancée Claire, whom he had known since their university days at Girton College in Cambridge. They were ushered into the splendid Grand Ballroom from where they watched the hour-long ceremony, although initially I was directed to the ornate Green Room where I received instructions as to the form of address to the Queen: 'It is Ma'am, as in Pam or in Jam, and then wait for Her Majesty to open the conversation' intoned the official who then advised that it was clear when your time was up as the Queen would proffer her hand. As you took it, she would give you a firm handshake; then, with a curtsy, it was into the ballroom to watch the rest of the proceedings. At the conclusion of the Investiture, I met up with the family for the official photographs in the Inner Courtyard and it was also a chance to catch up with other recipients. Alan Lawrence, who had been so supportive over the years working with me on many of my Women in Dentistry projects, was receiving an OBE for his contribution to public health dentistry, and was next in line with Tom Jones, the singer. Causing great mirth was the opportunity to have my photo taken with Roger Moore, receiving a CBE for his work with UNICEF: or, as reported in the dental press, '007 and M at the Palace'.

It proved to be an unprecedented few months, as cards and letters of congratulations flooded in, not only from colleagues and friends but also from people in my earlier life with whom contact had long been lost. 'Say it with flowers' was real and, wherever I went, the toast was in delicious champagne. Not so much appreciated was the execution of an original thought by some people, who insisted on greeting my arrival with the song from South Pacific: 'There is nothing like a Dame.'

I was also informed by the Garter King of Arms that as a Dame I was entitled to petition for a Coat of Arms and a Badge. However, when could I use it? I pondered whether attaching it to my supermarket trolley might hasten my progress through the check-out. I have still to put it to the test.

Chapter 16

Delivering change

'YOU NAME IT, THERE'S A GDC Committee looking at it' was the cryptic comment which appeared in the January 1997 issue of the *BDA News*. This was proof that the increased activity and resultant heightened profile of the Council was not only being noticed, but also ruffling feathers, especially amongst some diehards in the establishment who believed that the President, and the self-regulatory body, should emulate Victorian children and 'be seen, but not heard'.

So, as I entered my penultimate year as President, it seemed to me an opportune time to take stock and produce a summary document outlining progress so far, coining the title 'Delivering Change 1995–2000'. This would demonstrate to the profession, public, and, importantly, the politicians, that the GDC had achieved change although hampered by outdated legislation. It would also confirm that we were ready to shoulder the responsibilities enunciated by Government in its White Paper, 'The New NHS', which stated that 'professional self-regulation must remain an essential element in the delivery of quality patient services'.

To much acclaim, the GDC in 1997, under the chairmanship of Professor Fred Smales, published a revised dental undergraduate curriculum entitled, 'The First Five Years', which was to ensure that the dental course equipped students to cope with technological and scientific advances in the future. But it was also clear that education and training could not abruptly cease after five years and there was a call for a review to explore whether immediate postgraduate training should last not one, but two years. I was grateful that Professor John Murray agreed to my suggestion to chair a General Professional Training Committee, which, in aiming to be inclusive of all facets of the profession, resulted in a large membership. However, John's consummate skill and his widely held respect concluded with the publication of a landmark report, 'The Next Two Years', which has provided a sound foundation for subsequent developments through to the present day.

During my presidency I was fortunate to have around me very dynamic leaders among whom, with particular enthusiasm and innovative ideas, was Dr Jim Rennie, postgraduate dean in Scotland. He drove the debate on the necessity to ensure that dentists kept up to date after their initial qualification. The disturbing fact was that a dentist's name on the Dentists Register did not denote competence, just that he or she had paid the dues for the year.

I was delighted when Jim accepted my invitation to head the Recertification Review Group. Encouragingly there was general support, not only within the profession but also at the BDA, that the initial licence to practise dentistry should not be seen as the end of improving one's skill and knowledge. 'Lifelong learning is no longer an option for a professional: it is an obligation' became my mantra and often quoted from my President's address in 1998. As a result of the consultation on the document, the arrangement whereby dentists in effect reregister every five years, and are able to do so only if they can show that they have participated in a specified amount of approved postgraduate activity, gained universal acceptance. Developing the nuts and bolts of such a system became dubbed as the GDC's Millennium project and following the launch of 'Lifelong Learning in 2000', there has been steady progress towards an even more rigorous programme of revalidation for all dentists. Without doubt, UK dentists in this twenty-first century are well trained, re-assessed, and at the leading edge of the health professionals.

These policy initiatives in the educational field were fundamental and went well beyond the Council's traditional role. Another area of activity which had escaped the spotlight was the well-established visitation process of dental faculties in universities overseas, for example, in Australasia, Malaysia, South Africa and Hong Kong to verify that their course of study was qualifying dentists of the standard to gain entry to the UK Dentists Register and so permit them to practise dentistry in this country. Although the visits to the universities abroad were undertaken by teams of senior academics from the GDC, I sensed on my visits abroad a resentment at this colonial approach, when many of the countries, for example Australia and New Zealand, had established their own regulatory bodies to oversee and maintain standards. The cost, too, was not inconsiderable as it was borne entirely by the overseas university.

Another long-established examination, the statutory examination for dentists from overseas whose universities were not included in the visitation process, was brought into focus and again it was realised that it was inappropriate for modern-day practice. Putting it simply, what was needed was an examination during which the candidates could demonstrate their current competence, not the level of knowledge absorbed years ago to pass the qualifying exam. A great deal of work led to the establishment of the International Qualifying Examination (IQE) which has continued to evolve and been refined to reflect the changing practice of dentistry. Certainly, no tears have been shed for consigning the statutory exam to the history books. The existence of the IQE also meant that the visitations to dental schools overseas could cease, as recent graduates from the various countries were eligible to sit the new examination if they wished to practise dentistry in the UK.

In the late 1970s, a growing number of dentists were establishing dental practices limited to specific disciplines, for example orthodontics or endodontics (root canal therapy). Unfortunately, as far as the public was concerned this did not guarantee that these practitioners, most of whom had established dental premises in the high street, held competence in their claimed specialised area of dentistry.

In 1989, the General Dental Council instigated discussions with the profession about this unregulated state of affairs and the President, Professor David Mason, asked me to chair the GDC Distinctive Titles Working Party. This was an immensely exciting project, which gave me unprecedented background to this hitherto unexplored topic. After a couple of years, the findings were produced as a report, which was sent for consultation with the profession and consumer groups. Many helpful comments were received and incorporated into a revised document which was approved by the GDC at its Council meeting in November 1992. We all eagerly awaited implementation of the recommended Specialist Lists and Titles the following year.

However, the implementation was delayed as we were advised to await the imminent publication of two important reports on Specialist Training, the report of the chief medical officer, Dr Ken Calman, on Specialist Medical Training, and the report of the chief dental officer, Brian Mouatt, on UK Specialist Dental Training. This latter one was published in May 1995 and supported the implementation of the GDC's proposals to introduce specialist titles and lists and invited the Council to work with the health departments and the dental profession to give practical effect to these changes.

Ken Ray, long-time friend and colleague and now Dean of the Faculty of Dental Surgery, came to the GDC on a Sunday evening that May to pour over with me an advance copy of the Mouatt Report. It was crystal clear that there were areas of the Report that did not find favour with the traditional gatekeepers of specialist training, the Faculties of the Royal Colleges in conjunction with the Joint Committee for Specialist Training (JCSTD) and the myriad of Specialist Advisory Committees for each speciality, and Ken gave me early warning of the conflicts ahead. The inflammatory situation occurred because the Mouatt Report reaffirmed the GDC under the terms of the 1984 Dentists Act as the 'sole competent authority' with ultimate responsibility for specialist training and standards of practice in the UK, a role which we were advised we could not delegate. However, this was at variance with the terms of the Medical Directive where the General Medical Council was designated as one of the UK competent authorities with responsibility for issuing certificates, while a Council of the Medical Royal Colleges was designated as a second competent authority.

'Margaret, you must follow the medical model. Give up your right for the GDC to be the sole competent authority.' This message was reiterated on many public occasions by leaders of the faculties, dental specialist societies and the BDA, often delivered as a personal attack with a confrontational tone of voice or turn of phrase. I was in unfamiliar territory, portrayed as assuming the role of ogre. My reaction was to dig my heels in. There was no way that I was going to surrender the GDC's right, also enshrined in the European Dental Directives, won in 1980 through tough negotiations by our then current leaders, Professor Geoffrey Howe and Ronnie Allen at the BDA. I repeatedly asked myself 'Why were the colleges so anxious to take control from the GDC? What was their hidden agenda?'

During this period of frenetic activity around the specialist issue, letters of complaint were being published in the dental press and submitted to the Minister of Health against the CDO and GDC. Then the Chairman of the General Dental Services Committee, Joe Rich, aware of my discomfort due to the seemingly intractable situation, firmly stated his view. 'Margaret, why this crisis? You were the arch networker and an excellent listener. What has happened?' This fatherly enquiry stopped me in my tracks. I conceded that I had reacted badly to the bullying tactics and personal attacks. I resolved to activate my networking and negotiating skills to deal with the current impasse. Whilst I held fast to the principles and did not surrender the GDC's legal role to be the single competent authority, I began anew to seek a harmonious solution with all the stakeholders involved.

So, with the utilisation of Jane Gordon's legendary drafting skills, we prepared a partnership agreement between the Council, the dental faculties of the Royal Colleges of Surgeons and other educational bodies to ensure the maintenance of standards. Thus, an important milestone in the specialist saga was reached with the creation of the Accord, which was in essence an agreement among all the involved parties regarding future educational responsibilities, recognising the key roles that the faculties, universities and specialist societies played in the formulation of curricula and syllabi and in the monitoring of training arrangements. Peace at last broke out, nearly a year after the publication of the Mouatt report, when in 1996 the Accord was signed. Honour was restored and the stance taken by the GDC showed that it was prepared to prove its independence as a self-regulatory body operating within its legal framework.

On assuming the Presidency, in order to expedite investigation of new matters and the preparation of a report for Council, I created Review Groups who could invite the best people to take part, and membership was not narrowly confined to Council members, as had been the case with the traditional GDC committee structure. In addition one (or more) Task Group could be formed to study delineated areas and, after completion of the work and submission of its report to the Parent Review Group, it, like the Review Group, could be disbanded. For example, each speciality mentioned in the CDO's report would need a task group: oral surgery, orthodontics, restorative dentistry, paediatric dentistry, dental public health and the 'additional dental specialties' which did not require a medical qualification and were at that time hospital based, oral pathology and radiology.

It was clear to me that it was crucial that I appointed the right person to chair the Specialist Review Group. He or she needed to have the confidence of the key players, have outstanding powers of persuasion and negotiation, as well as the intellectual capacity to wrestle with the challenging issues, the new requirements, involving the length of time of specialist training, to be met before awarding the much coveted Certificate of Completion of Specialist Training (CCST) and the method of registering these select holders on lists to be accessible to the public. My choice of John Tiernan, an elected member with experience of general practice and later advising practitioners through his role at Dental Protection, the indemnity organisation, proved to be inspired as he discharged his mammoth task, or some would say the poisoned chalice, expertly and within an uncompromisingly short time-frame. As with all Review Groups there was flexibility to recruit members from outwith the Council and this facility was essential as the membership had to consist of the best brains available within the profession.

However, once the work of the Specialist Review Group was completed, I needed some mechanism in place to provide continuing advice to the Council. Again this would be a tough assignment and so I needed a chairman with the highest credentials and universal respect throughout the profession. I turned to Sir Ian Gainsford, a very safe pair of hands as the Chairman of the GDC Education Committee, who had retired from the Council following my election as President, because his term of office as the nominated representative of the University of London had finished. As recorded in the Minutes of the Council meeting, I dubbed him my Knight in Shining Armour for his willingness to take on this role. As it transpired, he chaired this newly created Specialist Training Advisory Committee (STAC) with great distinction and delivered its remit, which was to advise the GDC's Education Committee on all aspects of education, curriculum and implementation of specialist training and specialist lists.

The Council's Seal and the signature of the President and Registrar were affixed on a regular basis to GDC official documents. These could be letters appointing people to visit and report on the course of instruction given to undergraduate dental students or transfer forms covering sales of investments as agreed by the Finance Committee, actions which were formally reported to each full meeting of Council. The Council's Seal was attached to the Appeal Regulations which provided the mechanism by which unsuccessful applicants could contest the decision and, if successful with an appeal, gain entry onto the 'specialist list' and use the title specialist in their chosen discipline. Thus, my next task was to appoint a Director of Appeals, and this was the first, and probably the last, time that I interviewed, in company with Sir Ian Gainsford, four judges who were recommended for the post. His Honour Judge Ronald Howe was appointed and guided us successfully through the legal minefield of Appeal Procedure, as well as chairing a large number of appeals from unsuccessful candidates. In 1998, there were ten recognised specialities, with several new ones in the offing, so it was clear from the outset that the Appeals Panel would be kept well occupied for not just months but years, as it proved to be.

History will judge the success of the introduction of a formalised structure to specialisation and the accruing benefits for patients with the shift of specialist care from the hospital into primary or community care, a move in the NHS which continues apace in medicine as well as in dentistry. But, on my retirement, Tom Macadam, the longest serving elected member of the GDC, recounted his verdict on the highly controversial issue of specialisation. 'Here were the combined forces of the universities, colleges, and the profession pulling each other apart. Could it be done or was failure the only option? "I was not going to let that happen" is a phrase which appears frequently in a memoir entitled *The Downing Street Years*. The failure option was dismissed. Only recently, some eight years later, has the initial work of 1990 (The Distinctive Titles Working Party) been completed. Under your guidance the proposal passed through the Council and all parties were placated. It is a far from easy task to achieve anything worthwhile in this Council and this was of major importance.'

This unsolicited verdict was solace to my ears. For me, the Specialist Issue had been a cathartic experience and one from which I know I emerged a wiser and more mature president of the GDC.

For forty years the Council's Red Book, an A5 publication, *Professional Conduct and Fitness to Practice* issued to all dentists registering with the GDC, cited the ethical behaviour expected of a member of the dental profession and was accepted as the ultimate authority in consideration of disciplinary matters. Unfortunately, its tone was threatening and its language stilted. My experience amassed while editor of the *BDJ* was put to good effect as I encouraged a major revision of the Council's Red Book. So, in November 1997 *Maintaining Standards: Guidance to Dentists on Professional and Personal Conduct* was issued to 30,000 dentists with names on the Register. The change in focus of the publication majored on promoting good practice, stating in easily understood English those ideals of a professional and, in order to facilitate updating of different sections without having to reprint the entire book, it was presented as a hard bound loose-leaf folder with an index and biography for further reference or reading. Janet Collins at the GDC put in an enormous amount of time editing *Maintaining Standards* and it proved so successful that within two years we published a similar document, in the same format, for other members of the dental team on the rolls at the GDC: the hygienists and therapists. This ensured that the guidance issued by the GDC reflected the expectations of the profession and public in the approaching twenty-first century.

Neither did we shirk our responsibilities in the wider public arena and studied closely the report of the Nolan Committee in 1995 on Standards in Public Life. This set out clearly Public Service Principles: selflessness, integrity, objectivity, accountability, openness, honesty, leadership. The Council voted to accept fully these precepts and published a code of conduct for members which included the setting up of a Register of Interests so that any potential conflict of professional or financial involvement could be declared.

I have already referred to the disciplinary and health procedures available to the Council to deal with a wide range of problems facing dentists in its effort to protect members of the public. However, it became obvious that, in company with other health professions, a mechanism was needed to deal with dentists whose clinical skills were chronically lacking or seriously deficient and for whom the health or disciplinary procedures were inappropriate. Professor John Scott, a member of the GDC and Dean at the Liverpool Dental School, was enthusiastic to explore this issue and so I invited him to become chairman of the Poor Performance Review Group. He expertly guided them to formulate in 1998 a possible statutory scheme to deal with dentists exhibiting failing standards of dentistry.

Since the 1980s, the GDC cherished the idea of introducing a statutory scheme for patients who wished to complain about the private treatment which they had received, but whose only opportunity was to seek redress through the civil courts. Tom Macadam, the experienced general practitioner from Scotland, chaired a non-NHS Complaints Review Group with the aim of developing such a scheme. However, this initiative, despite Tom's heroic efforts, failed to gain acceptance with all professional groups, although they were at one that such a scheme was needed. As so often seems to be the case, the stumbling block was the method of funding. In fact, it was not until 2006 that a complaints scheme for patients receiving treatment outside the NHS, which had its own system for redress, was launched, by the Rt. Hon. Rosie Winterton MP, Minister for Health, and financed and managed independently of the GDC, with much credit due to an energetic and far-sighted elected general practitioner member of Council, Meredyth Bell, who lobbied long and hard to get the issue back on the GDC agenda – someone after my own heart who never takes 'No' for an answer. The volume of complaints, just over one thousand, heard in the first six months of operation of the new scheme confirmed that it fulfilled a long awaited and much needed service for patients. The need was also enthusiastically endorsed by the dental professionals, as the complaint could be resolved promptly in a fair, efficient and transparent way, often through the dental practice, so avoiding damaging confrontational disputes or lengthy legal battles.

Controversial issues, it seemed, were rarely off the agenda during my term as President. It was also healthy that there was an appetite amongst members to debate Government initiatives and their impact on the quality of NHS services. This was in stark contrast to previously held views that the proposed NHS Reforms should only be considered by dentists in the forum of the British Dental Association, or more specifically its General Dental Services Committee (GDSC). Thus, for example, when the Minister of State for Health, Alan Milburn, announced on 23 April 1998 in a speech to the BDA Conference in Harrogate that the Government was to produce a new strategy for NHS dentistry later in the year, a response was prepared putting forward the Council's views on the five challenges enunciated by the Minister in his speech. The contents of the letter sent to the Department of Health featured as an agenda item at the November 1998 Council meeting and there was lively participation amongst the members, especially as the GDC's document: 'Delivering Change 1995-2000' was clearly in accord with Government thinking.

Throughout my thirteen years as editor of the *BDJ*, I could guarantee that my postbag would contain letters on the topic of permitting dentists to use the courtesy title of doctor. Ian Simpson, an elected member of the GDC in the 1970s spearheaded a campaign entitled 'Legalised Use of Title of Doctor' (LUTD) with other protagonists, Douglas Barber and Rosemary Malik. Douglas Pike, in 1990, initiated the 'Call me Doctor' campaign and over one thousand dentists pledged support, each donating £10 to the cause as well as gaining full backing from the two powerful professional associations, the British Dental Association (BDA) and the General Dental Practitioners Association (GDPA). The crux of the problem could be found in Clause 26 of the 1984 Dentists Act which, while not specifically mentioning the title 'Doctor', made it clear that 'a dentist should not use any title reasonably calculated to suggest that he has any professional status or qualification other than that which he possesses'. For many years, the GDC had interpreted this in its Red Book, the ethical guidance to all dentists, that they may not use the title 'Doctor' and to do so meant that they were liable to the charge of serious professional misconduct. The Rolls Royce solution would have been to amend the Dentists Act, and Baroness Gardner of Parkes, herself a dentist and at one time a member of the GDC, had attempted to do so in 1983 when the new Dentists Bill was under debate, but her amendment was defeated.

However, I was sympathetic to the idea to permit the use of the courtesy title for several practical and, to me, commonsense reasons. On my travels abroad, to attend dental conferences, I was addressed, registered and given documentation with the prefix 'Dr' in front of my name. To delete it would convey to other participants that I was not a dentist. This applied when travelling in Europe, America, Asia and Australasia, although in many of these countries the initial dental qualification is a doctorate and not as in the UK a Bachelor degree. Another well-founded reason, I believed, was the increasing feminisation of the dental profession, so using the title of address 'Dr' provided for the patient immediate recognition of the dentist amongst the increasingly female workforce in the practice: receptionist, dental nurse, hygienist and therapist. Undoubtedly it would have been an advantage during my younger days working in the clinic at Cheshunt. To be truthful, I did not relish the 'Dr' debate plaguing my entire presidency as it had done throughout my editorship of the *Journal*. Fortunately, I was given great encouragement to open the issue within the forum of the GDC by Douglas Pike and it was also reassuring to know that in 1990 Martin Levy had persuaded the Conference of the Local Dental Committees to make it the policy of the General Dental Services Committee to pursue the use of the title of doctor. Additional pressure came from the BDA and GDPA, who decided to use the courtesy title in correspondence and internal communication with members, so ensuring that the matter would not go away. Indeed, if the ethical guidance currently in force was to be enacted, then thousands of dentists should be charged with serious professional misconduct for breaking the rules: the situation was surely untenable.

Therefore, I decided to place the item on the Agenda for my second Council meeting on 16 May 1995, with the proposal that the ethical guidance issued in the Red Book by the GDC should be amended through the deletion of paragraph 54. To me this seemed a neat and simple solution to a long-standing problem which had raged for over thirty years. I admit that I was completely taken aback at the lengthy, passionate and at times, acrimonious, debate which ensued, when opinions oscillated, making it difficult to judge from the Chair the consensus of the Council. Strong support came from Douglas Pike in an almost triumphant opening speech, followed by some of the elected members and professors. However, the views of many lay members and, to me surprisingly, of many of the elected women dentists were in line with the trenchant views expressed by Alan Fearn, in convincing rhetoric as behoves a city councillor and a national political candidate standing as he did for Parliament, albeit unsuccessfully, on five occasions. The result of the vote to remove from the Red Book the paragraph containing the prohibition against dentists calling themselves doctor was dramatic. On a show of hands, for the motion 19, against 20, with 3 abstentions. The motion was lost. This was not the decisive vote I had anticipated, nor the result to get the topic off the agenda. The BDA had been so confident that the motion would be passed that they had already prepared its Press Release and letters to members, all of which had to be pulped. The dental press also reported unkindly: 'Jurassic Park has moved to Wimpole Street.'

With the support of the Registrar Norman Davies and advice from the Council's solicitor, Paul Honigman, I put the item back on the Agenda for the next Council meeting on 14 November. 'Margaret, you are a bad loser,' taunted Alan Fearn, 'You can't bring an issue back in six months just because you don't like the result.' Maybe it was with undue haste, but I was determined not to be deflected. This time I introduced the debate from the chair, reading a carefully worded statement prepared with advice from the solicitor, emphasising that if the resolution to remove the paragraph from the Red Book was passed this time, there was no compulsion on any dentist to use the courtesy title 'Doctor'; it was to be purely a matter of choice for the individual dentist. Such were the interest and emotions generated by the topic this time, that the public gallery was crammed with exuberant and chattering dentists, who had to be admonished from time to time by the Registrar to maintain silence as the debate got under way. An early speech in favour of the resolution was from one of the original antagonists, Brian Lux. He recounted how he had been greatly influenced by the results of a survey, conducted by David Thomas, amongst dental students who overwhelmingly had voted to adopt the courtesy title on graduation if given the chance. However, despite announcing his change of heart, he added the rider that he personally would not use the title.

But Alan Fearn remained resolute to the end. He warned that 'there could be a legal challenge from the General Medical Council or Advertising Standards Authority.' Nevertheless, this time the vote on the recommendation to delete paragraph 54 from the GDC's own Red Book was decisive: 30 in favour, 9 against and 6 abstentions. Applause broke out in the gallery disturbing the usual hushed atmosphere. Realising the error of their ways the occupants beat a hasty retreat into Wimpole Street before they could suffer the ignominy of being asked to leave the premises.

By coincidence, the principal guest at the Council Dinner that evening was Sir Donald Irvine, the President of the General Medical Council. His opening words gave approbation to our decision. 'Hello, Doctors . . ., I congratulate you on taking this progressive action.' A threat from the GMC, as predicted by Alan Fearn, would not be forthcoming. The press coverage was positive and generous and I was thrilled to receive a magnificent bouquet and message from Douglas and the 'Call me Doctor' supporters, 'Grateful thanks to our very courageous President'. A letter was also sent by the Registrar to all practising dentists advising them that they could use the courtesy title Doctor without the risk of prosecution by the Council. But rumblings persisted and Michael Stern, MP for Bristol North West, secured an adjournment debate in the House of Commons on 19 January 1996 on the title of Doctor. The Minister for Health, Gerald Malone, responded and advised, 'that the Council has merely amended its own ethical guidance to dentists. It is quite within its own legal powers to do that.'

On the tenth anniversary of dentists being able to choose to use the courtesy title of doctor, a press reception was held in London on the evening of Tuesday, 1 November. Many of the early pioneers were present, including Douglas Pike, who led the 'Call me Doctor Campaign', and Derek Watson, and as President at the time I was delighted to recount in brief the steps leading to the historic decision a decade earlier. I was also thankful to be able to report that the frequently expounded misgivings by the antagonists had not occurred. Patients and public were not confused by the use of the title.

Today most dentists use the title 'Dr' which is explained on their notepaper or practice sign with the words 'dentist', or 'dental practitioner'. Younger members of the profession will have now forgotten that for thirty years interminable debates took place and reams of paper used, as letters were published on the topic in every available dental periodical. But there remains unfinished business. Until the 1984 Dentists Act is updated, the GDC and other official Government bodies refuse to use the courtesy title when in correspondence with dentists. Maybe the passage of a further ten years will allow acceptance through 'custom and practice'; surely then it will be time for another party.

⋆ ⋆ ⋆

When a child dies it is a heartbreaking experience for all concerned. When a fit child dies at the dentist while having treatment for two broken front teeth it is nothing short of criminal; indeed doctors and dentists have been prosecuted on a manslaughter charge for this tragic event.

Many may not realise that the history of dentistry and general anaesthesia are inextricably linked through the dentist, William Morton, who in 1846 in Boston, Massachusetts, demonstrated successfully the use of ether to produce unconsciousness for an operation. However, that occasion does not mean that dentists should consider it as their birthright to administer general anaesthesia for all time. In fact, up until 1997, dental students received practical instruction on how to give a general anaesthetic as part of their undergraduate curriculum. Nevertheless in the early 1990s, despite the advent of modern drugs, there was a marked escalation in the use of general anaesthesia, often provided in dedicated clinics for people afraid of going to a dentist for treatment. Ironically, over the years, it is the experience of 'the smell of gas' or 'the mask over the face' which has produced a cadre of dental phobics, lasting a lifetime.

'Death at the Dentist'; 'Child dies under GA'. These are just two of the disturbing headlines appearing in the national and local newspapers with alarming frequency. The statistics given by Dr Michael Rosen, a former president of the Royal College of Anaesthetists, writing in *The Times* in November 1998 made grim reading: 'Since 1990, at least twenty healthy children have lost their lives or been brain damaged unnecessarily' and concluded that it was time for safe dental anaesthesia.

Any dentist involved in the death of a patient was automatically referred to the General Dental Council and was called to appear before the Professional Conduct Committee. At the conclusion of a deeply disturbing and heart-rending hearing of a case in May 1998, as President and Chairman of the Committee I made the following statement: 'This case has raised fundamental issues in terms of the relative responsibilities of the professional qualified staff in the giving of general anaesthesia in dentistry. The Council will be reviewing its guidance in the light of this case.'

Using my well-established method of inquiry, I convened a Review Group on Resuscitation, Sedation and General Anaesthesia in Dentistry, with the specific task of reviewing the ethical guidance issued to dentists on the topic *Maintaining Standards*. Many knowledgeable colleagues in the specialised field of general anaesthesia for dentistry were called upon to give advice – Meg Skelly, a highly experienced and well respected dentist heading the Pain Control Unit at Guy's Dental Hospital, Professor Leo Strunin, the president of the Royal College of Anaesthetists, John Lowry, Dean at the Faculty of Dental Surgery of the Royal College of Surgeons, Professor Tony Wildsmith, who chaired the dental anaesthesia committee at the Royal College of Anaesthetists, and influential members of dental anaesthetic groups, Chris Holden, David Craig and Douglas

Pike, also a GDC member, to name a few. Indeed the Royal College of Anaesthetists and the Faculty of Dental Surgery were already hard at work producing a joint document 'Standards and Guidelines for GA in Dentistry', finally published in March 1999, setting forth clear and unequivocal advice on how to raise standards and improve patient safety.

It was a challenging task for the GDC Review Group to formulate the ethical guidance because it was necessary to balance a number of important ethical principles: proper respect for patients' wishes; the practitioner's duty to exercise his or her own professional judgement in deciding on preferred treatments and methods of pain control, and the General Dental Council's most important consideration, the protection of the public. What transpired was that the GDC guidance set out clearly the responsibilities of the dentist providing the treatment, the need for agreed written protocols in every dental practice as to the regime to deal with life-threatening emergencies, as well as ensuring that the general anaesthesia was administered by a specialist anaesthetist, fulfilling certain published criteria.

It was evident that this revised guidance was going to reduce dramatically the availability of dental treatment under general anaesthesia with the inevitable impact on patient services. Nonetheless, the continuing unnecessary loss of life was completely unacceptable. This was not a situation for compromise. Before I presented the amendments to the guidance prepared by the Review Group to the Council meeting on 10 November 1998, I shared it in confidence with the BDA's General Dental Services Committee and its chairman, Tony Kravitz. The BDA wanted to see a reduction in demand for dental general anaesthesia and also for encouragement to be given to patients to consider safer alternatives, for example sedation. However, its support ended there. The Association made known its opposition to the possibility that the GDC's recommendations would come into effect immediately: there would be no transitional period. Ahead of the GDC debate, the BDA on 6 November issued a press release: 'Thousands of patients will have their appointments for dental treatment under general anaesthesia cancelled at short notice.' So all eyes of the media were focused on the GDC on the morning of 10 November 1998. Tony Kravitz was interviewed on BBC Breakfast News, in advance of the Council meeting later in the morning, making again his point of the GDC limiting access to patients seeking dental treatment under general anaesthesia, especially if a decision was taken to introduce the changes forthwith.

After a full debate there was a unanimous decision by members to accept the revised ethical guidance on GA in dentistry and, crucially, that the revised guidance should have immediate effect. My statement to the press following the meeting is worth recalling: 'The GDC's guidance on GA has always been strict and has made clear that general anaesthesia for dental treatment is never without risk. The new guidance will build on this and stress that GA should only be considered if there is an overriding clinical need and the alternative methods of pain and anxiety control have been fully explored. The purpose of revising the guidance is to provide for better protection of the public whenever dental treatment involving general anaesthesia is given. In making this decision the welfare and safety of patients have been the Council's overriding concern.'

On the day of this historic Council meeting, a letter enclosing the revised guidance was sent to each dentist on the register, to dental hygienists and therapists, consultants in dental public health, to chief executives of health authorities, health boards and trusts and others providing general anaesthetic services through, for example, the Poggo Clinics. Everyone in the UK was advised of the changes in practice.

But the absence of transitional arrangements caused enormous disquiet, even outright anger. It was a new experience for me to receive hate mail through the post from dentists or members of their family inconvenienced through having to close down their general anaesthetic provision for dental treatment, which for some amounted to 100 per cent of their work. 'You have forced my husband out of business: how are we to make a living?'

On the day of the decision I was in and out of the broadcasting studios dotted around London giving radio and TV interviews. It was also an unnerving experience when I was ushered into a darkened room, with a view of Wimpole Street projected behind me on a screen, while a disembodied voice fired the questions. Much more relaxed was my appearance on *Watchdog* when interviewed by Dr Mark Porter. Unsure of my cues to start and finish I was cheerfully told, 'No need to worry, Margaret. I will give you a pinch, like this, to start, and two to stop.' The office staff were jealous as I regaled this episode, but did not share the same enthusiasm when I described the state of the BBC sandwich of cheese and pickle: a long way to go to reach the culinary standard of the Council.

For me it was morally defensible to introduce the changes in the guidance with immediate effect. If giving GA for dental treatment was deemed unsafe and unethical on 10 November, I could not see any reason to postpone the decision, knowing that a further fatality might occur in the intervening period.

I was reassured when, on my retirement, the chief dental officer, Robin Wild, commented: 'Some of your initiatives took real courage, for instance, your stand on the new guidance on general anaesthesia.' But my courage, in no mean part, came from the unwavering support given to me by Professor Leo Strunin, the far-sighted and indefatigable president of the Royal College of Anaesthetists. As crunch-time approached, Leo's mobile phone was in daily use and I also would, at short notice, grab a cab to go to his office in Russell Square to work through another raft of objections. But he went even further with his support and offered, from the day of publication of the guidance, to field the phone calls from anaesthetists seeking clarification on this or that.

Later, I was thrilled to receive an Honorary Fellowship of the Royal College of Anaesthetists and the greatest pleasure was to hear Leo give the citation at the splendid award ceremony held in the awe-inspiring British Museum. But these material rewards paled into insignificance. I had learnt so much from my colleagues in both disciplines on the journey to reach this momentous decision. Above all, I believe I had been able to make a difference: I had saved lives.

'What's going on today: is a soup kitchen opening here?' chirped a cheerful postman when he spotted a queue of some thirty people on the pavement outside the premises of the General Dental Council in Wimpole Street, an hour before its normal opening time of 9 a.m. Their quest was to secure a seat in the Council's small public gallery so that they could listen to a highly controversial debate about the recommendations for the future regulation of the dental team. The presidents and chief executives of all the dental auxiliary organisations had travelled from all parts of the country to be present because the debate was the conclusion of years of work, high hopes and aspirations, but a satisfactory outcome was by no means a foregone conclusion.

In earlier chapters you will recall my unwavering support for members of the dental team. My interest was intensified after I had visited the training school for dental therapists in Adelaide, Australia, and for the school dental nurses in Wellington, New Zealand. Then, after working alongside a dental therapist when practising as a community dental officer in the early 1970s in Cheshunt and later visiting the innovative schemes to develop new auxiliary dental personnel in the Netherlands, I became a staunch advocate for the dental team approach to the provision of dental care. Indeed, members of the profession were well aware of, and some not a little concerned at, the strong opinions I expressed on the issue. Many remembered the topic I chose for my maiden speech at the GDC in 1976, which was to support the change in name of the dental auxiliary to dental therapist, citing that an auxiliary in the English dictionary is defined as 'mercenary' or 'subordinate member', which was at odds with the wish to convey to the public and profession that they were valued members of the dental team.

As time passed at the GDC, I became eligible to be considered for the chairmanship of one of its committees, and I was delighted to be rewarded with the opportunity to chair the Dental Auxiliaries Committee from 1983 to 1988. It was while holding this appointment that I became a proponent for another undervalued member of the dental team, the dental technician. The leaders of the dental surgery assistants (dental nurses), especially a team led by Diana Wincott, who later became head of the dental nursing school at Guy's Dental Hospital, worked hard to develop a set of occupational standards and raise awareness for education and training through the formation of a Dental Surgery Assistants Standards and Training Advisory Board. It seemed to make sense to seek to establish a comparable board for dental technicians, a craft which was male dominated, although sharing the ultimate goal of statutory registration.

Thus, the GDC, on 3 April 1984, convened a meeting of all the representative bodies concerned with the education and training of technicians and this involved a staggering number, fifteen. There was an amazing turnout for the first meeting, each organisation sending a representative ensuring every aspect was covered – technicians, employers (dental laboratories), and dentists. The initial meeting was my first encounter with a trade union representative and as the GDC had called the meeting on its premises, and was providing the secretariat and administrative support, it had been assumed that I, as chairman of the Dental Auxiliaries Committee, would take the chair. But that assumption was grossly misplaced. Within a minute of expressing welcome to the delegates, I was challenged by the trade union representative, who demanded I vacate the chair while the meeting decided on the chairman. This was an aggressive, frontal approach and a new experience for me. I did not budge but was completely taken aback by the sequence of events. Indignantly, the trade union lady stuffed her agenda papers into her briefcase, stood up, and stormed out of the committee. I was steeling myself for a mass exodus but before I could speak one of the elder statesmen in the technician group, Harry Eastwood, more known for his forthright manner and none too sympathetic views of dentists, immediately assumed a fatherly role and reassured me not to be offended. They were delighted that the GDC was taking this initiative and would give me unanimous support as chairman of the meeting, now designated as the Dental Technicians Education and Training Advisory Group. It was certainly a baptism of fire and made me wary of any future encounters with trade union representatives. The woman did not return to participate in the deliberations but meeting her on a future occasion I found that she was a thoroughly nice person, but had only been doing the job she was paid to do. Over the years this experience has made me ponder whether the trade union of dentists, the BDA, would have done better with their negotiations if they had employed a professional trade union representative rather than a practising dentist, however committed to the cause.

Work continued apace and two years later the inaugural meeting of the Dental Technicians Education and Training Advisory Board (DTETAB) was held at the GDC offices, on Tuesday, 21 January 1986. The membership had been proposed by the advisory group and I was thrilled that confidence in me was expressed through my appointment as chairman for the first triennium. Thereafter, we decided that to maintain the confidence of the technicians, employers and dentists, the Board must be independent of the Council and self-financing. Ian Simpson, a senior GDC member, agreed during a debate in Council, 'that the GDC is seen to help to establish and observe, rather than continually running it, was commendable.' Dentists needed to learn to let go.

However, there was plenty of research to do during the first triennium and three subcommittees on manpower, education, and training and constitution were established. The convenors Les Ward, Bernard Smith and Geoff Garnett worked tirelessly, ensuring that the final recommendations of the Board were based on fact and ushered in a new era for dental technology. At the end of the triennium Colin Lee became chairman, followed subsequently by outstanding leaders in dental technology, Brian Gordon, Ian MacLeod and Tony Griffin. Sixteen years later, DTETAB metamorphosed into the Dental Technicians Association. While continuing to operate the voluntary national register for dental technicians, for which in 1986 DTETAB had assumed responsibility from the National Joint Council for the Craft of Dental Technicians and its now well-established educational and training interests, the new Association widened its scope to issue pay and terms and conditions of employment, offering membership services such as a legal helpline and indemnity insurance. I was thrilled to be invited as guest of honour at the inauguration in December 2002 at the Royal Society of Arts in London, when Tony Griffin was elected the first president of the Association. 'From small beginnings' was an appropriate truism. The dental technicians' patience and persistence had ensured the success.

When I assumed the role of President of the General Dental Council, the profession watched intently to see whether I would continue to champion my known areas of special interest – women and the dental team. However, as with perfect timing in 1993, a year before I was elected to office a groundbreaking report was published by the highly influential and widely respected Nuffield Foundation. The members of the Inquiry started from the premise that, in the future, treatment would be polarised into low-tech care for the young and high-tech for the old. They made many recommendations including that the low-tech work should be carried out by expanded teams composed of dental nurses, dental technicians and clinical auxiliaries, namely hygienists, therapists, orthodontic auxiliaries and clinical dental technicians. The Nuffield Inquiry into the Education and Training of Personnel Auxiliary to Dentistry went even further in proposing that all auxiliaries who work within dentistry should be registered with the GDC, an ambition stoutly promoted by all auxiliary groups. These were radical and provocative proposals and the profession was deeply divided on the issue. Importantly, Nuffield concluded: 'Despite the best efforts of many people, there remains a muddle and an inconsistent mixture of courses, assessment procedures and regulation for auxiliaries.'

It was widely anticipated that the BDA and many other dental and community organisations would comment on the report and so a response from the GDC was inevitable. Nevertheless, one of my first decisions as president was that this response was to be substantial and I could see that the main recommendations could be used as a platform to launch our own forward-looking proposals. So, steered by the gifted administrator, the assistant registrar Jane Gordon, relevant material was gathered on as wide a scale as possible, resulting in the preparation of a set of three consultation papers. Over 500 copies were sent out to various organisations in August 1995, inviting comments to be returned to the Council by 31 December. The GDC clearly indicated in its preamble support for the main thrust of the recommendations but attempted to examine in more detail how the proposals could affect the Council. Thus, the first paper dealt with the registration of dental auxiliaries; the next paper examined the constitutional changes that might be needed following registration with the Council, for example representation in the Council, and the final paper put forward the necessary amendments to the 1984 Dentists Act to facilitate change.

There was an unexpected and enormous response to the GDC's consultation process and it was encouraging that there was great support. 78 per cent of those replying agreed with the creation of a committee to be inclusive of all members of the dental team, the Committee for Professions Complementary to Dentistry, the latter term chosen as all-embracing for members of the dental team. This was to get away from the medical model of Professions Supplementary to Medicine; no more subservience or 'add-ons' as we moved forward into the new dawn of the dental team. But there were antagonists to the proposed changes and I believed that the opportunity to have a full and frank debate on the issue was long overdue. So the first GDC seminar on the Dental Team was organised for 5 September 1996 and held in the Bradlaw Suite at the Council's premises, which could accommodate ninety-four people. Surprisingly, everybody who was anybody wanted to be there. Invited delegates were begging for more tickets so that they could bring people with them. 'Just what is the GDC up to?' was a consistent riposte.

The morning session was devoted to short presentations given by a representative from each of eleven different groups, followed by a discussion session in the afternoon. However, sparks began to fly at the beginning of the seminar. 'I object to an illegal group being invited into the GDC,' voiced a BDA delegate. 'It's your role to prosecute them,' referring to the two representatives from the Clinical Dental Technicians Association. But the Nuffield Inquiry had called for the education, training, regulation and working arrangements for clinical dental technicians. Also, barely three months previously, in June, the Health Minister, the Rt. Hon. Gerald Malone, had specifically identified this dental worker when announcing in the House of Commons the proposed Dental Bill. This was a time to be inclusive, not exclusive, and so Chris Allen and Tony Ward stayed and took full part in the seminar, giving excellent presentations and making comments in the debate. What a change in fortune when ten years later the GDC took an exhibition stand at the World Symposium in Private Dental Technology and Denturism held in Birmingham, with Chris Allen playing a leading role in organising the event.

At the end of the seminar on the Dental Team there was a clear mandate to take matters forward and so a Dental Auxiliaries Review Group (DARG) was set up under the chairmanship of Jennifer Pinder, a long-time advocate of team dentistry and a talented GDC member who enjoyed support from team members. Again, a review group was chosen as the way forward because it meant that members could be chosen for their knowledge and experience as individuals and not as representatives of a particular group or organisation. Some notable GDC members did serve on the Group – Professor Frank Ashley, John Chope, Rosemary Khan and Douglas Pike. The remaining members from outwith the Council brought important skills and experience – Professor John Frame, Jane Holt, Pat Harle and Gordon Watkins. Terms of reference were formulated and the review group was given a challenging timetable, to report to the full Council meeting in May 1998. To facilitate work three task groups were set up, concentrating on different auxiliary groups: dental nurses; hygienists, therapists and the new orthodontic auxiliaries; and dental technicians, maxillofacial prosthesists and technologists, and clinical dental technicians. Scepticism abounded so I moved to reassure the doubters, in a press release issued following the inaugural meeting of the group a couple of months later, that nothing would be introduced without full consultation with the profession and appropriate consumer groups, but made it clear that the primary duty of the Council was to protect patients.

But concern lingered as many dentists believed the move to greater use of auxiliaries was unstoppable, possibly affecting their livelihood, and so used various strategies to make their point. At the 1997 annual conference of the local dental committees held in June in London, on the most notable day of Friday the 13th, I was surprised that the lead speaker to the motion, 'That this conference believes that the Dentists Act must not be amended to expand the role of auxiliaries without the agreement of the profession', was Gordon Watkins who was chairing one of DARG's Task Groups looking at hygienists, therapists and orthodontic nurses. The motion, as expected, was overwhelmingly supported by the delegates but it did not knock the GDC off course. Even more, to Gordon's credit, he continued committedly in his leadership role of the DARG task group.

But a year later the sniping was still in evidence. 'BDA accused of sabotage' ran the headline in the November 1998 issue of the *Dental Laboratories* magazine. So what was happening after the smooth passage of the DARG Report, presented by Jennifer Pinder to the GDC Council meeting in May 1998? It transpired that the BDA had at a very late stage, in fact two weeks before the DARG report was made public, decided to commission a report from J M Consulting, a management consultancy whom they had heard possessed experience of working with other regulatory bodies and health departments. Their report made it clear that they did not see the case for the registration of dental nurses or dental technicians on the grounds of public protection. This was a hard-hitting verdict on the core plank of DARG's work and Jennifer Pinder, understandably, reacted with amazement at its late appearance. 'This report from the BDA will confuse the profession: it is very discourteous.' However, Diana Scarrott, head of education and science at the BDA, defended its position. 'We felt there was another way of looking at the issue and commissioned the report to stimulate debate. It was not meant to compete with DARG.'

Despite this exchange, suspicion in some quarters remained and there was a degree of apprehension as to the official response which would be forthcoming from the BDA to the consultation paper published by the Dental Auxiliaries Review Group. Eventually, the BDA response was released at a stormy press event on 18 December, chaired by Gordon Watkins and supported by chief executive John Hunt at the BDA headquarters. It was clearly stated in its own press release: 'BDA delivers radical response on auxiliary use to the GDC', suggesting an alternative and more flexible approach to the work of auxiliaries and their regulation, making plain that 'it does not support registration of dental nurses or clinical dental technicians'. The Association further rejected the proposed term of 'professions complementary to dentistry' as confusing for the public, but stressed that this was not intended to demean those workers. Not surprisingly, the auxiliary groups were incensed. Bill Courtney, editor of the *Dental Laboratories Association Journal*, wrote, 'You will see a general theme running through the BDA paper which, summed up, amounts to: we dentists know best and we don't want uppity auxiliaries getting above their station.'

Bill Courtney had already forewarned about this state of affairs. 'Margaret Seward is forward thinking and because of that she has her enemies. Her effort to keep everyone engaged in talks has been prodigious. However, make your mind up time is approaching fast and with it comes Margaret's biggest test.' I was well aware that I was under enormous scrutiny. To gather together consumer organisations and distil into a report the 233 responses to our consultation document received over a six-month period from the dental profession, auxiliary groups, health authorities and councils, medical bodies and consumer organisations was an immense task. However, I was also cheered that the BDA joined forces with the GDC to organise a joint symposium 'Teams for Tomorrow' at the Association's annual conference in Torquay, the month before the scheduled debate on the GDC's response to the consultation at its May meeting.

With this tortuous journey to reach the final debate and decision by the GDC on the future for members of the dental team, it is not difficult to understand why so many people were queuing on 11 May 1999 outside the premises of the GDC to gain entry to the rather small public and press galleries in eager anticipation that history could be made, high hopes realised or aspirations dashed. The outcome was too close to call. As it transpired, the debate was of the highest quality and lasted unusually for two and a half hours, as so many members wished to take part. In brief, the GDC agreed to adopt the overall title for auxiliaries of 'professionals complementary to dentistry' (PCD) and to register the members of the dental team with the GDC. Also supported was the proposal to widen the role of hygienist and therapist and the suggestion that these health professionals could give an inferior dental block injection. This highly controversial issue had been repeatedly debated for nearly a quarter of a century. To me, at last, common sense prevailed. Joe Rich spoke strongly to encourage the move away from a long list of permitted duties by auxiliaries which undoubtedly hampered the development of individual members of the dental team possible through appropriate training from their supervising dentist.

The observers crammed into the public and press galleries could not believe their eyes or ears as one controversial decision after another was agreed, with little dissent. 'It looked as if the Council was on a roll – anything would get through,' commented a reporter when the GDC agreed to introduce orthodontic PCDs and clinical dental technicians.

That very evening I claimed in a Press Release that this was a 'New Era for Professionals Complementary to Dentistry' and further stated that 'The public should be greatly reassured by this landmark development in oral healthcare'. Finally, the 'Them and Us' philosophy was ousted: the face of dentistry would be changed forever. But the last word was to be with the BDA. Three days later, on 14 May, it published its press release. 'If, after changes in the law, statutory registration proposals for nurses are brought forward, the BDA will judge them on their merits.' Further, the Association commented: 'The Council's decision to introduce clinical dental technicians as a new class of registered PCD is ill thought out.'

Were new battle lines being drawn? However, it would fall to my successor and the Chairman of the Dental Auxiliaries Committee, Professor Colin Smith, a committed member of the Nuffield Inquiry, to implement the new GDC Policy. All I could do would be to watch from the sidelines.

'Power corrupts' it is claimed. Certainly I could see how power and the accompanying trappings could become addictive and that it would be easy to drift into standing for a second five-year term as President. However, anticipating this possibility, immediately after my election in 1994, I made it clear that I was a one-term only president: five years for myself, family, Council and the profession would be enough to cope with. Swiftly the GDC Legislation Committee recommended a change in its Rules and Regulations to reflect my wishes. 'A retiring President will not be eligible to stand as a candidate for re-election to the office of President.' This change was unanimously approved: no possibility for ambiguity this time.

Without doubt, during my incumbent five-year period, the workload had increased dramatically and I was spending on average three days a week at the GDC and many more hours reading papers or representing the GDC at a myriad of events. It was apparent that, with financial pressure on universities, hospitals and trusts, it would become impossible for anyone working in these areas to stand for the presidency, in effect excluding consideration being given to the best person for the job. The days of voluntary service to one's profession were rapidly coming to a close so, in anticipation, it made sense that an honorarium for the next president should be agreed before the call for nominations took place. The proposals were sympathetically and wholeheartedly approved and the initial honorarium was agreed at £20,000 per annum. I was touched when some members suggested that payment should be retrospective, which was not acted upon but which confirmed to me that it was correct to get the matter sorted before my successor took up office, and save potential embarrassment.

As you have read, my last full Council meeting was in May. However, there was no let-up in activity, indeed the reverse for the final few months in office. During my last week, in September, I was chairing for the last time a meeting of the Professional Conduct Committee. As we took a break for lunch, the Registrar handed me a piece of paper with a mobile phone number on it and said that John Denham, the health minister responsible for dentistry, wanted to talk to me urgently. 'Sorry about the poor reception but I am in a restaurant in Westbourne,' explained the Minister on receiving my call; he too was taking a lunch break from the Labour Party Conference in Bournemouth. 'I just wanted you to know,' he continued, 'that the Prime Minister will announce in his speech to the Conference this afternoon that, by October 2001, anyone who wanted to could find an NHS dentist by phoning NHS Direct.' This was an incredible pledge to make, as access to NHS dentistry was a fiercely debated problem. Thankfully, I consoled myself, it would not be my concern. By then I would be thoroughly enjoying retirement.

Leaving parties were soon in full swing and I was overwhelmed by the generosity of organisations wishing to say farewell and the variety of gifts to mark the occasion – from silver cruet sets and candelabra to cut-crystal bowls, vases and decanters of assorted shapes and sizes, all treasured and still in frequent use around my home. In particular, when indulging in my favourite pastime of giving dinner parties, the silver gift from the GDC staff of elephant place-name holders are on show and much admired. A less formal farewell in a local pub was hosted by the education department who organised the lunch-time party to include Eva Lembke, my secretary, who had put retirement on hold to remain working with me for the final months. The GDC was destined to become a quieter office without the gales of laughter from us two Leos.

But after five fulfilling years I too wanted to say a big thank you to the staff. It had been an exhilarating time of team working. It was also a time to say thank you to the many colleagues and friends who had played a central role in my life, so during the last week I organised the party to end all parties, 'The Seward Soiree'. Gordon, Colin and Claire, our son and daughter-in-law, came too and we danced to the same Salsa Band which had been such a great hit at their wedding a few months previously. We finished with a memorable Congo round the courtyard. This was surely a first for the Lansdowne Club in London.

But one further GDC function remained in my diary. I had been invited to return with Gordon to attend the morning November Council meeting, chaired by the new president, Professor Nairn Wilson, to receive tributes from Council members and to be dined out as guest of honour in the splendid Ironmongers Hall in the City of London with past and present GDC colleagues in the evening.

At the morning Council meeting I was completely taken aback at the nice things people can say about you: all your foibles are forgotten as you make your way out of office. Tom Macadam, who had joined with me twenty-three years previously, recalled what it was like in those earlier years and that the instructions from the chairmen to newcomers was simple: 'Do not attempt to be innovative and speak only if spoken to.' 'I have often wondered,' said Tom, 'what they thought of the rebellious 1976 intake. Margaret Seward was not to be silenced!'

Next came the chief dental officer, Robin Wild, who referred to me as 'the arch networker'. I believe that this and a sense of humour are the crucial skills to nurture if you are intent on making a difference. Robin continued, 'I was pleased to remind people that the GDC was already taking the lead on so many of the issues that are now recognised as government policy. Some of your initiatives took real courage, for instance, your stand on the new guidance on general anaesthesia.'

Professor Ronnie Laird, the longest serving nominated member and treasurer, who had proposed me as president, added his comments. 'Her term of office has not been without controversy. If it were so, we surely had elected the wrong person.' He further considered that the profession and public had benefited from my 'enthusiasm, guidance, cajoling and indefatigable energy', and, to my great delight, recognised, as did the five speakers, Gordon's unfailing support. He truly has been my rock in all my endeavours.

To a mixture of emotions there were more speeches in the evening when gifts were exchanged. I received from the Council members an exquisite gold brooch, shaped as a basket filled with sparkling coloured flowers made of precious gems, and a silver salver. In keeping with tradition, I presented a gift. I selected a silver sugar shaker dated 1921, a notable date in dentistry when the last dentist without a degree or licence was entered onto the Dentists Register.

What an extraordinary and long day it had been. The next day I arrived home laden with flowers, gifts, good wishes and a profusion of wonderful memories of my Wimpole Street years. Earlier, in 1989, Michael Watson had written when I failed to be elected as President that 'the GDC was not ready' for me. In truth, I was not ready for the top job at the GDC. The electorate had known best and confirmed my belief that organisations can best be served by the democratic election of members, rather than by appointment.

Ronnie Laird concluded his tribute, 'If I may paraphrase Mr Oscar Hammerstein, you have climbed every mountain.' He had forgotten that I now had a new mountain to climb: Retirement.

Chapter 17

International interludes

I HAVE ALWAYS ENJOYED TRAVELLING and even more so if it involved flying to reach the destination. My first experience was as a young girl of twelve when my parents decided to celebrate their silver wedding in style and fly to Scotland, en route for their special week's holiday in Skye, leaving me to stay with my cousin, Elizabeth Russell, in Troon. I can vividly remember the excitement as we entered the Viking aircraft at Heathrow and the amazement, once airborne, of looking below to see the patchwork quilt of fields, the doll-size houses and miniature cars driving along tiny roads. Barely an hour and a half later we landed at Renfrew airport, now the location of the bustling international Glasgow airport, and after a short car journey we were sitting at lunch with the family in Troon. The sheer speed of this form of transport was incredible, not only to us but also to our friends. Travel by air was not yet commonplace.

The incredulity continued when I announced to my colleagues halfway through my sixth-month term as the resident dental house officer at the London Hospital that I was flying to Canada for a holiday. BOAC, the precursor of British Airways, heralded as the world leader in jet travel, had announced a special fifteen-day return trip to Montreal in its new 707 aircraft for the princely sum of £99. Once there I would stay with my cousin, Betty, who had coaxed me into the bath when I arrived as a toddler at the Mitchells' home from the orphanage. Betty's husband, Peter, had emigrated with their family in 1949 to Montreal, in response to a request from the Quebec authorities for teachers fluent in French to teach English in the French-speaking schools; Montreal at that time was the world's second largest French-speaking city.

I left Heathrow at 1 p.m. on 7 October 1960, having been advised that there would be a refuelling stop of twenty minutes at Shannon airport. To me this was a name I usually heard on the radio's shipping forecast but now it was to assume greater importance because we all quickly disembarked to stock up on the duty-free goods. The flight time to Montreal was just over six hours and, with the local time some four hours behind London, the plane touched down mid-afternoon, at 3.30 p.m. This was to be my first experience of customs control: Canadian passport holders first, immigrants next, and visitors last. It was not surprising that by the time I arrived at the luggage carousel there was only one case remaining, but it was not mine. Suddenly, as flustered as I was, a passenger returned bearing my case and claiming his rightful one still on the carousel. With a great sense of relief I was finally able to enter the arrival hall and meet up with

Betty and Peter, who after the interminable wait, had almost come to the conclusion that I had missed the flight.

Montreal, on the St Lawrence Seaway, is a vibrant city, with the French influence evident from the attractively coloured and well-kept houses in the French quarter, to the profusion of sumptuous restaurants offering French cuisine. As my visit coincided with the autumn 'fall', we drove into the nearby Laurentian mountains to witness the full effect of the glorious changes in colour of the leaves set against a backdrop of a vast and deep blue sky. The famed maple leaf is primarily responsible for the bright red colour and features as Canada's chief symbol on souvenirs as well as the emblem on her flag. After visiting the main tourist attractions in the city, Mount Royal, St Joseph's Oratory, St Joseph being the Patron Saint of Canada, and McGill University, I turned my energies to scouring the large department stores – Eatons, Morgans and Simpsons for presents to convince my friends back home that I really had been to Canada on holiday.

Then the Duncan family came up with a fantastic suggestion: a three-day trip to New York, some 500 miles away reached by car through negotiating the famous Route 9. After collecting another cousin from Lake Placid, we stopped overnight at Saratoga Springs, the home of the famous spa where the only naturally carbonated mineral waters are found in the United States, east of the Rocky Mountains. Our overnight accommodation provided a new experience as we parked our car in front of our bedroom: it was a motel and, for ten US dollars for a room sleeping four, it was great value for us three girls en route for New York. Although the motel did not provide food, it did have television and it was here that I got my first taste of American TV, interrupted, it seemed, by never-ending commercials. Oh, how I hoped this would not happen to TV in the UK.

On reaching New York we checked in at the YWCA on Lexington Avenue for four US dollars per person per night, well within our budget. But before we could go sightseeing we had a mission to complete. This was to visit James Mitchell, a brother of my dad, living in the Bronx, who had emigrated to the USA after the First World War. As a regular user of the London Underground system, I was not daunted by entering the New York subway, although surprised to see armed guards in the carriages. But it did not prove to be as simple as I thought, especially when changing routes, which resulted in getting lost for nearly half an hour under Brooklyn Bridge, a far from salubrious spot for three ladies on their own. Incredibly, and with great relief, we managed to reach our destination in the Bronx after receiving impeccable instructions from a most helpful fellow passenger who, by coincidence when resident in England, had commuted on a daily basis from my nearest tube station when I lived at Enfield: Wood Green on the Piccadilly Line.

After visiting Uncle James we embarked with vigour to explore the 'Big Apple'. Soon we had cracked the road system. All streets run east-to-west, avenues First to Fifth run north-to-south and Broadway, crammed with theatres, runs diagonally across them all. We visited the United Nations Building, watched a Security Council in session, climbed the Statue of Liberty right into its torch, and took the elevator to the top of the Empire State Building. We ventured into Greenwich Village and Chinatown, grabbing a rest as we took our seats in the Radio City Music Hall in the Rockefeller Center. Lauded as the 'showplace of the nation', the programme during the week of 13 October 1960 included not only the world famous line-dancing Rockettes, but also a production of the play *Midnight Lace* with Doris Day and Rex Harrison appearing in the lead parts. Little did I realise that both would become acclaimed stage and screen performers in later years.

Inevitably, there was a shopping spree, visiting Macy's, at that time the largest department store in the world, covering two million square feet of floor space, Bloomingdale's, crammed with designer clothes, and the fashionable Saks on Fifth Avenue. But shopping was put on hold when a deluge of paper streamers and confetti rained down on an open-topped car. It was a 'ticker tape' parade in honour of Senator Kennedy in the run-up to the Presidential election the next month, on 4 November, when in fact Kennedy beat Nixon. It was an action packed and memorable three days: I had also fallen in love with New York.

Fortuitously, my travelling lust was satisfied with the opportunities offered to me each year through attendance at the World Dental Congress. In 1981, the venue was Rio de Janeiro in Brazil and I was assisting in drafting a programme for the half-day meeting of world dental editors, examining the impact of the electronic medium on publishing. Everyone was anxious to learn more about information technology but not only were many editors indicating that they would not be going to Rio for financial and security reasons, but potential speakers were also declining invitations to attend. Aware of the difficulties, Jan Erik Ahlberg, the FDI executive director, wrote to all participants at the end of April. 'In consultation with colleagues who are assisting me in preparing the programme, I have reluctantly come to the conclusion that the editors' conference must be cancelled and the programme rescheduled for 1982, in Vienna.'

With my autumn diary clear, I decided that this presented an ideal opportunity to act on Gerry Leatherman's advice. 'Margaret, get yourself to an American Dental Association (ADA) annual meeting and I will introduce you to people you should get to know, and then it's up to you.' The venue in 1981 was Kansas City, colloquially referred to as the 'heart of America' due to its central location. The sprawling Crown Centre, 'a city within a city' was owned by Hallmark Cards and crammed with apartments, shops, offices, restaurants, hotels and cinemas. I was fascinated with the exhibition in the Hallmark visitors centre showing changes in styles of greetings cards alongside political and cultural changes; evolution of the printing process; hard decoration techniques and a selection of the most outrageous and sentimental, if not sloppy, verses to suit every occasion. Naturally, I grabbed the opportunity to stock up with the original cards on offer for the fast-approaching Christmastide.

Gerry was true to his word and he introduced me to the 'movers and shakers', not only of American dentistry but the doyens in the world dento-political arena whom I watched in action round a committee table or in debate. I have never forgotten the privilege of speaking with the much loved and respected Harold Hillenbrand, who was in charge of the ADA for nearly a quarter of a century, and in Gerry Leatherman's own words about his contemporary and close friend, 'the greatest administrator that the world of international dentistry has ever known'. The influence of these two greats in my career is without equal and I have endeavoured to pass on their pearls of wisdom to as many colleagues as possible during my professional life.

Gerry also facilitated my attendance at the business meetings of the ADA, called the House of Delegates, lectures, workshops, table clinics, a trade exhibition of the latest technical equipment and dental products, and a very popular health screening programme for dentists. Featured among the table clinics were the winning entries of the student clinician programme, which was organised by Densply International. In each dental school, students were encouraged to undertake a research project and the winner then competed against the winning students from all the other USA dental schools. This innovative competition, instigated in 1959, was the brainchild of Harold Hillenbrand and Henry Thorton, Chairman of Densply International, and those successful participants were held in the highest esteem by general practitioners and academic staff. However, when I went to Kansas City, the programme had only been in existence in the UK for four years and was not so widely recognised by the dental profession. I was determined to raise the profile of our winner in 1981, Michael Heads from Leeds Dental School, whose prize was to demonstrate his table clinic alongside all the other USA winners in the main exhibition hall. Michael commented, when later he wrote for me an article on his experiences for the *BDJ*, 'Great importance is attached to receiving an award as it is a considerable boost to the student's future career.' Certainly this proved true for Michael as he became a very successful and popular President of SCADA, the Alumni Association of Student Dental Clinicians, undoubtedly raising the profile of the programme in the UK.

There was also no let-up on the social side. Surely it was impossible to accept so many competing invitations. Gerry again was ready with advice for me. 'Margaret, chat to someone for as long as to be polite, and then move on – and to another venue if possible.' This was how I learnt to 'walk the room' and, in so doing, avoid being trapped in conversation and miss the opportunity to meet new and interesting people and exchange words with a lone guest who did not have the benefit of a mentor as I did or who was not comfortable in an unknown environment.

However impossible it may seem, my attendance at my first ADA Conference was eclipsed by my incredible journey to the USA. The route to Kansas City entailed passing through a major gateway, New York or Chicago, changing planes for an internal flight to my destination. At the beginning of the 1980s, interest was aroused with the prospect of supersonic air travel and especially by the elegant British Airways Concorde. Then an unbelievable temptation came my way when the airline announced a promotional deal of a one-way flight in Concorde, from Heathrow to New York on selected dates. I began to dream whether it would be possible to fit my schedule into one of these available dates and fly at twice the speed of sound, at a cruising height of 55,000 feet, and complete the journey in a staggering four hours. With the time difference between the two cities it meant arriving in New York at the same time as leaving Heathrow – 11 a.m. Sharing my outrageous thoughts with my family, they encouraged me to research further this once-in-a-lifetime experience and jokingly suggested that I should trade in my accumulated daily 15-pence luncheon vouchers included in my monthly wage packet from the BDA. Gordon, pragmatic as ever, coaxed me further. 'Margaret, you are earning money, so treat yourself.' So I did.

On the morning of the flight, the Seward household was at fever pitch. I departed for Heathrow with the one-way ticket to New York by Concorde safely in my pocket, but with onward and homeward flights arranged on conventional economy routes, this time via Chicago. Check-in was swift at the readily identified Concorde desk, after which I was escorted to the designated Concorde lounge. Here, laid out in front of me, was the most gigantic and sumptuous buffet I had ever seen, with an unlimited selection of champagnes, wines and beverages. For someone who had been too excited to eat even a meagre breakfast, I unashamedly tucked into this welcome feast. It was a grand lounge, with comfortable, deep blue, upholstered chairs and sofas, writing materials available on the desks as well as telephones from which personal calls could be made, and for free. But who could I call? Gordon was operating on patients in the hospital theatre; Pamela, 17, and Colin, 15, were in classes at school, so I decided to share my excitement of the journey so far with Marjorie Gillate, my secretary at the *BDJ*. 'Marjorie, I wasn't checking up on you,' I hastily reassured her, 'but I couldn't pass up a free phone call.'

Suddenly, I realised that the passengers were being called to board the plane and as the lounge emptied I started to wonder if I had been forgotten. But all was well, and as I entered the aircraft I was aware of its narrow interior with only two seats on each side of the aisle. But these were different from any seat I had seen before; luxurious cushioned armchairs with all-enveloping wings on either side of the head rest so that on leaning back, your face all but disappeared from the view of your travelling companion. Even so, it was not difficult for my neighbour to realise that I was a novice on Concorde and revelling in my unique experience. In an American brogue, he kindly began to point out its special features. 'You see that mach meter at the front? When it signals Mach 2 we will be flying at twice the speed of sound.' I was astounded to think I was going to sample the fastest form of transport available at that time.

Immediately after take-off we savoured canapés with Champagne, Mumm Cordon Rouge 1975, and studied the grandly embossed menu card with its blue tassel; the lunch promised, and indeed was, a truly gastronomic experience. However, I almost stumbled at the starter course, 'Sevruga Caviar served with melba toast and lemon' – a very long cry from our family fare. I watched my neighbour intently to see how I should eat this without displaying my ignorance. Having survived, the marathon lunch continued: fillet of beef grilled and coated with Madeira sauce and garnished with morels and truffles, a tasty cheese selection, prior to the pineapple and figs in brandy, all washed down by choice wines, and the meal culminating in the offer, to accompanying coffee, of liqueurs and a cigar from the box of the best Jamaican Macanudo cigars placed in front of me by the steward. As I made a move to decline, my companion prompted me to accept. 'Take one for me,' he encouraged. I did not need a second bidding, as I was delighted to repay his good company. He had engaged me in interesting conversation. We explored the world of films and he cited the recent and greatly acclaimed *Chariots of Fire*. 'Do you realise,' he commented, 'that the stars of the film are not the actors whose names are virtually unknown, but the runners in the Olympic marathon? You don't need a big name to be a box office success.' He then moved on to breakfast television, asking for my thoughts, but as this programme had not yet arrived in the UK, I learnt more from him about what to expect once it reached our screens. During our chat he discovered that I was a dentist, heading for a conference in Kansas City. 'Where do you practise in London?' he enquired, and I explained that, as editor of the *BDJ*, I worked from my office in Wimpole Street. 'The only equipment available is in our museum so its mainly turn of the century dental chairs and antique instruments.'

'Shame,' he replied. 'Sometimes I need a dentist when I'm in London. Let me have your menu card and I'll give you the name of my dentist, in case you have time to contact him in New York, or he may be with you in Kansas City.' Then he added his name and handed the menu card back to me.

Starting our descent into John F Kennedy (JFK) airport, I glanced at the names he had written. I then looked more carefully at his name, for surely my eyes were deceiving me. It read: Robert Redford. I was tongue-tied. Just how had I failed to recognise him? It must have been those large wings around the headrest in our comfortable armchairs. My wait at JFK for my continuing flight to Kansas City seemed like an eternity, as I wanted to share this amazing encounter with everyone. I had been aware that the unique aircraft was used routinely by the captains of industry and millions of pounds and dollars worth of business was transacted in the sky. But I had not contemplated meeting a film star of such repute. *The Sting* was especially popular with UK audiences. Imagine my chagrin that I had turned down the opportunity to have 'RR' as a patient on a visit to London. Surely a colleague would have lent me his premises for such an encounter?

This daydreaming stopped as I picked up the phone to call home. 'Pamela, guess who I sat next to on Concorde? Robert Redford.'

'Lucky you,' she replied. 'Hang on, I'll get dad.'

'Gordon,' I exclaimed excitedly, 'I sat next to Robert Redford on the plane.'

'Robert who?' came the unimpressed reply. It was comforting to know that my husband would not only have failed to recognise the heart-throb of the cinema world but was also unaware of his existence!

As you can imagine this has become a treasured, and on occasions, embellished story when retold by friends and family. However, it does underline that throughout life we will have unexpected encounters. Hopefully, I won't fail to recognise Robert Redford if I have the good chance to meet him again.

At the conclusion of my first FDI Congress in Paris in 1979, I was invited to join the publications committee, as a consultant, and the working group which prepared the FDI newsletter, which was the medium of contact between the headquarters office in London, its member associations and individual members. Through these activities I was fortunate to establish friendships with the editors of similar dental journals to the *BDJ* in member countries around the globe: Guy Robert in France, Hans Reckort in Germany, Helmut Heydt in South Africa, Colin Wall in Australia and Henry Koehler in USA, to mention a few. As a fledgling editor, I learnt so much from these experienced and well-established editors in their respective countries. Fortunately, in journalism there is a strong cadre and without exception they welcomed me wholeheartedly and soon we were exchanging information on a regular basis and eliciting worldwide assistance with tackling a sudden crisis topic to hit the media, questioning the safety of mercury in amalgam fillings, or the excessive charges for dental treatment. We then wanted to meet together as a group during a Congress and so, in Hamburg in 1980, Hans Reckort, through his journal the *BDZ*, arranged a conference for dental editors on Saturday 6 October in the hotel adjacent to the Congress Halls. In Singapore in 1983 the emphasis changed to 'Ethics: What can editors do?' I spoke about the 'Editor's role in maintaining ethical standards and values and the urgent need to tackle salami science' as authors of research were attempting to get as many papers as possible out of one project and then seek publication in numerous journals. In Manila in 1984 we focused on the controversial issue of 'The image of the dentist' with speakers reporting their experiences from the USA, Malaysia, New Zealand and France, with a stimulating discussion opened by Helmut Heydt of South Africa. These half-day conferences were not confined to editors and the appeal of the topic was such that they were always well attended. Imagine our dismay when we were told that one of the recommendations of the Bomba Committee looking at the future of the FDI was to disband the publications committee, and in effect our conference of dental editors. I put up a spirited defence of the role of the editors at an open session convened to discuss the findings of the report, explaining the public relations power vested in each editor to promote the FDI through its national journals. 'What a short-sighted move to get rid of us' was my parting shot. This tactic worked, a communications committee was set up in 1985 and I was honoured to be appointed its chairman.

An initial task was to chair the first FDI press conference at the Congress in Manila in the Philippines, as well as arranging interviews requested by the local journalists for their papers or radio or TV stations. I had been fortunate to have media training from the BDA but putting it into practice at FDI Congresses was an opportunity not to be missed and for which I have always been most appreciative. Among the many anecdotes associated with the Manila conference, I recall one in particular when, at the rehearsal for the opening ceremony of the Congress, we were warned not to move from our seats or we would be shot. Security was at the highest level as the recent victor in the 'coup' to replace President Ferdinand Marcos was President Cory Aquino, but she was going to address delegates at the opening ceremony from behind a bullet-proof podium. The downside of the change in administration was that our visit to the Presidential Palace to see the famous collection of Esmeralda Marcos's shoes was cancelled. Indeed, as the week went by, civil unrest erupted and it was touch and go as to whether the airport would remain open, or if we could get to it, as most of the public transport system was on strike. I can remember the throngs of people at the airport desperately trying to leave the country, and the relief when Nora Borland, a great friend of the FDI over the years and the Spanish translator, and I, sitting together on the plane, felt its wheels leave the runway. We were safely bound for London.

In addition to the newsletter for members, the FDI published six times a year a scientific journal, the *International Dental Journal* (*IDJ*). Its original board was set up in Dublin in 1948 with Professor Harold Hubert Stones as Chairman and Editor of the *Journal*. He and successive editors, Professor Frank Lawton and Professor Roy Duckworth, had strong academic ties and all had held the post of dean at their respective dental schools. Roy, as scientific adviser to the *BDJ* had given me much appreciated advice and support when I was new to the editor's chair and I was reluctant to accept his resignation in 1982 on his election as editor of the *IDJ*.

However, I was delighted that on the retirement of Roy Duckworth, the BDA submitted my name for the vacant post. With another candidate, an experienced editor of an American Journal, we were called before the FDI nominations committee to explain our ideas for the future development of the *IDJ*. The BDA delegation worked hard lobbying on my behalf, an activity which seemed to occupy most of the time at social functions, much to the frustration of accompanying persons. On the evening before the vote, the leader of the American delegation told me, after quizzing me about my ideas for the *Journal*, 'Margaret, we are going to support you.' This was great news and clinched the outcome that I became the fourth editor of the *IDJ*, following the Congress in Singapore in 1990. As a result, I also assumed a seat on the Council, which greatly increased my contact with the senior members of national associations who constituted its membership. Further, I became a member of the scientific programme committee which gave me unsurpassed knowledge about the leading international lecturers and potential authors for the *Journal*. Soon my experience of my readership survey for the *BDJ* was transposed to the *IDJ* and, as a response to its findings, I included an abstract section, product reviews, guest editorials, supplements on specialised topics presented at the Congress and, with welcome additional advertising revenue, published the first articles with colour illustrations. There was a downside of becoming editor. I had to relinquish the chairmanship of the communications committee, but fortunately was still able to attend in an ex officio capacity, so supporting my good friend and successor Guy Robert of France.

Despite my ascendancy within the upper echelons of the FDI, I did not neglect my desire to improve the recognition for women dentists, not only in the UK but also on the international scene. For example, while in the Scandinavian countries women qualified in equal numbers as men from dental schools, few reached top jobs in the universities; most professors in dental schools were men. This even applied in Finland where one woman, Leila Telivuo, had broken the gender barrier to become the first woman elected as Councillor of the FDI. Leila was a great friend and role model to me and we made a lasting friendship, as one does through the family of the FDI. She was one of my key speakers when I organised a symposium about women in dentistry at the FDI Congress in Amsterdam in 1989. Entitled 'Any Room at the Top?', the aim was to look at the careers of women dentists. Karen Ahlberg, senior lecturer at the London Hospital and wife of the executive director of the FDI, who had wide experience of the position of women in the profession, having qualified in Sweden, spoke from a university perspective. The research angle was covered by Joyce Rees from the USA; a view of general practice in the UK by Shelagh Farrell, and Caroline Kaunda Mmembe from Zambia explained the difficulties of a career for women in developing countries. An excellent summary to open the discussion was given by Geraldine Morrow, who was actively seeking nomination as the first president-elect of the American Dental Association, which she achieved. She was installed as president on 9 October 1991.

The initiative of a women's programme in the FDI Congress was so successful that I asked if I could organise one in future years. This request was granted in Hong Kong and Barcelona when with the assistance of Lois Cohen we chose the provocative title 'Men in dentistry – will they survive?' It certainly caused hackles to rise and the lecture room was crammed to capacity in October 1998 with a good representation of both sexes in the audience. Lois Cohen's input into planning the contents of the programme was invaluable and, as a trained behavioural scientist and director of international affairs at the National Institute of Health in Bethesda in the USA, she had an impressive network of speakers from around the world to call upon. Michelle Aerden from Belgium mobilised the European women dentists into a group and collected valuable data to support her research project on the feminisation of the dental profession. Many individuals within the FDI gave encouragement to widen our activities from purely symposia, and through the financial support of Marsha Butler and Christopher Fox of Colgate, I organised a luncheon with a keynote speaker at the Paris Congress in 2000, which proved to be the forerunner of many successful luncheons and breakfasts for women dentists attending the Congress, providing a social occasion for discussing issues of interest or concern with colleagues.

More recently, the establishment of Forums within the structure of the FDI has allowed the formation of a Women Dentists Worldwide Forum, with a scheduled all-day programme during the Congress. It has also been rewarding to witness the baton for the organisation pass seamlessly to the next generation of women and in Dubai, in 2007, Christine Osborne, a past chairman of Women in Dentistry in the UK and T. C. Wong from Hong Kong and a Council member of FDI, coined a challenging title for the programme, '80 is the new 60' aimed at assisting dentists to understand the multifarious difficulties when treating elderly patients.

While it is inevitable to question the political correctness in providing an activity for women only, it has to be remembered that in some constituent countries of the FDI, equality of the sexes may exist in name but certainly not in action. Until discrimination within the dental profession is eliminated, I believe it is entirely appropriate for an international dental organisation to provide practical support and this is achieved superbly through the Women Dentists Worldwide Forum of the FDI.

Berlin is a city where I experienced the 'high and low' of my international interludes. As editor of the *British Dental Journal* in the early 1980s, quality clinical colour photographs to accompany the scientific articles were difficult to accomplish. The gold standard against which we measured our illustrations was set by an outstanding German publisher, Quintessence, based in Berlin. It was a long established family firm and the current managing director was Horst-Wolfgang (Dicker) Haase, a fiercely ambitious and gifted businessman, whose ambitions were tempered with philanthropic exploits demonstrated through forging links with the developing countries and sharing with them the fruits of his success in the continuing postgraduate education field. The quality of his dental books won the admiration of exceptional English clinicians, for example John McLean, Michael Wise and Nairn Wilson, who as authors also lectured on the popular symposia organised by Hasse. I was flattered to be approached by Dicker Hasse to see if the *BDJ* would act as an agent to market his books in the UK, but it was clear to me I was unable to share a promotional base with a strong competitor. This was fully understood and we remained firm friends and Gordon and I enjoyed celebrating his landmark birthdays in style. Subsequently, a London office for Quintessence Publishing Company was opened and run most efficiently by John Brooks. We established a healthy working relationship and I was pleasantly surprised when he suggested that we join forces and run a Teach-In together. This we did, in Sheffield, most successfully on the topic of photography with Phillip Wander and Peter Gordon as authors and speakers.

However, I remained curious as to how the colour illustrations in the Quintessence books were produced and to consistent top quality. 'Margaret, come to Berlin, and see for yourself' quipped Dicker, an invitation I readily accepted. So, in the early 1980s, I found myself in Berlin, visiting the Quintessence office in Ifenpfad, and enjoying delicious German fare with his family at home in the evening. 'I have arranged for you to cross to East Berlin tomorrow. I assume you would like to go?' announced my host at the end of the meal. There was no hesitation on my part; this was an opportunity to grasp. He explained that as a German citizen he could not go with me, but I would be driven by his foreign chauffeur and accompanied by one of his dental visitors from China, another country to which he extended the hand of friendship.

Berlin, after the Second World War, had been split into sectors, with the East controlled by the Russians, and the West by the Americans, French and British. In the early 1950s, when I visited my Latymer school penfriend in Feuchtwangen, I stayed within the US zone. During the summer of 1961, the Russians became increasingly concerned by the emigration of nearly fifteen hundred East Germans each day and, to stem the haemorrhage of skilled labour and professional talent, they sealed off the West. Overnight barbed wire fences were erected, trenches dug, windows of houses straddling the border were bricked up, tram and railway lines torn up and the infamous Wall was built, twenty-three miles running through the city centre, punctuated by lookouts and strictly controlled border points. Checkpoint Charlie was designated as our point of entry. As our car came level with the guard's cabin, an arm was thrust out to take our passports. The iron gates clanked behind us. It was distinctly eerie as the three of us waited for permission to proceed, with, for company, only the border police painstakingly searching our car for forbidden goods.

Eventually, we drove into the eastern sector but I had not prepared myself for the visual or emotional impact. In front of me the people were dowdily dressed in clothes and styles long since out of fashion in the West. Bombed buildings remained as ruins, small rusty cars were parked along the former magnificent Unter den Linden, a boulevard lined with lime trees, and the severely damaged triumphal arch, the Brandenburg Gate, was stranded in no-man's land. However still accessible, and the focus of our visit, was the world's major archaeological museum, the Pergamon. The splendour inside, compared with the drab exterior surroundings, was awesome. Of lasting impression was the reconstructed blue and ochre tiled Gate of Ishtar and the Babylonian Processional Street dating from King Nebuchadnezzar's reign, 605–562 BC. How sad, indeed criminal, that access to these and many other treasures was denied to residents in West Germany.

People can often remember what they were doing at the time they heard of a worldwide tragic event: the assassination of J. F. Kennedy, or the death of Diana

Princess of Wales. One such event for me was watching television with Gordon in the lounge at Hadley Wood, when the scheduled programmes were interrupted to show the East Germans knocking holes in the Wall and climbing through to freedom, without the fate which befell more than eighty men, women and children who, over the years, in desperation had tried to escape from the oppressive regime. The 'Iron Curtain' was at last coming down and on 9 November 1989, twenty-eight years after the Wall had been built, people power had won.

It was predictable that when I heard that the FDI Congress in 1992 was to be held in Berlin, I was determined to return to a country where the symbolic reunification had taken place on 3 October 1990. My delight was tempered with sadness as I realised it would be a Congress without the presence of my long-term mentor, Gerry Leatherman, who had died on 11 December 1991, at the grand age of 88 years. I was invited by Council to arrange a memorial session during the Congress in Berlin and this was planned to last an hour on the Sunday afternoon, with no other competing scientific or business meetings. The aim was that presentations would be given to cover a facet of Gerry's life not only within the FDI family, but also his outstanding contributions to worldwide dentistry over some twenty-two years as executive director and, latterly, as emeritus executive director. I sought the assistance of his long-serving former executive secretary, Mary Barker, whom Gerry acknowledged in his retirement speech in 1975: 'A time to say "Thank You" and "Farewell"; her wide knowledge and experience, poise and good judgement, her ability to lead and accept delegation and in turn to delegate and, perhaps most difficult of all, to work and share with me the problems of the FDI.' Luckily, Mary not only gave freely of her time to assist me complete the programme and memorial booklet, but also came to Berlin to reminisce about working with an exceptional leader of worldwide dentistry. A puzzle to many of us was that despite his countless number of honorary degrees and awards in tribute to his unremitting labours for his profession, his name never appeared in the civil honours list. This surely was a comment more on the inadequacies of the British system, rather than a reflection of the merit of a particular individual, a state of affairs that continues to be all too evident today.

But Berlin was also to be a turning point in my international career. Earlier in the spring of 1992, when I was attending the Asian Pacific Dental Congress in Auckland, as guest lecturer on the *BDJ* Teamwork initiative, Clive Ross, a vice-president of the FDI, took me aside one evening, in the company of the newly appointed executive director, Per Åke Zillen, and suggested I should consider standing for the presidency of the FDI. I had not entertained this thought because I was on Council in my role as editor of the *International Dental Journal* and I was aware of other senior Councillors who nurtured this ambition. Gordon reacted positively, 'Why not?' and I thus began to reflect on the idea and examine the practicalities because the appointment would necessitate a considerable amount of international travel. Fortunately, the FDI election timetable allowed sufficient time for forward planning, as first the office of president-elect would be assumed for two years before entering the two-year term as President. The next election for president-elect was to be in Berlin, which seemed to be too early as I still cherished the ambition to stand again in 1994 for election as president of the GDC. To hold two top jobs concurrently was out of the question, either for the organisation or personally.

However, several national organisations encouraged me to think seriously about the suggestion and, most importantly, pledged their support: the American Dental Association, the New Zealand Dental Association, and South African Dental Association, to name a few. I began to think more deeply about the proposition and started to assemble material together and draft an election leaflet for distribution to Council members and those who would have voting rights in Berlin. Did I really possess sufficient credentials or was I on an ego trip? Undoubtedly, I was soon to become president of the BDA and at the end of the one-year term in 1994, I would be retired and available, with good health and still plenty of energy, to take on the role of president. I had a long track record of involvement with the FDI, since 1978. I was well known on the international scene and had been invited to join the working group exploring the establishment of an African Regional Organisation within the FDI chaired by the speaker of FDI, Runo Cronström, who with his wife Cissi had been fantastic colleagues throughout my association with the FDI and most enthusiastic participants on many *BDJ* study tours. It was not difficult to convince myself that I should enter the race. The closing date for submission of nomination papers was fast approaching, so my next step was to approach the BDA for its support.

My decision, however coincided with a dramatic downturn in the relations between the FDI and BDA, which had been turbulent throughout the previous year. The cause was a not uncommon controversial topic – rent review and renewal of a lease. For some years the FDI had leased offices on the third floor and a couple of rooms on the ground floor of the British Dental Association's headquarters in Wimpole Street. With the expansion in activities of each organisation, there was a mutual desire for more office accommodation. Thus, there was considerable disquiet expressed by the FDI executive when, in April 1991, it received notification from its landlords (BDA) of the new terms for the next three years; increase in rent from £36,000 per annum to £48,750 with a substantial rise in rates from £8,000 to £25,000. Such dramatic increases had not been foreseen by the FDI and was not affordable within its budget. Immediately, two options were considered by its executive, a move to other premises or to negotiate with the BDA. This latter course of action was pursued and as a 'gesture of goodwill' the BDA offered to reduce the rent to £44,000 and the length of the lease to 18 months. However, after several months of deadlock, the chairman of council, Geoff Garnett, wrote to the FDI president, Ruperto-Gonzalez Giralda, to alert him that the BDA had served a statutory termination notice, as required under UK laws. At the same time, Norman Whitehouse, mindful of my position as *IDJ* editor and my close working relationship with the office of the FDI, thoughtfully sent me a personal note, reassuring me that the intention of this action was not to get rid of them, but to force negotiations along. Geoff Garnett, in his letter to Ruperto on 13 August 1991, expressed his regret at having to write about the renewal of the lease and concluded, 'Since the Association and Federation have worked so closely together for so many years, I do hope that we can resolve the current impasse without rancour. We understand your budgetary position and desire to expand, equally you must understand that we too must plan our budgets and that it is necessary to agree both the cost and length of any new lease in order for us to do so.' The FDI executive committee, Clive Ross and Per Åke Zillen, were also sent copies of the letter. The response, after further extensive consultations and consideration of parties and factors involved, resulted in a decision conveyed on 9 September 1991 to the FDI executive director to renew the lease for an 18-month period at £44,000. Concurrently, Per Åke Zillen continued his search for alternative accommodation and secured convenient premises to lease at 7 Carlisle Street on the south side of Oxford Street.

I recount these seemingly domestic events in detail so that it is possible to understand that relations between the two organisations were under intense strain, and to place into context future events. Disillusionment on the part of the BDA ran deeper than the terms of the lease. There were fundamental concerns relating to the policy direction of the federation and its relevance to the BDA and rumours were rife in the lead-up to the Berlin Congress that the Association might leave the FDI. Clearly, if this happened, it would be impossible for me to hold office as president-elect. Thus, my promotional leaflet remained in draft and I arrived in Berlin to convey my decision to my known supporters that I would not progress my candidacy. Gerry Morrow, president then of the ADA, offered to nominate me, as did other organisations. However, disappointed of course, I remained resolute. I fulfilled my commitments in Berlin, chaired the memorial session for Gerry Leatherman and then on the following day attended with Gordon the dinner given by the president of the German Dental Association (BDZ) in the beautifully restored historic Opernpalais, located in Unter den Linden, built originally in 1733 as a palace for the princesses. At that time, the business meetings in Berlin stretched for nine days and so, with my FDI commitments discharged, I returned to London to attend meetings of the General Dental Council.

The BDA was true to its word. At the meeting of the representative board in November 1992, the members voted to suspend its membership of the FDI for a minimum of one year, 'in view of the BDA's budgetary situation and reservations about the effectiveness of policy of FDI'. This groundbreaking decision was given extensive press coverage. 'BDA pulls out of FDI' reported Jeremy Cowan, editor of *The Probe* magazine. 'The British Dental Association's self-imposed suspension to take effect for a minimum of one year, thus saving £27,000 according to the motion put to the Representative Board by the BDA Council chairman, Geoff Garnett.' However, Dr Zillen told *The Probe*, 'that there was no such thing as suspension. If the member association wishes to resign, the constitution says that all subscriptions must be paid for the period of lapsed membership before it can be readmitted.' Predictably, members were unhappy. 'It was never mentioned that savings might not be achievable,' commented BDA members Jenny Pinder and Ario Santini.

It was strange to attend the following year, in August, the Congress in Gothenburg, Sweden, without a delegation from the UK. I found it an unhappy Congress, even although I was now president of the BDA, because people continually enquired, 'Is it true the BDA is not here because it is bankrupt?'; 'Tell me, what is the real reason for the Association's resignation?' A consequence of the BDA's action meant that my successor as editor of the *BDJ*, Mike Grace, was unable to be nominated to the communications committee and there was no official presence in General Assembly when a former president of the BDA, Professor Duckworth, was admitted to the list of honour for his role as editor of the Federation's journal, the *IDJ*.

My despair at the withdrawal of membership, coupled with the desire to put the record straight, prompted me to read a prepared statement to the Representative Board at its meeting on Saturday 6 November 1993. I expounded the benefits I had enjoyed as editor of the *BDJ*, especially through contact with colleagues who were editors in ninety-seven countries around the world. I selected a couple of examples of international cooperation when changing to the modern Vancouver system of references and acting as a dento-political Interpol in trying to combat plagiarism in scientific journals. I was able also to inform the Board of the significant part Norman Whitehouse had played in reshaping the FDI, especially as a member of the Bomba Committee of Inquiry and his successful term as UK National Treasurer. Likewise, I assured the Board that the valued contribution of Geoff Garnett in redrafting the long overdue new constitution and his knowledgeable chairmanship of an important working group on continuing professional development under the auspices of the Commission on education and practice would be sorely missed. I continued, 'I believe we have much to give the world of dentistry as we lead in educational development and we have many innovative ideas in health care delivery systems,' and the Swedish Minister of Health made a complementary reference to the recent Bloomfield Inquiry in the UK set up by Government. 'I would like to see the BDA regain its rightful place amongst the opinion formers in worldwide dentistry.'

Understandably, my intervention was not a popular move with the top officials and I was chided and reminded that it was out of order to question BDA policy as president: it was a non-political post. As far as I was concerned, it was the reputation and credibility of the Association that mattered. Suffice to say that, in

1994, it was a new start as, with John Hunt as chief executive and Bill Allen as Chairman of Council, the BDA returned to the fold. Writing in the *BDJ* on 25 August 2007 about the FDI, Stephen Hancocks concluded, 'The BDA is quite rightly a proud national member association', a state of affairs I hope will continue for many years to come.

My own personal involvement with the FDI continued unabated. At the 1995 Congress, I chaired the first meeting of a new section of ethics and dental legislation. 'Thank you for your excellent chairing; people have told me, and no surprise to me,' wrote Per Åke Zillen. Over the years I had closely observed the techniques needed to ensure full participation of people who do not have English as their first, or even second, language: clear articulation, moderate speed of delivery and absence of colloquial speech. In the FDI, English is the main language for the scientific and educational programmes, but French, German, Spanish and Japanese are additional recognised languages for which simultaneous translation or interpreters can be provided during the Congress. The new section became a success story through the prodigious and combined efforts of the secretary, Patrick Colgan from Australia, and Peter Swiss in the UK, who earlier in 1983 was very involved with an Ethics Working Group which was part of the Commission on Dental Education and Practice. In Seoul, Korea, presentations on the topic of informed consent attracted an unexpected number of participants, resulting in standing room only and a request for a bigger venue at the next Congress. Other sections asked to join us and so in 1998 in Barcelona, with the section of Dental Deans and Educators and under joint chairmanship with Don Allan, dean from Texas, USA, we examined 'Ethical responsibilities and rewards'. The following year in Mexico, 'The ethics and legal aspects of dental specialisation' was under the spotlight and a most informative joint session was held with the section of public health, the programme compiled with the assistance of Martin Hobdell, who had studied with me at the London Hospital and was now working in the USA. These activities, albeit time-consuming in organisational terms, were of great relevance to me in the discharge of my day-to-day responsibilities at the GDC, as I learnt from colleagues around the world how they tackled and sought solutions to the unfortunately escalating professional ethical and legal problems.

I continued throughout as editor of the *IDJ* and was extremely fortunate to have the support of a very able team at the FDI office in Carlisle Street, Stephen Hancocks, a talented assistant editor who had worked with me previously at the GDC, responsible for processing the scientific articles, and Sabrina Webber for production. With my term at the GDC as president approaching completion, I was determined to turn more of my attention to the *IDJ* and introduce some new features or even a face-lift to the design after the passage of nearly a decade. However, I was oblivious of the fact that a product called Xylitol would affect my future plans. The procedure followed for each paper submitted was standard and once the referee's comments had been received, the editor, taking these into account, made the decision to accept or reject the paper for publication. At the time involved, the claims espoused for the efficacy of Xylitol were controversial and commercial interest was riding on the paper's successful appearance in print. Both referees' reports, on this occasion, were critical and so I took the decision to reject the paper for publication in the *IDJ*. Per Åke Zillen was furious at my decision, as well as my outspoken views on management issues of the *Journal*, expressed at a subsequent editorial meeting. Thus, I was prepared that when I met with him a couple of weeks later, he would challenge me over my stance. What took me completely by surprise was that he told me that he had decided that I should resign as editor. Put bluntly, I was sacked, a new experience to add to my CV. At this stage in my career I was not going to compromise my decision with the promise of an FDI award; I would not be able to live with my conscience if I overturned my editorial principles of a lifetime.

I set about compiling a file of relevant documents and was heartened to receive calls from the scientific community pledging support for my stance. I explained the reason for my hasty departure, after ten years as editor, to Michelle Aerden, then on the FDI Council, and shared the documents with Bill Allen and John Hunt, now respectively chairman of council and chief executive of the BDA. I then flew to Paris to brief the president, Jacques Monot, on the position and to discuss the paper on specialisation which I had been asked to prepare for the next Council meeting. His choice of a delightful Parisian fish restaurant for lunch more than adequately compensated for my personal outlay on the trip. With these steps I believed I had satisfied my conscience and cleared my name. I did not wish the issue to become a crusade, although I do not deny that I resented the method of my departure; it was hurtful, if not humiliating, to end twenty-two years' involvement with the FDI in this manner.

But being a pragmatist, I accepted life must move on, and reassuringly, my friendships with colleagues around the globe remained undimmed. My eight years as editor of the *Dental Digest* of the International College of Dentistry did not end so unceremoniously when I handed it over to Cecil Linehan of Northern Ireland, who expanded its contents and embraced the new technology in its production. Rather, they spoilt me by electing me a Master of the College in 2007, an honour I was pleased to accept from the president of the European Section, Professor Phillip Dowell in the splendid City of Cardiff.

Over the years, I have been privileged to receive honorary membership of several American institutions – the American College of Dentists, American Dentistry International, and the American Academy of the History of Dentistry. Without exception, all these organisations in one way or another seek to promote excellence, professionalism, ethics and leadership in dentistry. Top of the list of annual invitations I receive is from the American Dental Association which granted me honorary membership in 1992, at the time when Gerry Morrow was

15. After collecting my insignia of DBE at Buckingham Palace with Gordon, Colin and Claire

16. Talking Points speakers in 2000; left to right: Roy Higson, Jacqui Garcia, Me, Sverker Toreskog and John Tiernan

17a. Members of the General Dental Council, 14 May 1997

17b. Key to photograph

1 J.P. Tiernan
2 J.N. Chope
3 C.J. Smith
4 J. Anderson
5 A.R. Grieve
6 Miss C.M. Doig
7 P. Langmaid
8 B.M. Currie
9 I.C. Benington
10 N.H.F. Wilson
11 H.B. Mathewson
12 F.P. Ashley
13 A. Harrison
14 D.C. McD. Pike
15 R. Raja Rayan
16 D.T. Herbert
17 P. Sutcliffe
18 K.B. Fanibunda
19 J. Scott
20 D.C. Rule
21 F.C. Smales
22 Mrs. J.I. Harbison
23 Mrs. R. Khan
24 J.L. Rich
25 J.J. Murray
26 Mrs. C.B. Abel Smith
27 T.T. Griffiths
28 T.S. Macadam
29 D.D. Di Biase
30 Mrs. R.M.J. Hepplewhite (Registrar)
31 Mrs. J.M. Salter
32 Mrs. S. Farrell
33 J.S. Rennie
34 N.H. Whitehouse
35 Miss J.M. Pinder
36 L.B. Lux
37 L.D. Kramer
38 A. Singh
39 Miss J.N. Aitken
40 J.R. Wild
41 Mrs. F.P.W. Simpson
42 W.R.E. Laird
43 Dr M.H. Seward (President)
44 D.A. McGowan
45 R.M. Basker
46 J.L. Williams

Not present: Professor D.A.M. Geddes, J.W. Frame, R. Green, W.J.N. Collins, T.R. Watkins

18. *At my Christmas Party; Lord Philip Hunt (left), Peter Swiss, President BDA and in background Bill Courtney, editor of the* Dental Laboratories Association Journal

19. *John Renshaw keeps an eye on me chatting with HRH Prince Charles*

20. *The Minister David Lammy MP, centre, launching the 6th volume of* Teamwork *in 2002. Left to right: Ken Eaton, myself, Stephen Lambert Humble and Ian Pocock*

21. *Unveiling my final plaque when opening the dental skills laboratory in the Northern deanery*

22. At my 70th Birthday Celebration; left to right: front row, Claire, Jake, Colin and Zoë; back row Sue (Claire's sister), Gordon, Pamela and me

TO ALL AND SINGULAR

DAME MARGARET HELEN ELIZABETH SEWARD

DAME MARGARET HELEN ELIZABETH SEWARD

Garter

Clarenceux

23. The framed illuminated document displaying the Seward Coat of Arms

CDO's Digest

A communication to all dentists from the Chief Dental Officer • February 2002

NHS dentistry: options for change

HAZEL BLEARS, Parliamentary Under Secretary of State for Health and the Minister responsible for NHS dentistry, in a speech to the House of Commons on 16 October, said that the Government's priorities were:

- Ensuring that everyone can access an NHS dentist if and when they need to do so
- Trying to improve the quality of service offered by NHS dentists
- Raising the level of oral health, particularly in children, and trying to tackle the inequalities that exist across communities.

These formed the basis of the Government's strategy document, *Modernising NHS Dentistry*, published in September 2000. This work was built upon by the Dentistry Modernisation Steering Group (DMSG), set up in December 2000 and chaired by the Chief Dental Officer. The DMSG reports have provided valuable input to the work currently being taken forward in the modernisation project *NHS Dentistry: Options for Change*. This project has also been informed by the input from a workshop held in June last year. There we looked at what was wrong with the present system, the likely drivers for change over the next five to ten years and what models were likely to emerge.

NHS dentistry has had problems since the introduction of the new contract in 1990 and the subsequent fee cut. Since then dentists have been increasing their work in the private sector, with a knock-on effect on access to NHS dentistry for patients. Last spring, the House of Commons Health Select Committee investigated this problem and concluded that the system of remuneration in the general dental services was the main factor, but also the lack of management levers for health authorities. They also called for a workforce review and a long-term strategy for NHS dentistry.

NHS Dentistry: Options for Change is led by the Department of Health, chaired by the Chief Dental Officer, and involves a wide spectrum of people from within the profession and outside including representatives from patient organisations and PCTs and the NHS Confederation.

Sub-groups were set up in September to focus on three areas of concern:

- Systems for delivery of dental care and remuneration
- Proposals for education, training and development needs of the dental team
- A new deal for patients – national standards for oral care.

The groups will report back to the main group and a report will be sent to Ministers in the spring.

One of our prime objectives is to bring dentistry into the mainstream of the NHS. The NHS is, however, changing itself. The balance of power is shifting away from the centre to local structures, especially to primary care trusts. One of the challenges of *Options for Change* is to see how NHS dentistry can be incorporated into the new order, to become fit for purpose in the 21st century.

Faces of success: Phillip Ratcliffe and his team from the Woodlands Dental Practice on the Wirral, winners of the Focus Awards for innovations in patient-focused dental care. Story, page 2

INSIDE ■ A better deal for all dentists ■ Dentistry fit for the 21st century

24. *CDO's Digest announcing* NHS dentistry: Options for change *and the winners of the first Focus Awards from the Wirral*

25. Receiving the Honorary DSc from the Chancellor of Portsmouth University, Lord Palumbo in 2005

the first woman president, because it never fails to rekindle the memories and thrill of attending the Kansas City meeting all those years ago.

However gratifying active involvement is in international dental organisations, it should not be driven by personal ambition and reward, nor the individual attainment of improved skills and knowledge. Rather, it provides the opportunity to pool resources and work together to improve, if not eliminate, the oral health diseases that afflict so many of the peoples of this world. From this international endeavour retirement is not an option.

Chapter 18

Latymer: a continuing thread?

I never really left Latymer. I suppose it was inevitable that, as a former head girl and remaining at home whilst studying dentistry at the London Hospital, I was the automatic choice as the leavers' representative on the Committee of the Latymer Old Students Association (LOSA). Its meetings were held on the school premises in Haselbury Road and each year there was the association's annual dinner at the Firs Hall banqueting suite in Winchmore Hill, which I had first attended as a guest when head girl. Regularly I organised a table from amongst our recent leavers and these events were well attended by the school's staff and governors. Once I was married, the net widened and many of our friends of schooldays with their partners swelled the attendance, making it a very enjoyable pilgrimage.

The arrival of our 'offspring' curtailed social activities and so I resigned from the LOSA committee, but kept in touch with many Latymerians and some of the younger members of staff who were stalwarts of the Saturday night badminton club at St Paul's Presbyterian church – Tom Spurgeon, Daphne Kennard and May Munns. May, as I learnt later, put my name forward as a possible guest speaker at the Latymer Junior Speech Day and Prizegiving, an invitation which I was thrilled, yet awed, to receive as it entailed not only an emotional return to my Alma Mater, but also giving an address to the junior pupils from ages eleven to thirteen, and to their parents, with eighty or so members of staff watching from their seats on the platform arranged behind the local dignitaries, governors, and headmaster. Just how was I going to keep a thousand people of disparate ages amused, as well as to deliver a serious message? I decided to rely on my profession. 'Many of you may like to see,' I continued after a few introductory remarks, 'how we are trained to take out teeth.' Instantaneously and en masse the pupils sitting in the side balconies with limited views of the platform rose to get a better position; they were not going to miss this practical demonstration, having convinced themselves that I was going to single out a 'volunteer' from the assembled platform party. The leg-pulling worked perfectly and after the peals of laughter had subsided the audience listened intently to the more conventional 'pearls of wisdom' expected from a guest speaker.

Less than two years later, I took a phone call from one of the governors, Professor Pickard. 'Margaret, send me your CV. A vacancy has occurred on the governing body and I want to put your name forward as a Foundation governor.' I was surprised to be asked, but I did not need a second bidding to dispatch the information requested. 'Pick', as Professor Pickard was affectionately known, was a pupil at Latymer in the 1920s and became a distinguished member of staff at the Royal Dental Hospital in Leicester Square in London. He was also internationally acclaimed as one of the UK's leading restorative dentists, undertaking teaching and examining assignments at home and abroad, as well as writing the definitive manual on operative dentistry. To be approached by such a senior figure in my profession was immensely flattering. Also, at the age of 41, with the work involved with the 1975 study on women dentists nearing completion, I was open to another challenge and the opportunity to become more closely involved with the affairs of Latymer School, which still held great ties for me as I was now experiencing a new role, parent of a pupil, my daughter Pamela.

I found myself straight in at the deep end because in the 1970s there were no induction sessions or handbooks extolling the skills and attributes required to be a governor: it was a case of learning on the job. As far as Latymerians past and present were concerned the functioning of the Foundation appeared to be a closely guarded secret. Thus, I arrived for my first meeting of the governing body, on 24 September 1976, held traditionally on a Friday evening in the handsome setting of the heavily oak-panelled library, named in memory of a great and influential headmaster at the turn of the century, Richard Ashworth. Never had I dreamed as a library monitor when I was busily replacing borrowed books in their rightful places on the shelves that, at some time in the future, I would be sitting in that grand location as a Foundation governor of Latymer. Up until that point my contact with governors was either a polite greeting at the annual dinner or observing them over a seven-year period as a pupil, watching them process, at different speeds dictated by age or infirmity, down the long central aisle of the Great Hall of the school, before ascending the steps onto the stage to take up their designated seats in front of the several rows of members of staff resplendent in their black gowns and colourful academic hoods.

So who made up the governing body of the Latymer School? The instrument of government ratified in June 1955, granting the school voluntary aided status, also decreed that the governing body was to consist of fifteen persons, ten being Foundation governors and five representative governors who were appointed on the nomination of the local councils, originally Enfield, Edmonton and Middlesex. It was further stipulated that of the ten Foundation governors, one was to be appointed by the Senate of the University of London and this place was held by Professor Pickard, and a second one was to be appointed by the Vicar and churchwardens of All Saints' Church in Edmonton. However, there were no rules or caveats concerning the appointment of the remaining eight Foundation governors and it soon became clear that it was a self-selecting and appointing group.

The chairman, Mrs Gladys Child, MBE, an energetic octogenarian of slight build with an inborn love of music and literature, hailed from Wales and had spent her working years in the teaching profession. On retirement she became involved in local politics and rose to become Mayor of the Borough of Enfield and I soon discovered her political pedigree was not unique. Alderman Mrs Amy Emsden and Alderman Ted McNern were also former Mayors and Mrs Emsden was a very influential past-chairman of the Borough's education committee, and brought a wealth of inside knowledge to the governors' deliberations. Old students were also well represented by Frank Conisbee and Eileen Amos, so my arrival as a past pupil was not untoward. With so many of the governors excelling in political debate, I was exposed to the fascinating intrigue and point-scoring which took place during the meeting. As a newcomer to the formal conduct of committee meetings with structured agendas and resolutions, I was shocked at the strength of expression of an opinion or disagreement with a proposal which to my untutored ear verged on rudeness. I also became aware for the first time of the political impact on educational issues. The representative governor, Councillor Len Warren, of the minority socialist party at that time, was obliged to enunciate the party line as it was against selective and voluntary aided schools and was fiercely advocating comprehensive schooling. My respect for Len was unwavering for, after making his party's view known in debate, he would then work tirelessly towards ensuring the furtherance of Latymer's great traditions. After all, Edward Latymer's original bequest was to clothe and educate eight poor boys living in the Ancient Parish of Edmonton: surely true to the Socialists' ideals?

I noticed how for each item on the agenda the chairman, after a suitable passage of time, would firmly bring the debate to a close, give the decision, and then move on to the next item. Edward Kelly, the headmaster, was strategically seated on Mrs Child's right-hand side. Although his secretary, Mehra Cartwright, was in attendance as Clerk to the Governors, it was Edward Kelly who prepared the minutes. Seated to the left of the chairman was another official, the Secretary to the Foundation, Ken Gooch, who was the senior partner of a well-established local firm of solicitors. He too was a former pupil of the school and his role was to be responsible for the financial transactions of the Foundation's assets, the extent of which was a closely guarded secret. He also worked closely with the school architects, K. C. White, a London based firm, who had the oversight not only of the school buildings but also of the Foundation's property mainly centred in the Hammersmith area. The business was complete within a couple of hours and finished with a cup of coffee, accompanied by a very thick slice of cherry fruit cake purchased that afternoon by Charlie Geeves, the school caretaker, at the local Marks and Spencer.

Although it was a most agreeable introduction to the governing body, I was soon to become aware that initial discussions and preferred decisions were taken by a core of Foundation governors who were available to attend meetings held in the afternoon in the headmaster's room. Neither the chairman nor Eileen Amos drove and as I was able to organise my work schedule to be available in the afternoon I soon found myself invited to join their inner circle, the Finance and General Purposes Committee, as well as acting as chauffeur for Gladys and Eileen, which in itself gave me an unrivalled insight into personalities involved and workings of the Foundation.

I only had to wait a few months for my first taste of the impact of political diktat, if not interference, in the delivery of education. The Government, at that time a Labour administration, had made it clear that it intended to abolish the selective sector, direct grant and voluntary aided schools. The Education Act of November 1976 put the future of Latymer in the balance and on 17 January 1977 the Department of Education and Science wrote to the local education authority with a copy to the Latymer Governors asking for a reply, stating how the school would be organised in the future to give full effect to the comprehensive principle, citing that the current arrangements for admission of pupils to Latymer were based, 'wholly or partly, on selection by reference to ability and aptitude'. The governors were expected to formulate their reply within six months but, helpfully, the local education authority was asking for deferment to September to fit in with its scheduled meetings.

Nor did it pass unnoticed that the Rt. Hon. Shirley Williams MP, the current Secretary of State for Education and Science, having sent similar letters to all education authorities, promptly withdrew her daughter from the Godolphin and Latymer School for Girls in Hammersmith, which, as a direct grant school, was also under threat as not providing comprehensive education. It is commendable that parents wish to provide the best possible education for their children and it is not unknown for senior members of government to remove their children from local state schools and send them to independent or strongly performing schools in the selective sector outside their residential area. However, it remains disappointing that 'practice what you preach' is not a staunchly held adage amongst politicians, irrespective of political affiliation. I was nominated to join a specially convened governors' working party to prepare our reply. The generosity of the benefactors and traditions of Latymer nurtured by many generations was not going to be relinquished without a fight. The issues to be considered by the working party were clearly identified: Latymer as a comprehensive school but with variations, as a sixth-form college, or as an independent school. I was asked to assess this last concept and consider the prospects of Latymer as a fee-paying school. I set about gathering information about independent day schools in the north London neighbourhood which could be viewed as competitors in the private sector. Surprisingly, it was a sizeable list: Highgate, Channing, North London Collegiate, Haberdashers' Aske's, St Albans, and the City of London, all single-sex schools. I presented my findings to the special meeting of governors on 6 May 1977 and showed that Latymer would be unique in offering co-educational private education and was in a sound financial position to go independent. However, the governors found difficulty in reconciling this way forward with the intention of the original Latymer bequest to educate poor boys of Edmonton. In fact the Borough was relieved that we did not want to pursue independent status; the local education authority was already short of secondary school places and the loss of over one thousand at Latymer would be catastrophic for them.

I was fortunate, considering my junior status on the governing body, to be included in the small group which travelled to London to meet a leading Counsel, Leon Brittan, at his chambers. This meeting was facilitated by one of our parents, Leonard Bromley, QC, and the advice of the leading Counsel and recommended text formed the basis of the governors' reply to the local education authority. This was my first brush with the upper echelons of the legal profession and I was greatly impressed by Leon Brittan's quick grasp of the issues and his depth of understanding and was attracted to his manner of delivering legal advice incisively. I watched with no little surprise that after a distinguished parliamentary career in the House of Commons he became the Tory European Commissioner and was eventually ennobled as Lord Brittan of Spennithorne.

It was essential that the governors were not bulldozed into making a swift decision to suit the Government's timetable, rather that pre-eminence was given to the future of Latymer School. Thus, the initial reply, supported by ten governors with the labour representative, Councillor Len Warren, voting against, stated that it was too early for the governors to take a view and that extensive consultations were needed with all the groups who had legitimate interest in or affiliation with the school. This involved the headmaster in an enormous amount of extra work as he set about convening a series of meetings to canvass views of parents and old students. No stone was left unturned as to the possible future development if, as desired by government, Latymer became a comprehensive school. Building on its special reputation for excellence in music, I was delegated to report on the possibility of establishing a distinctive feature such as music, with the consequence of music specialisation featuring in the admissions procedure. At the end of four parents' meetings held in June 1977, the vote showed an overwhelming majority happy to accept this proposal. With this positive endorsement of Latymer as a specialist music centre catering for gifted and talented musicians mainly from within the Borough, further exploration of the proposal and advice were obtained from Professor Brian Trowell, Professor of Music at King's College London, and Mr Friar, the music adviser to the local education authority. A less radical approach was also floated – Latymer as a comprehensive school, but with a specialist wing to take some thirty to sixty pupils each year, with some of the places open to be filled from outside the Borough.

Again with advice from Counsel, a letter from the governors was prepared, incorporating these ideas, and was sent to the Department of Education and Science after its unanimous adoption at the special meeting of governors on 4 January 1978. Six months later, on 22 June, a reply arrived from the Department of Education and Science stating: 'the proposals submitted by the governors appear to the Secretary of State to be unsatisfactory' and 'requires the governors to submit to her, within one month, further proposals'. She also made clear that our current suggestions did not satisfy the comprehensive principle as defined in the Education Act 1976. She went further to request that we should clearly state that 'arrangements for admission of pupils will not be based wholly or partly on selection by reference to ability or aptitude'.

There then started a constant exchange of letters between the secretary of the Foundation, on Counsel's advice, and the Department of Education and Science, contesting the unreasonable demands for a reply 'within one month', citing the approaching summer holiday period. It was reassuring, as this legal tussle hotted up, that Leonard Bromley, QC joined the Foundation governors, filling the vacancy created by the resignation of Mr Roberts, whose place I took on the Finance and General Purposes Committee. Eventually, a letter was sent to the department, in October, challenging the given date of September 1980 for implementation of the Secretary of State's proposal and suggesting that September 1981 would be more realistic. This was brinkmanship in action for to pursue protracted negotiations was in Latymer's best interest, as a general election was only twelve months away. We as governors had to keep our nerve, sit on our official letters and stick together in our resolve.

We had two cards up our sleeves: firstly, the local education authority supported our view, and secondly the shadow Secretary of State for Education and Science, Norman St John-Stevas, later to become Baron St John of Fawsley, made it clear to us that if a Conservative Government was elected, Latymer would remain a voluntary aided grammar school. On 3 May 1979 there was a rout of the Labour Party and the Tories were swept to power with the Rt. Hon. Margaret Thatcher MP becoming the first woman to hold office as Prime Minister. The governors met the next day and ceremoniously shred their individual letters demanding compliance to the Education Act. It was a close call for Latymer changing its character and becoming a comprehensive school.

Each Foundation governor was appointed for a five-year term and it was a matter of automatic renewal, if the governor was willing to continue to serve. Gladys Child completed her term in June 1981 and intimated her wish to retire from office as chairman, although to continue as a governor. There was unanimous agreement that the current vice-chairman, Professor Pickard, should assume this role and he was duly elected at the full governors' meeting on 26 June. However, I had become aware that the headmaster had approached Leonard Bromley to fill the vacancy of vice-chairman and my competitive streak surfaced when it dawned on me that succession was prearranged. No one could doubt that Leonard was an eminently suitable person as he had made an enormous contribution, not only combating the threat to our voluntary aided status, but also in carrying out assessments of the Foundation's investments, mainly large blocks of flats – Latymer Court and Colet Court in Hammersmith – and had given advice as to how the Foundation's income could be enhanced through selling and reinvesting in less high maintenance and in modern property. Cheekily perhaps, I believed I had also contributed in many fields since becoming governor, some two years before Leonard Bromley who joined in 1978. Certainly, I had been vocal in my support for a parent-teacher association (PTA) and, having experienced the threat to our future, the backing of the parents proved crucial. I was pleased to be on the working party chaired by Professor Pickard, eliciting views of governors and teachers as to the feasibility of establishing a formal PTA, and a meeting of parents was called for Wednesday 11 January 1978 to gauge opinion. I can well remember the meeting, which was held in the Great Hall, and despite a typically cold winter evening the parents kept coming until the Great Hall was crammed to capacity. Parent after parent spoke eloquently about their support for the proposal but in the end their enthusiasm was not matched by the headmaster and staff, and so the idea was quietly shelved. Another of my crusades was to highlight the need to introduce computers into the life of Latymer and, perhaps to occupy my time fruitfully, I was asked to convene a joint governors and teachers working party to prepare a report and make recommendations, which I willingly did.

Both these initiatives were viewed as controversial and perhaps not compatible with a senior role on the governing body. I shared my disappointment that I had not been given the chance to put my name forward with Diana Baylis, who immediately countered, 'I assumed you had been asked. I will support you and put your name forward.' A vote for the position was held at the Annual General Meeting of the governors on Friday 26 June 1981 and I was elected vice-chairman. I learnt from this episode that modesty is not necessarily a virtue when seeking progression in one's career or public life. You have to be prepared to speak up if you wish to achieve the next rung on the ladder and it is far better than harbouring a grievance of what might have been.

I learnt so much from Pick, not only in the technique of chairmanship, but also in the appreciation of the poetical works of Yeats and Keats. Gordon and I enjoyed his generous hospitality at his home in Daventry, Northamptonshire, 'The Nuttery'. He, with his wife Daffy, ran a market garden harvesting hazelnuts and sending snowdrops and spring blooms to London distributors. Pick, a sprightly 72-year old, thought nothing of the round trip from his home to attend governors' meetings, concerts and the entire breadth of extra-curriculum activities offered at Latymer. He proudly claimed that his greatest achievement was to appoint Geoffrey Mills head teacher to succeed Edward Kelly when he retired at the end of the summer term in 1983. Geoffrey was a local boy made good, as he attended the Enfield Grammar School, a fierce rival of Latymer, especially on the sports field. He was a graduate of Clare College Cambridge and had an exemplary track record of being a headmaster of the Manhood High School and Community Centre in Selsey, Chichester. Sadly, the promising time ahead for Pick to work with Geoffrey Mills was brought to an abrupt halt by the relentless and rapid progression of a debilitating deafness, for which no hearing aid or treatment was available and which made his conduct of governors' meetings impossible. Pick's decision to relinquish the cherished chairmanship after barely two years at the helm was seen as a very courageous step. So, at the annual general meeting of governors held on Friday 24 June 1983, our roles were reversed. I was unanimously elected chairman and Pick vice-chairman. I was so grateful to have his continuing support and advice as he worked tirelessly, assisting with the essential paperwork generated by the admissions procedures and researched and prepared a model report on the utilisation of the Latymer field centre at Cwm Penmachno, and its sustained viability as the governors bore full financial responsibility for its operation.

As a pupil in the fifth form in 1952, I shared in the great excitement when the headmaster, Mr Davis, told us at a morning assembly that the governors had purchased a large mansion, Stapleton House, with adjoining fields in nearby Potters Bar, Hertfordshire, to create a centre for field studies. Most appealing to us was his idea that three coaches of pupils would go there every day to study Art, Biology, Games, Geography and Drama. In practical terms this meant that each of us would have a day in the country once a fortnight, and for many of the children at the school at that time it presented a rare opportunity to escape from the bricks and mortar of London suburbia. Unfortunately, the grand plan floundered, due to a combination of the expense of building materials in the post-war period and the failure to obtain planning permission for the necessary alterations and extensions.

When Dr Trefor Jones succeeded Mr Davis as headmaster in the 1960s, he was keen to resurrect the concept of a field study centre and discovered within the Snowdonia National Park a disused village school in Cwm Penmachno following the demise of the local slate quarry industry. So, in 1966, the Latymer Foundation purchased, renovated and re-equipped the school, now called Ysgol Latymer, to provide residential accommodation initially for thirty pupils, gradually expanding to sleep nearly fifty. At Cwm there was the opportunity for pupils to take part in a spectrum of outdoor activities, from orienteering to canoeing, mountain cycling to hill walking, and for sixth formers it provided an unrivalled resource centre for the pursuit of Biology, or Geography at advanced level. But there were other pursuits not strictly academic. The musicians found it a conducive environment to practise for their numerous concerts and music tours, and the Latymer Madrigal Group excelled under its able conductor, Michael Brewer, who later became director of the Manchester Chetham's Hospital School of Music, but not before they won in 1973 the school class of the BBC programme, *Let the People Sing*. An additional benefit was that teachers were viewed in a different light away from the structured school environment. Our son, Colin, recalls how his maths teacher, Terry Jacob, would assume the mantle of storyteller par excellence at bedtime, with gripping ghost stories leavened with a dose of Winnie the Pooh. Pupils wrote in glowing terms to the school magazine: 'I think everyone will agree that a trip to Cwm is not to be missed, as great fun is had by all. Yes, even the staff enjoy it.'

With the arrival of demanding health and safety legislation and new fire regulations there was suddenly the need to increase considerably the expenditure on Cwm, an expense underwritten entirely by the Foundation. There was a tough decision to be made: governors spend money on Cwm or sell it. The headmaster solicited the views of the parents, staff and pupils and the result was an overwhelming 'Yes, keep Cwm.' Therefore, at the beginning of November 1986 the governors undertook a first: to mount a campaign to raise money for 'The Cwm Penmachno Appeal' with a target of £60,000 to cover the cost of the improvements which were explained in detail in an attractive brochure and sent to all parents and old students. The campaign was successful in that it raised the profile of the field centre; its existence ceased to be taken for granted. The governors were also greatly encouraged when one of the members of staff, Jim Ridge, was appointed warden and he encouraged volunteers from the senior pupils to help with internal decorating and general maintenance.

Generations of pupils would speak in revered terms about Mrs Williams and her mouth-watering home-baked apple pies. She lived in the cottage next door to Ysgol Latymer and was employed by the Foundation to prepare meals for the pupils and staff. I only knew about her cooking by repute and so decided, when I was attending a dental nurse conference in Llandudno, that on my departure I would drive home with a detour to Cwm Penmachno. It raised my spirits to escape into the beautiful Welsh landscape and then alight upon the school nestling in the valley. But, knocking on Mrs Williams's door brought no response, except the appearance of the next-door neighbour. 'She's in chapel but will be back at midday.' Sure enough on the stroke of twelve Mrs Williams was spotted walking along the road and within minutes was giving us tea and scones in front of a roaring fire in her cosy parlour. 'Have you been to Latymer?' I soon enquired. 'No, I haven't; I have never been to London,' she replied. An invitation was quickly extended to visit and after some gentle persuasion she agreed to travel with her assistant, Mrs Archer, to the 1991 Speech Day and Prizegiving. A couple of members of staff, with whom she was familiar from their visits to Cwm, gave them a whistle-stop tour of the major London tourist spots and amazingly on the way round Covent Garden exchanged words with a former pupil working there: Latymerians indeed get everywhere. A tumultuous reception awaited her in the evening at Speech Day and as I drove them back to their hotel in Holtswhite Hill, Mrs Williams, choked with emotion, confided that she had realised a lifelong ambition to come to London and, to combine this with a visit to Latymer, made it a precious occasion. It also pulled me up to realise how fortunate I had been in my job to travel the globe and yet people within our own country had not even had the opportunity to travel to the capital.

Speech days and prizegivings, as Mrs Williams found, could be moving occasions when the very best of Latymer and its achievements were on show, not only to the parents, but also to the guest speakers. Traditionally, two were held at the end of the autumn term, one for junior pupils and the second for the senior pupils and recent sixth-form leavers and, as chairman, I conducted the proceedings. Over the years I was fortunate to meet and introduce many luminaries who had incredible life stories to tell and to observe how brilliantly able they were to communicate with the audience: it was a ripe arena for me to pick up tips on public speaking.

Lord Tonypandy at the speech day in 1987 reminded us how he had risen from childhood poverty in a Welsh mining town in the Rhondda valley to become the Rt. Hon. George Thomas MP, the 133rd Speaker of the House of Commons, and only the second elected Labour MP to hold that position. He represented Cardiff Central but enjoyed universal acclaim. Even Mrs Thatcher as Prime Minister praised him on his retirement, referring to his 'kindness, wisdom and integrity with the call to silence, "Order, Order", intoned in his strong Welsh lilt'. At speech day we were all so captivated by his talk that there was no need to call anyone to 'order'.

The following year the balance was redressed, with the guest, Mrs Angela Rumbold, CBE MP, the Minister of State for Education and Science in the Conservative government. She was responsible for implementing the 1986 Education Act which required governors to present an annual report to a specifically convened meeting of parents and to produce a school prospectus. In a way this was regularising a speech day custom at Latymer when the headmaster and chairman presented a résumé of the year's activities. The Secretary of State for Education and Science, the Rt. Hon. Kenneth Baker, had summed up the preceding Education Reform Bill of some 169 pages in three words: 'Standards, freedom and choice'. Idealistic sounding words, but there were numerous proposals which the governors had to consider carefully – opting out of LEA control, the introduction of a national curriculum with tests, the setting up of attainment targets, the organisation of regular assessments, to name just a few. As governors we were pleased to have the opportunity to hear the minister's comments, as all these proposals brought a lot of extra work for the governing body as well as for the headmaster and his staff.

But guests were not confined to politicians. Among them were Sir Wilfred Cockcroft, a former chairman of the secondary examination council, Sir Gordon Wolstenholme, director of the CIBA Foundation, Viorica Bergman, Trustee of Womankind, with aims to improve women's lives in the developing countries, who had been a member of the inquiry to investigate the condition of women in prisons, and Mary Warnock, Headmistress of the Oxford High School who had chaired the committee of inquiry into special education. Today, as Baroness Warnock, she is an acknowledged philosopher and is consulted over many of our pressing moral and ethical issues.

Chairing speech days also provided me with a unique experience in how to cope when addressing an audience of over a thousand people, an experience which was unexpectedly put to the test in 1992 in Orlando, USA. I had been invited to the dinner of the American College of Dentists and was not unduly surprised when, in true Disneyland style, Mickey Mouse escorted me to the head table for dinner. I did not think there was anything untoward about this as I was president-elect of the British Dental Association at that time. But a surprise was in store for me, for which I had not bargained. As we approached the concluding coffee, I idly turned over the menu card lying flat on the table. There emblazoned on the card was my name: I was down to speak. Unprepared, I turned in panic to Gordon sitting beside me. 'Margaret,' he said, 'imagine you are addressing all those parents from the Latymer stage.' His calming words had the desired effect and I was greatly relieved that the speech was enthusiastically received by the unsuspecting diners. However, so as not to be caught out again at official functions, I take along a precautionary 'few words' in my handbag, just in case!

From my business experience in managing the *British Dental Journal* I had been surprised that the administration of the Foundation was linked with the school office. I believed that a dedicated governors' room was needed to enable the chairman to deal with correspondence, and to provide a readily accessible small meeting room and storage facilities so that Foundation minutes and documents could be secured. Geoffrey Mills was supportive and fortunately at that time redevelopment was taking place at the south end of the school to provide sixth form accommodation and adjoining seminar rooms. It was easy to identify a suitable room for governors' use. It also seemed an ideal opportunity to relieve the school secretariat of the escalating amount of Foundation business and, with the impending retirement of Mehra Cartwright, to appoint a part-time secretary to the governors and Foundation. This proved to be an inspired and popular appointment and Sue Lawn was warmly welcomed to her first governors' meeting in December 1984, and continues effectively and efficiently to discharge this role almost twenty-five years on. Old students were quick to assist in furnishing the room with, in particular, a beautiful polished oak conference table and chairs donated by May Sanders in memory of her husband, a well-loved local headmaster as well as a former pupil of the school. But the modernisation did not stop there. It was clear that the conduct of the Foundation business needed to be streamlined and so the monolithic finance and general purposes committee was replaced with three: finance, buildings and estates, and education. In addition the composition of the governing body, where a lifetime of experience especially in local government dominated, needed to be balanced with specialist skills in order to discharge the increasing and wide-ranging responsibilities. At that time, certain posts in the voluntary sector were subject to age criteria: magistrates had to retire at 70 and judges, albeit paid, at 75. Other professional organisations had started to stipulate an upper age limit, after which a candidate could not offer themselves for election. All this seemed eminently sensible so I introduced this topic to a governors' meeting. It was a tense debate so I was surprised, yet relieved, at the acceptance of the principle and Ted McNern, now 80 years of age, was a staunch advocate for the proposal. Then, due to failing health, two governors resigned and were followed by Leonard Bromley after his appointment to the Judiciary.

So, in 1983, as chairman, I was encouraged to identify four possible recruits. This was a golden opportunity to build a new team and I set about identifying potential governors. I organised a lunch-time meeting with Tony Trathen, a chartered accountant and a former pupil and parent of a Latymer pupil. He was very positive about the suggestion and said he was looking to undertake some voluntary work and could think of nothing more rewarding than the opportunity to contribute to the future of Latymer. This he certainly accomplished and Tony became a parent Foundation governor and in due course a most effective chairman of the finance committee and vice-chairman of the governing body. As Professor Pickard's position as the University of London representative was still vacant, I approached Eric Ballard, a graduate of the University and a civil engineer and senior partner in Laings, the multi-national construction company. His appointment was ratified by the senate in 1984 and, likewise, he was an inspired choice to lead the buildings and estates committee. He too shared a pedigree with Geoffrey Mills as an old boy of Enfield Grammar School. The governors then suggested that I should approach the chairman of the Latymer Old Students Association and I was delighted that Don McQuistan was appointed unanimously, as he brought with him much needed highly technical knowledge. The fourth vacancy was filled by a much respected local solicitor, Frank Forney, who gave sterling support to the governors and to me personally when he succeeded as vice-chairman. Thus, within a period of fifteen months, the complexion of the governing body had changed profoundly and I considered it was fit for purpose to support the headmaster and cope with the inevitable period of change which would face Latymer with the numerous edicts emanating from central government.

With the arrival of the new headmaster the governors deemed it appropriate to raise again the topic of involving parents more formally in the life of the school. Geoffrey Mills was incredibly sympathetic to the idea and suggested an Association of Parents and Friends (APFLS). I was privileged to take the chair at the Open Meeting for parents held on 4 April 1984, and such was the enthusiasm shown for the project that a steering committee was formed, with the headmaster in the chair, until the time when the parents could get to know each other and elect their own officers. So the launch of the association was marked by a wine and cheese party on the evening of 10 July in Latymer's small hall and, gratifyingly, 300 parents indicated that they would be present at the annual general meeting on 9 October, and 29 had submitted their names for election to the committee. Here, at last, was the organisation I had dreamed of, to engage in activities which supported the school and to advance the education of pupils and to foster good relationships between staff, parents and others associated with the school.

The Foundation was also delighted to share its financial load. For example in 1985 it spent its income on the renovation of the three-manual pipe organ in the Great Hall installed in memory of a former headmaster, Mr Davis, the purchase of new pianos, and employing a professional librarian part-time, which was an innovation in the whole Borough, as normally a member of the English department took on this role. In addition, there was provision of new technology facilities, modernising the staff room with kitchen facilities as well as general maintenance. The shopping list of the fledgling association under its first chairman, Howard Farthing, was equally impressive. There was no shortage of 'wouldn't it be nice to have' items. In fact its first purchase was a TV camera at the princely sum of £413 which, it is reported, remains in working order. In total over the years until 2005 when APFLS celebrated its 21st anniversary it had procured equipment and resources for the school in excess of £300,000. Of greater importance was that bonds with the school and between parents were strengthened through the organisation of fund-raising and social activities – balloon races, car boot sales and an annual fête.

When Dr Jones came as headmaster to Latymer in 1957, he remarked on 'its drab appearance' due to a failure of decoration over many years. When Geoffrey Mills arrived in 1983 he made a similar observation, alighting on certain areas which were causing the governors concern, in particular the science facilities. Amazingly, despite the physical inadequacies, the school continued to enjoy an enviable science reputation and amongst the alumni was Professor John Horlock, who became an international authority on turbo machinery and power plants, and who capped his distinguished career through becoming Vice-Chancellor of the Open University. However, a visit to the laboratories where John and I had studied was instantly recognisable: the old wooden benches in serried rows were still in everyday use. This Dickensian provision was definitely not conducive to embracing modern teaching methods, attracting or retaining staff and, most worryingly, not compliant with current health and safety legislation. It was not scaremongering; it was true. Every one of the science laboratories in the school was a potential hazard to the pupils and staff who studied in them.

As chairman, on behalf of the governors I had repeatedly submitted plans to the London Borough of Enfield for financial support to refurbish the twelve science laboratories and each year the application was rejected. Contesting the disappointing decision, I was politely told that there were other priorities in the Borough, citing, as an example, children sitting in a classroom with a leaking roof and buckets strewn over the floor to catch the rain. Patience began to evaporate and so, when we submitted a further application to the Borough in August 1991, we enclosed as many supporting letters as possible to strengthen our case. The Borough's science adviser reported that 'the overall condition of the laboratories has deteriorated further and the introduction of more practical work by the pupils as required by the national curriculum put the creaking facilities under pressure.' Another letter on the same theme was written by the education safety officer: 'There is a lack of gas isolation and electrical protection in some areas.' It was at this time that I got to know our new architect, John Harvey, who now phased the project, hoping that this made the bid more attractive for capital expenditure during 1992 to 1993. This time we covered every possibility. I wrote letters to anyone who could influence the decision and this included the politicians: 'In view of the emphasis placed by the Secretary of State (Kenneth Clarke) in his recent speech on the provision of acceptable science facilities and Latymer's endeavours during the past five years to provide such facilities, we do hope this year that our submission will meet with positive and encouraging results for the morale of the science teaching staff, pupils and parents.' In addition, I sent a request for a meeting with the Minister for Education and Science, Angela Rumbold. Indeed this concerted effort paid off and modernisation of the science facilities was completed. However, the expenditure of time and energy to achieve this urgent improvement, by the headmaster, staff, Borough science and safety advisers, local MPs and governors, was incredible. Nevertheless, for me the exercise had two great spin-offs: I began to understand and appreciate the power of the art of lobbying and I forged a working understanding with John Harvey, whose architectural advice I was able to benefit from later when president of the General Dental Council.

An item on the agenda for my second meeting in the chair became a recurring and continuous theme: Latymer's admission policy and procedure. In the early 1970s, on average there were two applicants for each place and selection was assisted by the excellent pupil profile provided by primary headteachers, many of whom from their considerable experience, had developed their own nomenclature. Many parents began submitting letters outlining their offspring's extracurricular activities and so to rationalise information a parent questionnaire was designed and circulated to all applicants. However, in the 1980s, the headteachers felt under increasing pressure with the rising popularity of Latymer and so through the director of education they asked that the governors should consider including an objective test in its admission procedure. With the headmaster and some governors, I attended a meeting at the Enfield Civic Centre convened by the Director of Education, Mr Gordon Hutchinson, when the primary school headteachers voiced their concerns and suggested ideas as to the way forward. Any proposal of testing made me uneasy as an 'eleven plus' failure, although I was placated when it was explained that the advocated non-verbal reasoning test indicated a level of ability for reasoning which does not depend on verbal input or quantitative skills. This test would be taken on the school premises and it was agreed that the governors reserved the right to change the format of the test, insisting that it was to be a subsidiary to the all-important primary school profile.

With these provisos the test was included in the admissions procedure for the cohort entering Latymer in 1984. However, any thought that the test might act as a deterrent to would-be applicants, was ill-founded. In 1988 the number applying for one of the 180 places rose to 865 and a waiting list system was introduced. More refinements were added as the numbers continued to escalate; in 2005 more than 1,600 children sat the first test and about one-third went on to take a second test. Organising all these stages of the admissions process threw a tremendous load on Denise Blackwell and her school office staff. It also placed her in the front line to cope with the varied and ingenious ideas devised by parents to get their child into Latymer. 'I was once offered a free weekly hair-do if the child got in and a huge gold necklace,' recalled Denise when interviewed for the *Latymer Link* magazine. She went on to say firmly, in rejecting the offer, 'Does my hair look that bad!' and heard no more.

However, some parents could not accept that their child had been unsuccessful and so lodged an appeal. A panel was convened in the Spring term with an independent chairman, a Foundation governor not involved in the initial selection process, and a representative from the Borough. The headmaster had also to be available and this was an extra commitment to his already horrendous workload. The Governors' Room provided an ideal quiet venue for the panel to conduct the hearings, which could continue for well over a month. Oversubscription to good schools throughout the country remains a perennial problem. We all strive to secure the best for our children but there are instances when we have to accept that not gaining a place at an academically oriented school may be in the child's best interests, contrary to parents' wishes. This can be a most bitter pill to swallow.

Sometimes, implementation of government legislation can bring change for the good. This was the case concerning the membership of the governing body when, through the implementation of the new Education Act in 1995, elections were held for two teachers and one parent governor. Mrs Wray and Ian Tarling were elected by the staff and Howard Farthing, chair of APFLS, was elected by the parents of the school. Interestingly the new rules also stated that the four representative governors from the Borough could not be of the same sex and so Councillor Geoffrey Leigh retired in order to be replaced by a woman, so as to comply with the law. It was also around this time that a vacancy arose for a University of London representative, as Eric Ballard, having moved to Cornwall, indicated that he did not wish to stand for another five-year term. With others, I started to cast around for a likely candidate and remembered that Tom Taylor, whose father had been chairman of governors, would be eminently suitable as he held a degree from the University of London and had qualified at the London Hospital, later to rise to become a consultant anaesthetist. He recalled in an interview for *Latymer Link* magazine, 'Margaret Seward asked me to become a governor in 1989; I knew her when she was in a gymslip in the first year and I was in the fifth form.' Tom proved to be an excellent choice because, in due course, he became chairman of the finance committee and my vice-chairman, and when the University abolished the post everyone was delighted to be able to retain his skills in the role of a Foundation governor.

As you will have appreciated, during my chairmanship I was faced with an endless stream of reports and consultative documents to digest, especially concerning the future funding of schools. Fortunately, Geoffrey Mills worked tirelessly to ensure that we all understood the full implications of the many changes on the horizon. During his headmaster's report at Speech Day in 1990, he announced the latest – Local Management of Schools (LMS). In brief, this entailed granting to each school a sum of money from which it had to cover all its running expenses, including salaries of teaching and non-teaching staff. As is the case with this sort of scheme, there was a complicated formula to follow on which the eventual allocation of funds was based. Nevertheless it did seem to provide a welcome change, a flexibility and autonomy in the way that Latymer could spend its money. Not surprisingly, it was not long before much needed redecoration and adaptation in the school was undertaken, swiftly and effectively. But nothing, it is said, is as permanent as change and so within another two years we were grappling with a proposed change to our status, from voluntary aided to grant maintained. Such a fundamental shift demanded a full consultation with parents after the governors had considered carefully the 'pros and cons' of the move. The governors unanimously agreed that grant maintained status (GMS) was the way forward for the future and so a ballot of parents was conducted by the Electoral Reform Services. With just a few days to spare I was able to announce the result at the 1992 Speech Day, reporting a 71 per cent response rate. Seventy-eight per cent said they wanted Latymer to apply for grant maintained status, 22 per cent were against. The mandate was unequivocal for the governors who then had to embark on drawing up official proposals and preparing press notices, all actions stipulated under sections 62 and 63 of the Education Reform Act. Once submitted to the Secretary of State, the governors had to wait patiently for the final decision which, with great relief, approved the change in status of Latymer from a voluntary aided grammar school to a grant maintained school, taking effect on 1 September 1993. In its wake, new ways of working were introduced. Of particular relevance was the establishment of two posts, a responsible officer and a bursar. This was a new venture for Latymer and in a short time it became evident that the latter appointment was not working out as hoped. However, the incumbent sealed his own fate when, on returning from a business trip abroad, I tried to contact by phone my secretary on my direct line. As I did not get a reply, I went through the main school switchboard, to be told that the bursar had instructed that the chairman's direct line be disconnected, certainly not an action to endear when his performance was already under review. On occasions, 'someone's loss can be someone's gain' and this was indeed the case when one of our Foundation governors, Geoff Abell, decided to make a career change after twenty-seven years with the National Westminster Bank, latterly responsible for international specialist finance, and apply for the now vacant job of bursar. Geoff and the post have been a great success story for Latymer. It made so much sense to have someone with professional expertise managing the school's millions of pounds turnover and ensuring that there were always sufficient resources to pay the bills, keeping an eye on the opportunities to bid for special project grants, as well as making sure that the premises provided a safe and good working environment. In addition, there was a myriad of small accounts for extracurricular activities: trips to Cwm, tours abroad, ticket sales for concerts and plays. My learning in financial management took a great leap forward at this stage, with an understanding which could never be gleaned from A–Z books on finance.

While 1993 was a notable year for achieving grant maintained status, it was also a year of attaining excellence in national examinations results. When Geoffrey Mills arrived in 1984 he lamented the fact that 26 per cent of the fifth form pupils had failed to achieve five passes at Grade C or above at O level. 'Last year,' he enthused, 'the failure rate has fallen to one per cent.' However, there was much to celebrate when Latymer achieved the accolade of the best A level performance of any maintained co-educational school. League tables may be decried, but they can be a welcome indicator for parents and give encouragement to the staff. These outstanding results were soon picked up in the press. The entry in the *Daily Telegraph* Schools Guide reported, 'Latymer pupils are lively, articulate and demanding' and in the summary stated, 'exceptional school, highly recommended'. Governors basked in the reflected glory, but remained humbled by the enormous dedication and ability of the headmaster and his staff to reach this pinnacle in under ten years.

However, we did not confine our attention to the past and present. We indulged in blue-sky thinking as to what school facilities might be required to satisfy the educational ambitions of the year 2000 and beyond. I sent a letter to all heads of departments informing them of the Millennium project and that the working party would be chaired by Roy Smith, a governor and former pupil. Importantly, I stressed that before work commenced we wanted the views of the staff and gave details of a meeting to be held at lunch-time. The attendance was overwhelming and it was a delight that we nearly ran out of sandwiches. The ideas came thick and fast. One was the possibility of building a performing arts centre to foster the growth of already well-established areas, music, drama and media studies, with the building having a dual purpose providing conference facilities in the evening and during school holidays. Another suggestion was for a sports hall complex with a modern gymnasium and fitness rooms which, likewise, could be available to the community for hiring out during holidays. The staff had also in mind smaller projects: multi-resource-based learning centre, design studios, improved dining accommodation, enlarged computer facilities, creation of staff and reception areas to include interview rooms. Subsequently, many of the staff committed their thoughts to paper. There was a surfeit of ideas and the challenge came when attempting to convert the vision into reality. It was not until several years later when the Latymer Foundation mounted an ambitious fund-raising campaign for a new performing arts centre and sports hall that real progress was made. It was a costly project, £5.6 million, but this did not daunt the chairman of the Latymer Campaign Steering Group, Andrew Vallence-Owen, or the headmaster, as they set about applying to the national lottery, trusts, grant-giving bodies, as well as encouraging parents and former pupils to make gifts or covenants. It became a professional operation with a campaign office and dedicated staff, glossy information brochures and video. No fund-raising opportunity was missed.

It was a testament to the single-minded endeavours of so many that the performing arts centre was opened in June 2000 and appropriately named the Mills Building in recognition of Geoffrey Mills's undisputed driving force behind the entire planned development, from the initial stirrings of the idea in 1990. But with only part of the grand plan complete the campaign committee, still chaired by Andrew Vallence-Owen, continued to raise funds to build the sports and dining hall complex. Indeed there was more than enough to keep Niki Aresti and the campaign office fully occupied. Perseverance was rewarded when on 18 May 2006, HRH the Princess Royal officially opened the spectacular new sports and dining hall complex. Now one is left to ponder, how did we manage without them?

All Saints' Church in Church Street, Edmonton, was inextricably linked with Latymer, as a place on the governing body was reserved for the incumbent vicar. A tangible sign in the church was the memorial installed in 1983, comprising coloured tiles laid on the chancel floor to depict the Latymer crest and motto, and was dedicated when I attended my first Foundation Day Service in my new role as Chairman of Governors. This was always an auspicious day in the governors' calendar as we paid homage to our founders and benefactors, and the service was attended by the Mayor of Enfield and the senior pupils who walked, form by form with their teacher, along the half mile from school to church. Amazingly, it rarely rained to prevent this annual pilgrimage on Ascension Day. The pupils were rewarded with an afternoon off school while the governors, staff, former staff and old students gathered in the school for a sit-down lunch. Nearing the end of the proceedings I would rise to thank the two guest preachers, the junior pupils having their own service at the school, and say a few choice words. However, in May 1994, I sprang a surprise. I announced my retirement as chairman and as a governor, to take effect from the end of the summer term. Although I had shared my decision with Geoffrey Mills, most of those assembled were unaware that during the previous week I had been elected president of the General Dental Council for a five-year term of office. With this appointment, and a consequential move away from the area to Bournemouth, it was clear that I would be unable to give the full commitment needed to chair the governing body. Always mindful of Professor Pickard's example, I resigned.

Nevertheless, in the remaining few months, there were many issues to take forward which we had mapped out at the first retreat for governors held one Saturday earlier in the year at the Royal Chase Hotel in Enfield, when we also had our first attempts at structuring our mission statement, an exercise gaining favour in the business world. Inevitably, my retirement meant a vacancy for a Foundation governor and suggestions were invited. For my own part I had got acquainted on the journeys by train to work from Hadley Wood with Dr Andrew Vallence-Owen, a local resident shortly to become the parent of a pupil. I had known him by repute when he was working at the British Medical Association, before his more recent appointment as medical director of BUPA. I shared with him the fact that a vacancy had arisen on the governing body. He expressed interest and was appointed unanimously, and was soon fully involved as the energetic and visionary chair of the Latymer Campaign Steering Group.

Presiding over my final governors' meeting at the end of the summer term was emotional for me. Coming to an end was active involvement with Latymer for more than half a century – seven years as a pupil, twice as a parent (Pamela and Colin), an old student, six years as Foundation governor, and eleven years as chairman. I was well aware that I would miss enormously the friendships forged throughout these years and the camaraderie amongst the governors. I realised that I thrived on committee work; it was my relaxation and hobby and every aspect of my involvement with Latymer had sharpened my belief in teamwork as fundamental to achieve success.

As chairman, I learnt the true meaning of governance and management, areas which can so often lead to conflict and misunderstandings when the final line between the two is inadvertently breached. Success is definitely built on trust and I will always be grateful that my chairmanship coincided with Geoffrey Mills's reign as head teacher whose devotion to his job, his pupils and his family must be without equal and who would kindly and wisely steer me back into my governance role if in my enthusiasm for Latymer I spilled over into his rightful domain of management.

At my last meeting in July, a worthy candidate, Ian Pilsworth, was elected to succeed me. On taking the chair he invited me to join the governors, with Gordon, at a farewell dinner to be held at the luxurious West Lodge Hotel in Hadley Wood on 14 September. It proved to be a memorable evening for both of us. I was thoroughly spoilt with laudatory speeches and, even more, with generous gifts. When Sue Lawn enquired what I might like as a leaving present I went for the practical option: a new set of saucepans to replace the rather battered kitchen utensils. However, I had not bargained to receive a magnificent range of Prestige copper-bottom pots and pans, which will outlive me, yet be a constant reminder of my Latymer connection. I was going to miss Sue Lawn enormously. We worked so well together and she, uncomplaining, had put up with my idiosyncrasies, my illegible handwriting and lengthy tapes, all with good humour and complete loyalty. How fortunate I had been.

The Association of Latymer Parents and Friends presented me with a highly-polished piece of teak, salvaged from the old benches in the science laboratories at the time of its refurbishment, with a smart bronze plate inscribed: 'Once a Latymerian, always a Latymerian'; profoundly true. Then it was the governors' turn to spring a surprise. The curtains between the hotel dining room and conservatory were drawn back to reveal a group of senior pupils performing under the baton of our charismatic music director, David Elliott. There could not have been a more enjoyable surprise because music at Latymer had been a special part of my association with the school. I attended regularly the many concerts throughout the school year as well as the other events in the school's calendar, with the privilege of enjoying the performances from the chairman's reserved seat in the front row in the Great Hall, with Geoffrey Mills in his designated seat in the front row on the opposite side of the central aisle.

I have endeavoured to return to Latymer for special events, although not as often as I would have wished but, reassuringly, I still recognise some of the familiar and much-loved faces of the Latymer family. Most recently, the Richmond Herald at the College of Arms, in designing my badge, has incorporated the cross crosslet from the arms of the Latymer Foundation.

Yes, Latymer does remain a continuing thread.

Chapter 19

My second retirement

When I completed my term of office at the General Dental Council I was in the unprecedented position of having an empty diary for the entire month of October. Thus, it seemed to me it was an opportune time to indulge in the luxury of mixing professional pursuits with holidays by taking in a couple of annual dental conferences in exotic locations: the American Dental Association (ADA) in Honolulu, and the World Dental Federation (FDI) in Mexico City.

Mark Twain called Hawaii 'the loveliest fleet of islands that lies anchored in any ocean' and after my visit I agreed unreservedly. Honolulu was the venue for the ADA Conference and, in keeping with local custom, my colleagues had dispensed with their dark suits or tailored outfits in favour of brightly patterned Hawaiian shirts or blouses: informality was the order of the day. Once in each decade the American dentists descend on Honolulu and on this occasion in such great numbers that many had to seek accommodation on neighbouring islands. However, Gordon and I were fortunate to stay in Honolulu at the impressive Royal Hawaiian Hotel, known colloquially as the 'Pink Palace of the Pacific' which was the first hotel to be built on the island and designed in Moorish style with strikingly beautiful pink turrets. Particularly attractive was the easy access to two miles of Waikiki beach and its famous white sand, which we discovered was not its own but transported by barge from Papohaku beach on the nearby island of Molokai. But this did not deter us from sampling the delights of this ethnically diverse culture from its cuisine, including the famous macadamia nut pie, to its spectacular entertainments of traditional hula dancing and fire-eating.

There was also a packed scientific programme to enjoy, as a conference of around 60,000 delegates can attract world-class speakers, so I had no difficulty in filling my three days – attending lectures on team building, ethics in publishing, communication techniques and the latest innovative clinical treatments. As an honorary member of the ADA, I was included in the guest list to special events and so I spent one evening at the official residence of the Governor of Hawaii, and his wife Mrs Cayetano, in Washington Place, a historic wooden building with its own exhibition of impressive memorabilia. However, it was a more sombre visit to Pearl Harbour, where massive loss of life occurred, when the USS *Arizona* was bombed and sunk in December 1941. It was a grim reminder of the tomb of 1,177 men below the ocean as we viewed oil, still escaping from the engine-room, spreading out as a dark streak on the water's surface.

Without the pressure of work commitments, I was able to take another holiday before the start of the FDI Conference in Mexico City at the end of October, and so headed off to Cancun with Gordon to join up with a group of English travellers heading for the Yucatan Peninsula to explore the evocative Maya ruins of Tulum, climb the monumental pyramid at Chickén Itza, and discover Uxmal set in a jungle clearing in the Puuc Hills. Mexico City claims to be a 'city of superlatives', as the oldest and highest in the North American continent, as well as the most populous city in the world, while clinging to its deeply entrenched Aztec heritage.

Gordon particularly looked forward to coming with me to FDI Congresses because he would receive a cordial invitation to join the excellent spouses' programme, organised to occupy the ladies while their husbands attended the Council and business meetings which took place several days prior to the opening of the Congress; Gordon seemed completely at ease with his inclusion as the only man in the group. Very occasionally, the organiser of the spouses' programme extended the invitation to the 'other halves', as happened when Señora Laura de Acuna, the wife of the Mexican Councillor, arranged a lunch-time gastronomic feast in her garden with speciality dishes of different regions prepared and cooked for us by women in traditional costume. Certainly this experience was more acceptable to my conservative palate than the pre-Hispanic delicacies such as chillied worms or crispy fried grasshoppers! On the trip to the de Acuna home by coach and on our journey to the conference centre each morning in the hotel shuttle bus, we were accompanied by police outriders on motorcycles, ensuring no stopping at red lights. No chances were taken with the cargo of affluent dentists, especially in view of the fact that during the previous spring the US State Department warned of 'critical levels of violent crime against tourists'.

As well as my involvement with meetings related to my role as editor of the *IDJ*, I chaired the section of ethics and dental legislation. Following an invitation from the section of public health dentistry for a joint meeting, Professor Martin Hobdell, a colleague from my student days at the London Hospital, assisted in assembling a whole day's programme which I co-chaired with Dr Anne Nordblad from Helsinki. This was a successful venture and collaboration became a familiar feature on the FDI programme. If my second retirement could continue with this agreeable combination of work and play, I would be extremely content.

On my return to the UK at the beginning of November, two important events were rapidly approaching: firstly the generous farewell dinner at the Ironmongers Hall, which I have recounted in detail in Chapter 16; second, an all-day conference to be held on 19 November at the Royal Society in Carlton Terrace arranged by the UK Conference of Postgraduate Dental Deans and Directors (COPDEND) and the National Committee for Continuing Postgraduate Education in Dentistry (NCCPED). I was scheduled to welcome the participants who came from almost every major UK organisation in dentistry and who collectively had experience of initiatives in retraining and retaining of dentists in the profession. Many members of the dental press were present and I was reported as claiming that the issue 'had been treated as the Cinderella of dentistry' and that, despite the repackaging of the Retainer Scheme since it was launched in 1980, it has remained the profession's best kept secret'.

An update of my previous women surveys, in 1975 and with Pippi McEwen in 1985, was presented by Professor David Gibbons from Guy's, King's and St Thomas's dental school, followed by Ken Eaton, director of NCCPED who gave the latest statistics on the dental workforce, including the European dimension. He left us pondering the fact that in recent years a total of 850 dentists had disappeared without trace from the Dentists Register, dentists we could ill-afford to lose in view of the shortage of practitioners, and realising that an efficient and effective 'keeping-in-touch' scheme could have paid dividends. The morning session was crammed with further thought-provoking presentations: Christine Osborne of Women in Dentistry, highlighted the need for local mentoring; David Smith, the chairman of COPDEND who had the idea of the conference, spoke in his role as postgraduate dean of the Northern Deanery, lamenting the situation that the potential of the 'Keeping in Touch' scheme had not been realised and that only a minority of dentists leaving practice had heard about it. Alan Lawrence, who expertly organised the entire day, described a typical refresher course for dentists wishing to get back to practice from his experience gained at the Royal London Hospital since these courses were started in 1989 and, to emphasise its success, Haydee Hatzell spoke about her participation in the most recent one.

The initiatives in medicine to deal with their similar problem were shared by the postgraduate dean, Dr Elisabeth Paice, who, when challenged as to how they had acquired larger sums of money to maintain retaining systems in medicine, gave sound advice, applicable to most enterprises: 'establish the demand, then set the budget'. Lunch was almost forgotten as I chaired a lively panel discussion to end the morning session. The first speaker was Robin Wild, the chief dental officer, who emphasised that 'it was now an urgent issue and high up on the dental agenda'.

The speakers during the afternoon contributed a continuing feast of information for postgraduate dental deans to produce strategic plans to improve retraining and retaining for dental practitioners and, as observed by the final speaker, John Tiernan, 'it was a matter of working together to make it happen'. As we dispersed, Robin Wild casually remarked to me that I was going to be approached to undertake a project on women which would involve travelling but, with no further elaboration, I was left to wonder what he had in mind.

On my return from Mexico, besides the daunting piles of letters and journals, there were also numerous answerphone messages. One was from the personal assistant of the Permanent Secretary at the Department of Health, Chris Kelly, extending an invitation to lunch. This proved to be a delightfully relaxed occasion as we talked about my time at the GDC, and shared my future plans. As I was now retired, I seemed to have become the first choice to peer into a crystal ball and do some 'visioneering' in dentistry. Already, I had several lectures lined up for the spring: April in Washington, speaking at the American Association of Dental Schools, 'Expanding horizons – where do we go from here?' and, following the same theme a fortnight later, I had been invited to give the Tom Farrell lecture at the Dental Practice Board annual conference in Eastbourne. The month of May promised to be equally occupied with presentations, as I had been selected as one of three speakers to take part in 'Talking Points in Dentistry', the biggest dental postgraduate event in the UK. Over 3,000 of the dental team were destined to pack into nine venues around the UK in as many days, so popular was this Roadshow, hosted by Stafford Miller since 1986. My travelling companions were to be Roy Higson, an ever-efficient organiser and compere, John Tiernan, and Sverker Toreskog from Sweden, both acclaimed as lecturers of master class quality. My three-quarter hour presentation was expounding on my favourite topic: 'Teamwork Opportunities' which neatly coincided with the launch of the 240-page fifth volume and CD, 'Practice Management with Teamwork'. While this promised to be a fun-packed fortnight, beforehand I had plenty of work to keep me occupied, compiling my lectures.

I also retained other commitments. I was delighted to be re-appointed a member of the Denplan Advisory Committee and to continue on the Board of the Quality Assurance Agency in Higher Education (QAA). I had been appointed in 1997 as one of six independent directors when the Agency was established in response to one of the recommendations of the Inquiry into Higher Education, chaired by Sir Ron Dearing, which considered that the absence of a single agency within the UK to ensure an integrated process of quality assurance was seen as a grave disadvantage. To have as companions around the boardroom table leaders in higher education, vice-chancellors, principals or chairmen of governors from notable universities and high-fliers from the world of industry, was not only a privilege but also a challenging intellectual experience. By 2000 the Board of fifteen people, had appointed a chief executive, prepared a consultation paper, 'Agenda for Quality' containing proposals for a new framework for quality and standards in higher education, and relocated from London to modern offices in Gloucester, and I had also been assigned as the QAA representative on the Joint Committee with the NHS executive and was therefore involved in planning how to develop the potential of personnel within the health care team.

No sooner had I returned home to Bournemouth from the lunch with Chris Kelly, than I received a phone call from Robin Wild, enquiring how I felt about undertaking the study on women dentists. Much to his astonishment I replied that the topic had not even been raised. This prompted a phone call from the head of the dental branch at the Department of Health, suggesting I might like to undertake a study about women dentists as they wanted to encourage them back to work, especially after career breaks. What a change in fortune. After all the frustrating, and at times protracted, negotiations I had had with the Department of Health to secure funding for my two surveys in 1975 and 1985, I was now being offered the opportunity to garner up-to-date information. Amazingly, I felt ambivalent towards the suggestion. Surely it was time now for a younger woman to take up the baton. Nor could I contemplate undertaking a study without the assistance of Don Neal, my statistician, who had died a few years previously, but when I raised this as an issue I was informed that this should not be seen as a problem because I would be able to work with the professionals in the Statistical Division at the Department of Health.

Somewhat reassured, I agreed to travel to London to discuss further details about the project which they had in mind. In the meantime, I began to draft a possible protocol to take with me for discussion. 'Yes,' I told myself, 'women's issues were still close to my heart.' At Richmond House, the Department of Health's impressive office in Whitehall, I met with the head of the dental branch, Helen Robinson, and was joined by members of her team and by the statistician Jim Stokoe. Here was someone with whom I had immediate rapport and as the discussions progressed I felt confident, even enthusiastic, about the whole idea, and the outline of the survey began to take shape. This time I would use the increasingly popular research tool of focus groups, as well as depending on the tried and tested postal questionnaire and submissions from professional organisations. However, I would need strong administrative support and was relieved that Laura Wiles, who had worked with me at the *BDJ* as assistant editor and production editor on Teamwork publications, was willing to be employed as project leader. Her job would entail organising the focus groups, collating responses and coordinating production of the report in collaboration with Jim Stokoe, Pam Murphy and other members of the statistical team who would process the completed questionnaires sent to the 8,355 women dentists in England.

Gradually I was warming to the prospect of the study and viewed that it had the potential to keep me occupied for a year or so, appreciating that there would be fluctuations in the level of activity. A contract was agreed and I was told that I would be designated as Adviser to the National Health Service Executive of the Department of Health. Suddenly, I realised that there was no turning back, when I was informed that the Health Minister with responsibility for dentistry, Lord Philip Hunt, would announce on Friday 16 June that the department had commissioned a new study of the experiences and ambitions of women working in dentistry: the NHS, at long last, wished to be better employers. 'Dame Margaret will canvass opinion as widely as possible . . . she will make her recommendations to the department in March 2001.'

This was an incredibly tight schedule, so, with no time to lose, a letter was despatched on 4 July to fifty-four national organisations requesting a response within three months to seven questions and aiming to discover, amongst other issues, whether the schemes in operation to assist women at work or to attract them back after a career break were proving successful.

Undoubtedly due to the unprecedented press coverage given to the study 'Better Opportunities for Women Dentists', there was a great response – 119 written responses from major organisations and prominent individuals. Encouragingly, the British Dental Association compiled its response after extensive consultation amongst its members, which included a limited survey, a focus group, and interaction on its website. This ringing endorsement and support from the BDA was in stark contrast to the attitude taken in 1986, which resulted in the formation of the Women in Dentistry organisation. It seemed that, at last, the BDA was aware of the real barriers facing the increasing number of women, not only in the workplace but when trying to play a full part in the committee structure of a male-dominated and led trade union. The forward-looking thinkers had realised that this was more than a survey: it was a superb opportunity to influence future strategy on the role of women in the profession, as well as to improve the practising life experiences of all dentists.

Adhering to my maxim that the quality of the results and value of a survey depend on the time and effort expended on designing, refining and piloting the questionnaire, I beavered away with Jim Stokoe and his statistical team to have the questionnaire ready for despatch at the beginning of November. At the same time, focus groups were arranged around the country and the first one was fixed for 9 August in London and would be viewed as a pilot to test the format and conduct of future groups, as well as to ensure that the questionnaire covered the main issues of concern. Each focus group was held in the early evening for a couple of hours, ending with an informal chat over coffee and sandwiches and I was reliant on colleagues in each region to furnish me with ten names of people whom I could approach to take part. The willingness of dentists, men and women, to be involved, was remarkable and emphasised to me how much they relished the opportunity to share their views and to make their frustrations known in a closed group. I led each group with Laura and the plan was to traverse England in two weeks – Taunton, Runcorn and Solihull first, followed by Newcastle, York, Sheffield and Slough. The Talking Points Roadshow in May was to prove invaluable experience.

As a family we enjoy marking birthdays and my 65th birthday was no exception. Colin and Claire came to stay for the weekend in Bournemouth and on my return from the hairdressers, Claire handed me a note of a phone call she had taken while I was out. 'Can we book a phone call for Monday morning?' ran the message from the personal assistant to Chris Kelly, at the Department of Health. Naturally, I was surprised at the identity of the caller but I had to contain my curiosity as my homecoming was well past office hours. On Monday, when the phone call was eventually made, I discovered that it was to set up a meeting with the Permanent Secretary for the next occasion I was in London. I explained that I was holding the first focus group at the Royal Society of Medicine in Wimpole Street on the Wednesday evening and staying overnight. Because a meeting had already been arranged to meet the dental branch later on the Thursday morning to give a progress report on the women's project, a time was fixed for me to see the Permanent Secretary beforehand without further explanation. I was left to speculate as to why Chris Kelly wished to see me. Perhaps he too was interested to discover how the study was progressing, given its high profile through the Minister's statement when it was commissioned. Alternatively, I mused, in view of the publication of 'The NHS Plan for England' the previous month, he may have considered that, as a recent past president of the GDC, I would be a suitable candidate to chair the proposed Council for the Regulation of Health Care Professions which had the interesting remit to oversee the existing professional regulatory bodies, of which one was the General Dental Council.

After being ushered into the beautifully appointed office of the Permanent Secretary and exchanging pleasantries over a cup of coffee, I was completely unprepared for what followed. They were asking me to deliver the dental strategy. This was a bolt out of the blue. The idea had not been entertained in my musings because the dental profession had been waiting with increasing impatience and frustration for the appearance of the dental strategy promised two years previously by the former Health Minister, Alan Milburn, during his keynote address to the BDA at its annual conference in Harrogate. Then, as a postscript, Chris Kelly added that I would also be the Chief Dental Officer (CDO). The rapidity of these two extraordinary suggestions left me reeling. I thought I must be dreaming because I was not aware that the CDO post was vacant; the present incumbent was not due to retire for another year. Of one thing I was sure; it would be impossible to commute daily from Bournemouth to Whitehall, or work full-time, as I was still very involved with the women's survey. When I shared these latter thoughts, I was assured that they were not insurmountable and he clearly appreciated that I was more than a little bewildered by the rapid turn of events. Chris Kelly handed me a draft copy of the strategy, inviting me to take it away to read and to convey my decision about the job by the time he returned from annual leave at the beginning of September. I had less than three weeks to make up my mind.

As I left Richmond House, I could still not believe that I was in possession of the most wanted document in dentistry. I crossed Whitehall and made straight for St James's Park so that I could sit down and have a look at the draft dental strategy, away from prying eyes. Excitedly I scanned the opening chapters but when I read the opening paragraph in Chapter 4, I stopped. 'The skills of the whole dental team will be maximised and used to the full.' A couple of pages later I noticed that the GDC's proposals, which had been approved at my final Council meeting in May 1999, were listed: the statutory registration of all professionals complementary to dentistry (PCDs), the creation of new team members, the clinical dental technician and orthodontic therapist, as well as allowing dental therapists to work in general dental practice. 'The Government supports the principles behind these proposals.' Was this to be the opportunity to deliver my dream of team dentistry?

I made my way back to the BDA headquarters in Wimpole Street for a prearranged meeting to give quotes about the women's project for inclusion in an article that was being prepared for the *BDA News*, a magazine sent to all members of the Association. Then I met, by chance on his way out to lunch, Michael Watson, the BDA Policy Adviser and a shrewd commentator on the dento-political landscape. By now, after the morning's unprecedented excitement, I was ready for a bite to eat, so together we made our way to a nearby hostelry. It did not take long for me to learn about the BDA's despair and mistrust of the Government's intentions for NHS dentistry, the absence of the dental strategy and, as a consequence, the lack of rapport with Department of Health officials. How amazed he would have been to know that the 'absent' dental strategy was inches away from him, concealed in my bag!

Anxious to share the morning's extraordinary events with Gordon, I phoned home to arrange that he would meet me at Bournemouth station and that we could go straight out for dinner at our favourite Chinese restaurant, as we had a lot of talking to do: I did not want cooking and washing-up to distract our thoughts.

By the time I had finished describing the sequence of events, Gordon, much to my surprise, was enthusiastic and confident about my abilities in the role. 'Margaret, make a success of it and they'll send you to the Lords!' Gordon could see the potential for delivering many of my long-cherished ideals, although he realised that the job was no sinecure. The challenge, however, extended beyond teamworking with which I felt comfortable. It was about improving access to NHS dentistry and ensuring that the Prime Minister's pledge, 'that by September 2001, everyone can get dentistry by phoning NHS Direct', would be honoured. When I first was told about the pledge I was in my last month as President of the GDC and only too thankful that it would not involve me. Now the ball would be firmly in my court. I was acutely aware of my shortcomings in specific service areas and wondered if I was too old to learn the intricate world of general dental practice in the NHS. Some days I felt confident and elated, on other days doubts and misgivings took over. I walked the beach, prayed for guidance, and pondered in the beach hut until, one day at breakfast, Gordon, losing patience with my procrastination, urged me to make up my mind. I wrote the letter; I accepted the job.

There was little opportunity for second thoughts because I was preparing to fly to Stockholm on 6 September to attend the annual meeting of the Association for Dental Education in Europe. The timing of the conference was fortuitous because I was able to hear from many colleagues about their concerns, not only about the non-appearance of the dental strategy but also the future direction of dental education. This all provided essential background information but my biggest test was keeping my secret to myself. However, before leaving Stockholm on the Friday morning, I had been asked to phone Chris Kelly to finalise arrangements. Although he was delighted that I had accepted the job, he asked me to consider working for three days, not the two days I had suggested in my letter. I agreed and so became Chief Dental Officer for England on a fixed-term contract for one year, approved by the Civil Service Commissioners. As I looked out over the rain-drenched Swedish countryside from the taxi conveying me to the airport, I realised that my life was about to change dramatically: my second retirement was postponed.

Once again there was no time for reflection because the second wave of focus groups would begin on Monday 11 September, in Newcastle. Coincidentally there started a shortage of petrol at the pumps due to blockades in France and other parts of Europe as protests took place about increasing fuel prices. In this country there was panic buying, with long queues at petrol stations resulting in rationing, and even the troops were put on alert as the situation deteriorated. By the time we reached Sheffield on the Wednesday, we phoned round the evening's participants to see if they wished to conserve their dwindling supply of petrol rather than use it to drive to the focus group. Not one person wished to opt out. Laura and I were humbled and appreciative of this positive response.

While we were travelling south there had been frantic press activity from the department because they wanted to arrange a day for the launch of the dental strategy and my return to London for the focus group in Slough on the Thursday seemed to present a good opportunity. However, as the petrol crisis deepened, it was decided that it was unseemly to hold a press launch and also a focus group and so Slough was cancelled. Rescheduling for the strategy launch was proving a nightmare as after the Monday of the following week I would be unavailable. Each year when I was working, we had looked longingly at a trip organised during September to America by our local tour operator Bath Travel – fly Concorde from Bournemouth to New York and, after a few days there and in Boston, return to Southampton onboard *Queen Elizabeth 2*. It was Gordon's turn to sample the delights of Concorde travel, even if we did not encounter Robert Redford! Unfortunately, in mid June our dreams were shattered when we watched in horror the television coverage showing Concorde engulfed in flames at the Charles de Gaulle airport in Paris, resulting in all Concorde flights being grounded. The tour operator offered an attractive alternative package: fly in the recently unveiled British Airways upper-deck club class seats to New York, generous reimbursement for 'distress and disappointment', and an allowance to spend on board. We had no intention of forgoing the holiday for the launch of the delayed dental strategy.

On the last possible day, Monday 18 September, members of the dental press were ushered into the Minister's office in Richmond House at lunch-time for a briefing on the dental strategy. Then, in a complete surprise to the assembled journalists, Lord Hunt announced that I was taking over as Chief Dental Officer with specific responsibility for implementing the dental strategy. The dental journalists were not slow to comment. 'The appointment is breathtaking: firstly the post wasn't advertised and secondly it had not been made public that Robin Wild was retiring early,' wrote Caroline Holland in *Dentistry* magazine. John Renshaw, chairman of the BDA executive body, passed his verdict. 'To get a quart out of a pint bottle is something which even Margaret might struggle to contend with.' Many senior members of the profession were very angry that the CDO's post had not been advertised. I began to wonder if some had nurtured ambitions to succeed Robin Wild on retirement and that I had scuppered their plans. I almost felt flattered that my appointment prompted questions from Lord Colwyn, a practising dentist, in the House of Lords enquiring 'whether the position of the CDO had been advertised and, if so, when?' and commenting additionally on the part-time nature of the appointment which the profession read as downgrading the existing full-time appointment. To have the distinction of my name recorded in Hansard, the official report of the Parliamentary debates in the House of Lords, was a new experience but this action alerted me to the disquiet in the profession at the manner of my appointment and it began to dawn on me that some believed that I had crossed the divide between profession and government under the wrong circumstances. I was poacher turned gamekeeper. Caroline Holland enunciated clearly in her column, 'In working for the Department of Health, Dame Margaret is putting her undoubted popularity at risk. That's a high stake to play for.'

Thankfully some comments were more encouraging. Professor John Scott, chairman of deans of dental schools, wrote on their behalf to offer warm congratulations; Peter Kurer my first *BDJ* teach-in lecturer, expressed his delight that 'You have been taken away from the dole queue . . . and thrilled that someone of your experience is going to make it available to the Department.' These supportive comments, while encouraging, added to the pressure. Their high expectations must be fulfilled. It was somewhat eerie to realise that I was now to occupy a post for which I had been rejected when I applied in 1986 at the time of George Gibb's retirement. In retrospect, how wise the members of the appointment panel had been. Even now with fourteen years' additional experience I still felt unprepared for the challenges ahead but I was determined to succeed.

I arrived at Richmond House on Monday 2 October 2000 to start my civil service career at an age when most people are officially retiring! My role as the conduit between the Government and profession was to ensure that the Secretary of State, the Ministers, the Department of Health and numerous Government agencies received appropriate and timely advice in respect of the practice of dentistry and promotion of oral health. The onus was also on me to transmit concerns and comments from the profession to the relevant Government officials. Not much work was done on the first day as I tried not to get lost in the maze of offices and corridors within 79 Whitehall, the Department of Health's headquarters in London. I will always be grateful to Ian Cooper, a dental colleague, who took me under his wing and organised the security pass which I soon appreciated was the key to entry to many department areas, as well as to permit travel on the department's shuttle bus, which assisted greatly in getting to different buildings within the NHS Estate – Skipton House and Hannibal House at Elephant and Castle, and Wellington House at Waterloo. These short trips were also invaluable for meeting colleagues and exchanging information and were far more convivial than a taxi ride. Equally important on the first day was to find a place to live during the week and so, later in the afternoon, I visited several likely premises with the estate agent and finally chose a one-bedroom flat in a magnificent mansion, 105 Hallam Street, directly opposite the accommodation provided by the General Medical Council for its President, Sir Donald Irvine. I felt I was in safe territory and we often met getting our milk and breakfast supplies at the little corner shop nearby in Great Portland Street, and along the road I could catch a bus for the ten-minute ride to Richmond House.

Day two, and I was in at the deep end: an invitation to join an away-day/ conference for the senior management team of the Health Services Division being held at Orton Hall in Peterborough, so it was hot-foot to King's Cross to get the train in time for the start of the conference at 2 p.m. Retreats have always been my favoured way of team building and this lived up to all expectations: superbly organised, objectives and ground rules clearly defined, and for me a unique opportunity to meet, crucially, the senior civil service managers – the branch and division heads based in London and in Leeds headquarters. The entire proceedings were expertly guided by the Health Services director, Dr Sheila Adam, whose skill, knowledge and friendship proved invaluable to me during my time as CDO. She was a much loved mentor to me and to countless others working in, at times, an impersonal and elephantine organisation.

Nevertheless, I was under scrutiny by my new colleagues from inside the civil service; the extraordinary speed and method of my arrival had not gone unnoticed. After an afternoon of presentations we were invited to assemble in the bar prior to dinner to celebrate the promotion and departure of a division head. As a newcomer, quietly sitting watching the jovial occasion get underway, I was suddenly drenched with effervescing champagne as the cork exploded from the bottle. It was an ice-breaker I had not expected. Later, after dinner when the group reconvened to write on a post-it-note about each individual in response to the comment 'Something you do/did which impresses me', the episode in the bar was clearly uppermost in their minds. 'Coped brilliantly with champagne in unusual places'; 'Such aplomb when he poured sparkling wine over you'; 'Good fun, no pretensions'. My induction had been swift and unorthodox, but as I returned to London, I felt I had an affinity with a hardworking, highly-motivated and fun-loving team. Furthermore, I realised that I was not expected to know everything, but that in the large NHS organisation there would always be someone who did. It was useful too that I learnt from the away-day of the wider implications of the NHS Plan and the different workload that would result if the predicted General Election took place in 2001. I was challenged by one of the participants who was intent to improve the health of the prison population. 'Why don't you do something about improving prisoners' oral health?' Why not indeed; I would make it my business to improve the quality and availability of dental services in prison while Chief Dental Officer.

During the second week in my job the long-awaited press release was issued by the Department of Health. 'The Permanent Secretary of the Department of Health, Chris Kelly, today announced the appointment of Dame Margaret Seward as the new CDO. Dame Margaret will succeed Robin Wild, who is taking early retirement from 1 November . . . Now that the strategy has been published, Robin has decided to take this natural break to retire a little early. I wish him and his family many years of well-deserved and happy retirement together,' he said. The critics, the agitators, had now to accept with this announcement the finality of the situation. The Phoenix had risen from the ashes: Margaret was back in a top job.

Not anticipating a return to work in addition to the trip in September to New York, we had also planned to attend the annual meeting of the American Dental Association in Chicago, when, at the luncheon of the Pierre Fauchard Academy, I would receive the coveted honorary fellowship, but throughout there had been no suggestion that these prior engagements should be cancelled. My return to the hub of dental activity in this dramatic fashion was not lost on the Americans. 'Sacked by FDI and head-hunted by Government,' squealed Helen Cherrett, Director of International Affairs, a cry repeated by many overseas colleagues. The arrival of the new millennium had prompted many organisations to focus on the future and the ADA was no exception. 'Today's vision; tomorrow's reality' was the title of its inquiry. In addition to written evidence requested from different dental communities, the Committee of Inquiry held three public meetings to receive oral evidence and share views on the project. My visit to Chicago coincided with the first forum so I was able to tap into the creative thinking outside the UK; the challenges in my new role had global significance. My international contacts nurtured over the years were again set to pay dividends.

My first appearance at a national conference in my new role as Chief Dental Officer was on Thursday 19 October at the scientific meeting of the Oral Health Promotion Research Group which was being held in the fascinating meeting facilities of the Brunei Gallery of the School of Oriental and African Studies in London. When I arrived at registration time there was already palpable excitement amongst the delegates awaiting the arrival of their special guest, the Health Minister, Lord Hunt, because the conference had been chosen as the platform for the announcement of the Government's response to the York Review on water fluoridation which had been published the previous month by the University of

York Centre for Reviews and Dissemination. It was also expected that he would comment on the dental strategy and, of particular relevance to the audience, focus on one of its key themes, which was to involve the community when tackling poor oral health amongst the deprived in society and announce initiatives to promote oral health in new ways through Health Action Zones and Sure Start Schemes aimed to reduce health inequalities and combat poverty.

I was especially interested in the York systematic review of water fluoridation whose authors had examined twenty-six studies on fluoridation, many of which I was familiar with because, when editor of the *British Dental Journal*, I had published the scientific papers about the studies. The good news from Lord Hunt was that the Department of Health had asked the Medical Research Council (MRC) to set up a working group to advise on what additional research was needed to strengthen the evidence available to support the introduction of water fluoridation. Further, he indicated that the Government would encourage health authorities (HAs) with particular dental health problems to consider fluoridating the water as part of its overall oral health strategy, as well as to hold further discussions with water companies and local authorities.

This was a tremendously exciting announcement because I was a staunch advocate of water fluoridation, having seen children with vastly reduced levels of tooth decay who either were fortunate to live in areas of the country where the optimum level of fluoride (one part per million) occurred naturally in the drinking water or in enlightened areas, such as Birmingham, where fluoride had been added to the water supply to achieve the necessary level. My father had also been committed to water fluoridation although, during the early fifties, heated debates took place amongst the public and within the dental profession. A great friend of my father from his student days at Glasgow University was Tom (Mac) McClelland who was vehemently opposed and acquired notoriety by mounting anti-demonstrations in his home town of Andover. Mac was also a frequent visitor to our Enfield home and, as an impressionable and inquisitive teenager, I listened to the many lengthy arguments between Mac and my father. Such a grounding was also to prove valuable when, as editor of the *BDJ*, I would receive letters for publication on fluoridation, although twenty years later most of the opposition from within the dental profession had disappeared. The professional debate had shifted to the medium of fluoride delivery – milk, salt and toothpaste – due to the inordinate delays in getting water fluoridation introduced on a national scale. However, Lord Hunt's pronouncement had returned water fluoridation to centre stage. I was determined that, as CDO, I would do all I could to move the debate along to a positive conclusion.

It had been arranged that at the end of the Minister's speech I would make my way to the next event in my diary, a policy retreat organised by the dental hospitals and schools: 'Planning for the Future'. 'We are going back to the department,' whispered one of the ministerial aides. 'Do you want a lift?' I had to pinch myself to wake up to the fact that I was now 'one of them'. I accepted the ride and was able to benefit from the instantaneous debrief with the Minister and officials and to catch up on future planned activities around the dental strategy. I had arrived at the conference under my own steam, by tube; now I departed in the Minister's car – my life had certainly changed.

Later in the afternoon, when I reached the Four Seasons Hotel at Manchester airport, the conference had been in full swing for nearly two days. I was billed to speak for forty-five minutes before dinner and all were anxious to know about my commitment to dental education and its future development from my new position at the Department of Health. I felt comfortable to be amongst colleagues with whom I had worked over the years: the former Secretary of the BDA, Norman Whitehouse, now professor and dean at Cardiff dental school; Jim Rennie formerly of the GDC who was the prime mover and encourager for me to get recertification off the ground, and Bob Ireland, a keen supporter of dental therapists who ran an innovative training programme in Liverpool and advocated that they should be allowed to work in general dental practice and not solely confined to the community or hospital dental service. In my talk, I explained the thrust of the dental strategy and assured them that I was looking forward to working with them to deliver the highest quality of dental education for future generations of students. Suddenly, I discovered after dinner that everyone wanted 'to have a quiet word' and conversations continued well past midnight. Listening was going to be central to my success as CDO. Indeed to be known as a good listener and one who can keep a confidence is crucial to anyone aspiring to a leadership role. I was determined while in the job to adhere strictly to my long-held belief.

My first month in the new post had been action-packed although every minute proved to be an enjoyable and valuable learning experience. There had also, during this period, been a change at the top of the Department of Health due to combining the roles of Permanent Secretary and NHS Chief Executive, and as a consequence I was disappointed to say farewell to Chris Kelly, now Sir Christopher Kelly, as he took early retirement. The new mandarin was Nigel Crisp who arrived to much acclaim from those who had worked with him previously in the wider NHS. However, I was immensely looking forward to a relaxing weekend at home in Bournemouth with Gordon and a close friend, Tom Fellows, who as Chairman of the Community Health Council in Oxford was also extremely complimentary about Nigel Crisp's abilities; so all augured well for the future.

Our planned Saturday walk was aborted because of heavy rain but it did not dampen our spirits as we set off to the theatre in the Poole's Art Centre to watch *The Mikado* performed by the gifted local Gilbert and Sullivan Operatic Society. On retiring to bed after an extremely enjoyable evening, we decided that if the weather was dry on the Sunday morning we would rise at a reasonable hour and after breakfast take our postponed walk. Luck was in: the sun shone and Tom had joined me in the kitchen as I was preparing breakfast when I heard a loud thud on the ceiling above. As Gordon was still upstairs, I called up from the hall, 'Are you okay?' Getting no reply and seeing all the doors shut, I ran upstairs to see if he had heard me. As I entered the bathroom, I saw Gordon on the floor unable to move or speak. I shouted to Tom, 'Gordon's had a stroke'. The ambulance arrived quickly and soon we were on our way to the Royal Bournemouth Hospital. After several hours in the accident and emergency department, Gordon was transferred to a bed in the acute admissions unit and I was informed that there would be several days of investigation before his transfer to the stroke rehabilitation unit at Christchurch Hospital. The gravity of the situation was now beginning to sink in. Gordon's stroke was confirmed and while, thankfully, there was only transient weakness of his limbs, he had been left with dysphasia, the inability to speak or write. I was due that Sunday evening to return to London in readiness to chair the high profile national roll-out Conference organised jointly by the NHS Executive and NHS Confederation the next day. This was to be the first major step in implementing the dental strategy and delegates included the chairs and chief executives of health authorities, community health trusts, primary care services, and consultants in public health. Scheduled first in the morning was the keynote speech by Lord Hunt who was going to make important funding announcements. Now I faced one of the most difficult decisions in my life. Did I send my apologies or go to London as planned? Gordon was settled for the night, the ward lights had been dimmed and as I took my leave Gordon raised his arm and waved. I collected my car, drove to the station and, with a heavy heart, caught the last train to London.

After a fitful sleep I rose to find that gales and torrential rain had battered most of England with resultant flooding; power lines were down and trains severely delayed or cancelled. With torrential rain still lashing down I decided to get to the hotel, the Swallow International in South Kensington, as soon as possible, having been told that surrounding roads were under water and Gloucester Road and Earl's Court tube stations were closed. It soon transpired that I was the lucky one, as the organisers were taking phone call after phone call, conveying apologies from delegates who were unable to make it or who would be delayed. Then a message alerted us that the Minister travelling from Birmingham would be delayed, with the request to re-schedule the programme so that he could speak in the afternoon. No sooner was this organised than there was a further message from the second speaker, Ian Carruthers, Chief Executive of Dorset Health Authority, informing us that he was marooned, as no trains were running from Poole to Waterloo. 'I will fax his presentation,' said Jenny his PA, 'and the CDO can read it.' This was a great disappointment as no one reading his script could transmit the fervour and determination of Ian to improve dentistry's position in the NHS. 'Dentistry,' he had written, 'is in "catch-up" mode and health authorities should take forward this new challenge.' This was a welcome and laudable aim but it needed Ian's vigour to motivate some of his more reluctant fellow chief executives.

Gradually, delegates trickled in and the prospects for a successful conference were improving, especially with the arrival of two of the three anticipated speakers after lunch. When I had finished reading Ian Carruthers's speech 'Local action in Practice' I was passed a note. 'Minister now back in Birmingham – will not make it in time – you could do speech but NO ANNOUNCEMENTS.' This was devastating news. Many had battled to get to the conference and some were still arriving just to hear the Minister. I decided not to share the news until after lunch because I was sure even under these extraordinary circumstances, a new CDO reading not one but two speeches in succession would not endear me or my cause to senior NHS managers.

Miraculously, my luck turned. The Minister had set out again as the weather was improving and he expected to arrive by tea-time. My challenge was now to keep the delegates until he came. Finally, with great relief to all, Lord Hunt arrived just before 4 p.m. and in his speech announced the location of forty-nine new Dental Access Centres as part of the drive to make NHS dental care more easily available. In addition to this expenditure of £23 million, the Minister also announced the allocation of a further £4 million to the Dental Care Development Fund with the intention that health authorities would get much needed financial assistance to provide more NHS dentistry. After a shambolic start this was indeed a positive note on which to end.

But even more good news was to come when Gail, the secretary taking all the calls during the day, came to me with a message from Margaret Norwood, our minister's wife in Bournemouth: 'I've seen Gordon in hospital, he has had a comfortable night and is doing well.' Gail then added, 'I can't believe you were able to chair the conference under these circumstances. No one would ever have known.' Certainly it had not been easy, but to keep occupied was probably less stressful than sitting worrying at home.

Tom Fellows also phoned to enquire how Gordon was doing. 'Okay,' I volunteered. Tom continued, 'I expect you will be giving up your job?' Events had happened so swiftly that I had not yet thought through the implications. Gordon so wanted me to do it. What was I to do?

CHAPTER 20

'Yes Minister'

GORDON HAD NO INTENTION OF GIVING UP. Doctors were amazed and delighted with his rapid progress so that, within a couple of weeks, he was transferred to the stroke rehabilitation unit at Christchurch Hospital whose excellence of best practice within the NHS had been recognised with a coveted Beacon award. While physical disabilities from a stroke are readily apparent, dysphasia, the inability to communicate, is a hidden disability and can be difficult for people to understand and devastating for the person afflicted. It seemed especially cruel for Gordon, who had spent his professional life teaching students, lecturing, writing textbooks and articles, that the blood clot had damaged the areas of his brain responsible for these activities.

I was given an appointment to meet the speech and language therapist who had been assigned to look after Gordon while on the ward. She came straight to the point. 'Your husband has severe dysphasia so I will tailor a programme to help him to learn to speak and write again. Next time, bring me photos of your family, labelled with their names, and easy reading material of his favourite topic. These simple requests were soon delivered along with a paperback book to accompany the 1999 TV programme *Walking with Dinosaurs*, which became a well-thumbed reading companion. I attended some of the speech therapy sessions with Gordon and to observe the skill and patience of the therapist is an education in itself. She gently, yet firmly, rebuilt Gordon's vocabulary linked to recognition of objects, as well as ensuring that I understood that the speed and extent of the nature of the recovery varied with every case, citing a general prognosis of six to twelve months for major improvements, although progress can continue well beyond that time. It was also as important for me to learn to give that extra time for Gordon to process what he was hearing and what he wanted to say. However frustrating for all concerned, the temptation to finish a sentence or take over the entire conversation for the sake of speed or clarity must be avoided as it impedes recovery and undermines the patient's confidence. I was further encouraged, when meeting new people, to be up front about Gordon's disability during the initial introductions. Armed with this information, people are not left confused, wondering 'Is he deaf or daft?' Certainly this advice has never failed and makes social contact for all concerned less daunting. From the outset, friends were enormously supportive and we all admired Gordon's tenacity and determination to conquer this setback as he methodically completed the 'homework' set by the speech therapist.

At the beginning of December, Gordon returned home and it was now time to discuss the future. 'Would you like me to give up as CDO?' A horrified expression passed over his face, followed with a very discernible 'No.' Now I had an ever greater incentive to succeed: I would do it for Gordon.

While Gordon was in hospital, I kept busy touring the regions to speak at the conferences convened to launch the Dental Strategy. The south-east regional launch took place on 23 November and just a month into the job I was beginning to grasp the depth of anger felt by the profession, not so much about the contents of the strategy, but the fact that they had been excluded during its preparation. No wonder there was mistrust of Government's intentions, a fact I shared with the Minister. I suggested that engagement in the implementation stage was now crucial to its success and wondered if I could convene a steering group of key players, not only to consider the next steps but also to provide new thinking on the main topics identified in the report. I quickly realised that I was fortunate to have a Minister knowledgeable and committed to modernising the NHS dental services, but also one who wanted to draw a line under the past and to build constructive relationships with the profession. Lord Hunt asked me to chair a steering group and to submit names for possible membership, reminding me not to forget to include representatives from patients' groups and the NHS Confederation Organisation, of which he was chief executive before his ennoblement in 1997 and his Government appointment as Parliamentary Under-Secretary of State for Health. The popularity of this move was seen by the positive response to invitations issued to prospective members of the Dentistry Modernisation Steering Group (DMSG), or as John Lowry christened it, 'Dame Margaret Seward's Gang'. It was easy to identify six topics to explore: information technology, educational continuum, quality and regulation, workforce and re-skilling, inequalities of oral health care and patient communication. I soon selected the task group chairman and allocated members to an appropriate group and then allowed each group to work in its own way, preparing a document for consideration by the parent steering group.

Concurrently, the Minister was determined to engage the profession and this was confirmed in an interview published in *BDA News*. 'I realise this (the strategy) is a huge work programme which is why I want to start immediately, together with the BDA, on a shared agenda for turning vision into reality.' Lord Hunt was an astute and hospitable politician who understood the value of an informal get-together over dinner to iron out differences or to share thoughts for the future. Thus, on 18 December, the Minister invited John Renshaw, the Chairman of the BDA executive board, David Hewlett, who had just been appointed head of specialist health services, the dental branch coming under his aegis, and myself, to an evening meal in the Peers Dining Room in the House of Lords. Frank discussions took place and there was total agreement for a new start. Integral to this was the need to develop regular informal communications between the

Department of Health and the BDA outside the necessary and well-established formal negotiating procedures. Immediately, arrangements were made for such a meeting which took place in the New Year, and which I chaired, and we heralded it as the start of 'The New Dawn'. The idea of continuing the informal dinners on a regular basis with alternate hospitality was also confirmed, with John Renshaw offering that the BDA would host the next dinner in two months' time, fielding a wider team from the BDA to include the chairmen of committees, Sue Greening, Tony Kravitz, John Craig and the new BDA chief executive who would, by then, be in post.

It is worth recording how many of the suggestions aired at the December dinner became translated into positive action. The Minister was anxious that the establishment of the 'New Dawn' should be conveyed to the profession, at the same time making sure that they were aware that the Government understood and supported dentists and valued their contribution to the NHS. He was very conscious of the fact, stated over and over again by John Renshaw, that 'the 1992 fee cut is still seen as a scar running through the profession and has never been put right'.

It was considered that a joint venture between the Department of Health and the BDA would be a powerful signal of cooperation and so a competition was organised to identify the best NHS dental practice of the year in England, with the winners attending a high-profile awards ceremony at which the Minister would present the certificates. This idea became translated into the highly successful Focus Awards, a subject I will return to later. As the dinner progressed, a further suggestion was floated: to bring together five or six people from the Department of Health and the Association for a workshop. Led by a skilled facilitator they would brainstorm the future and design the ideal NHS dental service. York was proposed as a possible venue and the meeting would be conducted according to Chatham House Rules, the accepted phrase implying that discussions would be treated with total confidentiality. We were all fired with enthusiasm to undertake some 'horizon scanning', although only too aware that previous attempts in the profession – Tatterstall, Pavitt and Bloomfield – resulted in a lot of talk but little action.

For me, I remain convinced that good communication is key to establishing productive working relationships: everyone values being kept in the picture, so I was relieved that when, during the dinner, I floated the idea of producing a newsletter which would be sent to all dentists in England, John Renshaw enthusiastically supported its publication. Thus, in the spring of 2001, the first *CDO's Digest* was published, later followed by the CDO's website, both important vehicles for conveying news of Department of Health initiatives and progress on delivering other areas of reform.

Another, but controversial, issue raised was attendance at the annual dinner of the Local Dental Committees and while it was always anticipated that a

Government official would be the guest speaker, it was not normally viewed by them as a favourite engagement to have in their diary. Lord Hunt was encouraged and reassured by John Renshaw that the profession would be more than delighted if he would be prepared to come for a second time in June. Now knowing that he would be welcomed, and checking that I was going as CDO and that an invitation would be extended to David Hewlett, the Minister made it clear that he would look sympathetically at an invitation when it came: this was a coup for John.

What an evening it was: a relaxed atmosphere with good food and wine, frank discussions and propagation of new ideas, a convivial method of sorting out long-standing problems and the opportunity to move forward together to seek the solutions. There was also a welcome rapport emerging between the Minister and the blunt and forceful-speaking Yorkshireman, John Renshaw, who had previously been portrayed within the department in a less than complimentary light.

As Parliament was in recess over Christmas and New Year, I was able to spend time in Bournemouth with the family and to mull over the events of my first three months in office, and also to think through my plans for the remaining nine months which had to culminate in delivering the Prime Minister's Pledge. Reflecting on the emerging positive atmosphere there was no doubt that this was enhanced by the arrival of two senior figures, one at the Department of Health, David Hewlett, a civil servant with experience in the wider NHS who brought well-honed interpersonal skills and a determination to modernise the working practices of the dental branch with all its stakeholders, not just the BDA, and to create a coherent primary care dental service fit for the twenty-first century. Over at the BDA a new chief executive had been appointed to take up the reins in the New Year. However, once Ian Wylie's appointment was confirmed during the autumn, I was asked by the Minister to bring him to the Peers Dining Room for tea, when I had my first taste of their Lordships' delicious teacakes which I knew would do untold damage to my girth if eaten regularly. It became clear during that initial encounter that Ian's previous experience and the influential contacts which he developed, particularly as head of Corporate Affairs at the King's Fund, the independent health think-tank, would be invaluable, as indeed proved to be the case.

Before my appointment I was aware that my predecessor had had limited secretarial assistance and in discussions about taking the job I stipulated that I expected to have adequate administrative support. I was cheered when the head of the branch decided to create a new post and trawl for a person to work as my private secretary, and take on some additional pieces of work relating to education and manpower. In the civil service, job vacancies are advertised internally with selection through an interview process. There was considerable interest shown in this new post with a good number of applications received by 1 December, the closing date. An initial sift was conducted by the line-manager-to-be and I was presented with two strong candidates for final selection. It was to be my good fortune that I appointed Steve Collins, who was currently working as Parliamentary Liaison Officer/Correspondence Manager for the Food Standards Agency and had held previous posts in the Department of Health, and was conversant with parliamentary work and procedures, an area in which I was still on a steep learning curve. He swiftly created an effective and efficient Private Office, took on the role of secretary to several standing committees, ensuring that all the paperwork was delivered on time and to a high standard, and accompanied me on official visits which continued unabated. Early in January, when I made a trip to Bristol to launch the Dental Strategy, I found myself pampered, as Steve made all the travelling and meeting arrangements and was on hand to set up, during the conference lunch break, a radio interview on Radio 4's *You and Yours* programme with John Renshaw in the London studio. From comments received over the years it never fails to amaze me how many people hear these chat shows on the car radio or in the shower. On this occasion, Stella Saunders, the regional dental officer in the south-east, picked up the trailer for the interview on her car radio and on reaching her destination, assembled her team to listen and then e-mailed me: 'I thought it left a positive impression of good working relations between yourself and John Renshaw . . . and I was pleased that you slipped into one of your answers the benefit of water fluoridation.' I was encouraged to receive this comment for I was convinced that without the cooperation of the profession it would be impossible to deliver the Prime Minister's Pledge on time and, for me of greatest importance, deliver a modernised NHS dental service for patients.

However grateful I was to have Steve Collins's assistance, it did not solve the secretarial problem of dealing with the escalating correspondence, taking phone calls, maintaining files and sorting my engagement diary in view of the increasing requests for lectures and visits, including opening many of the newly-established access centres. I still wonder how many of the plaques I unveiled remain in situ, and perhaps a tour of the locations could be an interesting way to occupy me in retirement. When I began in October, I was allocated a secretary to share with the 'out of hours' medical team working in the adjoining office, but due to their increasing workload there was little time left to share. I became increasingly frustrated and, failing to resolve the situation locally, I took my problem to the top of the personnel department at the Department of Health. Later, I was to learn that in the civil service this is not the conventional way to do things.

Nevertheless, it brought an immediate response, as I was contacted by a kindly man from the personnel department who had been delegated to resolve my problem. He fully appreciated my untenable position and suggested that I should meet a woman who had been on secondment but had now returned temporarily to the personnel department, and who was hoping for a permanent placement working for a senior person and a job with greater responsibility. This brief pen-picture sounded promising so we arranged to meet at the end of the following day. Although it was a cold January afternoon, I was completely unprepared for the arrival of a woman swathed in a spotty fluffy 'fur' coat, matching hat, and rings on every finger with beautifully manicured fingernails decorated with eye-catching designs. She had a twinkle in her eye and an infectious laugh and there was immediate rapport; a sense of humour is essential for anyone to work with me. I was soon to discover that her knowledge of the civil service was encyclopaedic after a lifetime working in different departments: she was the very sort of personal assistant I needed. I was confident that with Steve as my Private Secretary, we would make a strong team to grace the Office of the Chief Dental Officer. Thus, Sonia Chadband was offered the post and started on Tuesday, 5 February, and like Steve remained with me throughout my tenure as CDO; no one could have wished for more loyal colleagues.

It was fortuitous that my Private Office was at last sorted because on 14 December we were advised that the Health Select Committee would undertake an inquiry into dentistry with the following terms of reference: 'To examine whether the Government's strategy, *Modernising NHS Dentistry: Implementing the NHS Plan*, will improve access to NHS dentistry in the long term.' There were glum faces around the dental branch on hearing this announcement and the reason, as I was soon to discover, was that it meant more briefings and reports at a time when we were focused on delivering the Prime Minister's Pledge and implementing the various new initiatives. However, parliamentary select committees have a vital role to play in our democracy and exist to scrutinise the work of Government departments. Each committee comprises about a dozen MPs from all political parties and submits a report of its findings to Parliament, to which the department under scrutiny must respond within a stipulated timescale. The committee is assisted by its own appointed scientific adviser, in this instance Bryony Soper, and invitations are issued to interested parties to submit written evidence. It is obvious that the time available to hear oral evidence is strictly limited and even those selected as witnesses are encouraged to commit their comments to paper. The taking of oral evidence was scheduled for the morning of 15 February and it is customary for the Government's team to appear at the end of the session. Representatives from the British Dental Association, the General Dental Practitioners' Association, two health authorities and two general dental practitioners had already made their points of view known to the committee, so we fully anticipated being grilled by members of the committee on areas of concern raised during the morning in addition to opinions which would have been submitted in written memoranda from individuals and institutions. Preparation was akin to a finals oral examination and trying to 'spot the questions' could be a true bonus.

I can remember, as if it was yesterday, arriving suitably attired in my smartest outfit at the St Stephen's entrance to the House of Commons en route to give oral evidence to the committee. After passing through security checks, compulsory for everyone irrespective of my Department of Health's identification badge, I quickly checked the lists displayed in the grand Central Lobby of the House of Commons to find out where the hearing would take place. Then it was hot-foot along the long corridor, off which were the individual committee rooms, where I met up with Lord Hunt, the principal witness for the Government, and the head of the dental branch. We did not have long to wait – 'The Committee is ready for you', and we were ushered into a small, heavily panelled room, its high windows overlooking the Thames, and tightly packed with members of the profession, as well as those who had already given evidence, and the press. The atmosphere was tense and sticky: it had been a long session. We were escorted to the three vacant chairs behind a small table in the middle of the room and positioned in front of the committee members arranged around a horseshoe-shaped table with the chairman, David Hinchcliffe, Labour MP for Wakefield, seated at the centre. I took the chair to the left of the Minister and was forewarned that he would invite me to deal with questions or comments on clinical matters. For the initial ten minutes or so the Minister was completely in control and obviously satisfying the committee with his knowledgeable replies. Suddenly, I found myself in the firing line as Dr Peter Brand, the Lib-Dem MP for the Isle of Wight, referred to written evidence which he had received from a dentist citing the findings of a survey in 1994 which demonstrated the low success rate (10 per cent) of NHS endodontic (root-canal) treatment measured against European technical standards. I dug deep into my memory bank but endodontics was well outside my expertise. I countered, stating that 'there was no hard evidence to suggest that the quality of NHS dentistry is not up to the standards patients expect' and pointed to the various regulatory systems in place. Dr Brand was too astute to be deflected from his quest for percentages. 'Send me a note giving the numbers of root-canal fillings that fail,' which kindly let me temporarily off the hook. However, I felt much more at home during our half-hour grilling when I was asked about the dental team and my ongoing review of women dentists, especially as I was able to share some preliminary findings and trends which had been prepared for me by Jim Stokoe, our senior statistician at the department.

Once the committee had departed, yet still with adrenalin pulsating through my veins, I joined the people gathering outside in the committee corridor exchanging experiences about the morning's proceedings. I was far from happy about my answer to the endodontic 'googly' but my dental colleagues, whom I thought would have enjoyed seeing their CDO put on the spot, were quick to console – 'Rather you than me' – and then we all went off for lunch together.

The Parliamentary Relations Unit, better known in the civil service as 'Parly' operates within a strict timetable and we were given a week in which to read the transcript of the oral hearing and make amendments and then, again within strictly defined guidelines, to proofread the printed version of our submitted written evidence. It was in this submission that Lord Hunt made the Government's case for a long overdue review of the dental workforce and so it was most encouraging that, in the Final Report of the Health Select Committee published on Tuesday 27 March, not only did the Committee endorse the proposed review of the workforce, but also recommended that it should 'cover the whole dental team and take account of the CDO's review of women dentists' working practices and further advise on the frequency of subsequent workforce reviews'. The Committee further stated unequivocally that 'we consider that the GDS (General Dental Services) remuneration system is the heart of the problem' and observed that, despite comprehensive reviews in the past, 'it remains unchanged'. The concluding paragraph of the Committee was hard-hitting: 'We believe there are serious concerns and that (the recent report) *Modernising NHS Dentistry* lacks the weight to alter fundamentally what is a deteriorating situation. We would suggest that a longer term strategy for dentistry within the NHS is still badly needed.' This was in accord with the reason for convening the Dentistry Modernisation Steering Group so that blue-sky thinking of future issues could be undertaken, which could contribute to the design of a longer-term strategy for dentistry.

Despite my initial misgivings, when I observed the concerns in the dental branch at the time the inquiry was announced, and the enormous amount of additional work for my private secretary, Steve Collins, who took responsibility for assembling all the relevant paperwork and managing the timetable, which he accomplished admirably, I remain convinced that the critical and independent examination of a topical issue by the influential House of Commons Select Committee brings benefits, as the recommendations provide powerful levers for change.

Personally, I found the appearance before a select committee a unique experience, as has been testified by Dr Susie Sanderson, the first female chair of the BDA Executive Board, who appeared some seven years later in front of a Health Select Committee to give oral evidence in an inquiry into the workings of the new 2005 contract in dentistry. She wrote in the March 2008 issue of the *BDJ*: 'I didn't sleep much the night before. There was a lot going round in my mind. Huge responsibility. I needed more information at my finger-tips than I'd had to have in my head for finals. Could I remember the relevant figures? Crucial not to mislead.' I can identify with every sentiment expressed and, like Susie, I would not have missed this high-profile opportunity to speak about dentistry.

Working closely with Ministers deepened my admiration as I watched them juggle so many competing demands on their time at Westminster, as well as the needs of their constituents on whose vote they depended for a seat in the House of Commons. The enormity of a Minister's portfolio was daunting. Dentistry could be just one of twenty or thirty areas of responsibility, each craving attention. Clearly, Ministers depended on civil servants to brief them on various issues and as Edwina Currie MP candidly admits in her book *Life-Lines*, 'I cannot watch *Yes*

Minister because it is too close to real life.' Edwina was correct in her appraisal of the TV programme but I did enjoy watching it and remained ever hopeful that I would pick up hints and tips for my job along the way.

As a fledgling Chief Dental Officer I was tutored on how to produce Ministerial briefings, and made aware that the Minister has limited time to read or assimilate detailed briefs. This is where my editorial experience was useful and I quickly learnt that the secret was to commit key points onto a single sheet of A4 paper, avoid a surfeit of statistics, point out controversial areas or 'elephant traps', and suggest possible responses and conclude with the all-important, 'Line to Take' which encapsulated the department's position on the particular topic. The results of one's efforts could be heard when the Minister spoke in the debate in the House; omissions were soon laid bare under questioning from members on the Opposition benches. Those responsible for preparing the briefing would normally slip into the designated area in the Chamber at the time the Minister was due to rise to make his statement, which too often was late in the evening near the end of the business of the House. Dentistry was not the most captivating of topics and in the House of Lords where our Minister made his statements it could be most eerie, as many of their Lordships would have already departed. Our presence was not only to hear the outcome of the debate, but also to be available to provide additional information or clarification. No direct contact with a Minister was permitted but he could 'send a note' and the skill was to write quickly a succinct response which was then delivered back to the Minister.

I soon also became conversant with the means of obtaining decisions from the Minister through the use of written minutes, termed 'submissions', which were sent to his Private Office. It was not unusual before the request was agreed for the Minister to wish to discuss further details with those responsible for its preparation and I would attend such meetings as appropriate. Contact with Lord Hunt was also through his regular 'stock-take' meetings when we were given the opportunity to convey progress on the dental agenda and benefit from his advice and encouragement. There were additional opportunities for civil servants to use writing skills: drafting speeches for public engagements or providing certain paragraphs, taking into account the Minister's style of delivery and most importantly, allowing time for his amendments; briefings for visits initiated by the department or invitations from outside organisations; Parliamentary questions, either written or oral for which again the reply had to be concise yet structured when the Minister gave the response from the Dispatch Box.

It was impossible to meet with every organisation or deputation who wished 'to have a word' with the Minister, as often as not to voice frustration at the long delay of some legislation or problems with new working practices. When a request came from members of a dental association, my advice and that of others within the branch, would be sought as to its standing or claim for a meeting and the pen profiles of those attending would be prepared.

When I was President of the General Dental Council and we were granted a date for a meeting with the Minister, it was usually after much pressure and persuasion on the CDO. However, once a date had been secured in the Minister's diary, our deputation would be carefully chosen and rehearsed, for we did not wish to squander the precious time. We would arrive at Richmond House, check in at the reception desk and then wait to be escorted up the long and very grand sweeping staircase to a waiting room near the Minister's suite of offices. There was no opportunity to get lost; when the Minister was ready to see us (and they always seemed to be running late), we were collected and shown into the Minister's office, when I was always surprised to see the CDO and officials from the dental branch already in the room. Now, with roles reversed, I discovered that we were not called until the Minister was free; unlike our visitors we did not have to hang around. Then when the call came we would take the back stairs to his office and go through any last minute changes or additions to the already supplied briefing, before the delegation was shown in.

It could be frustrating for all sides, as happened on more than one occasion, when just as we reached a critical stage in a long-awaited meeting, the Division Bell in the House would sound and the Minister would have to dash off to cast his vote, normally being ferried there and back in his chauffeur-driven car, although with the congestion of London traffic around Parliament Square some found it quicker to go on foot.

The relentless pace of life as a Minister is awesome and demands total commitment, extraordinary stamina and complete understanding and support of family and friends due to the frequent and prolonged absences from home. Self-inflicted maybe, but I am grateful that there are talented people who take on this role to preserve our democratic society.

The excitement of the Health Select Committee was not allowed to distract us from ensuring that health authorities fully understood their role in delivering the Prime Minister's Pledge. This was the first time that each authority had to produce dentistry action plans in which they had to set out the extent of its access problem and, more importantly, its plans to resolve the situation. I was greatly relieved that Lord Hunt realised that we needed an 'enforcer' and at his request a consultant facilitator, Mike Waterland, was appointed. He was an inspired choice, having recently retired as the Chief Executive of the Birmingham Health Authority and was thus able to establish rapport as he understood the difficulties facing authorities in tackling their new role. With unlimited energy and enthusiasm, Mike visited the regions and every chief executive in each health authority and within a few months he had signed off many dentistry action plans, or provided additional funding to enable the authority to reach its objective. My spirits soared for, with Mike's input especially when we shared speaking engagements, I began to believe that delivering the Prime Minister's Pledge by the end of September was now a real possibility.

It is worth recalling that the Pledge was predicated on the ability of people with dental problems to use NHS Direct, the 24-hour telephone helpline which aimed to do for the health service what cash machines had done for banking. Patients would be assessed through a triage system based on whether their clinical need was routine, urgent or emergency, and then be provided with information about their nearest dentist offering NHS dental treatment.

However, after several months in the post, I was discovering that many of the NHS exciting initiatives and accompanying generous funding were focused on doctors and nurses. Was the exclusion of dentists intentional or historical? I decided it was now time to challenge this state of affairs, starting with one of the Department of Health's 'Big ideas' which was the setting up of National Service Frameworks (NSF) in various areas of health and social care, from coronary care and mental health to strokes and cancer care, the aim of which was to empower authorities to improve services.

In charge of the NSF for Older People's Care was a delightful, youthful-looking and highly approachable consultant geriatrician, Professor Ian Philp, to whom I conveyed the dental profession's dismay that they had not been included in any of the early discussions regarding the development of the framework. My personal approach brought a positive and immediate riposte from Ian. 'I would be delighted to meet with the BDA.' He did and also gave an excellent interview for the Association's *News* magazine about his role as Tsar, the media's title for the men at the helm of the various special areas of health care. At one stage they tried to dub me as Tsarina, but I did not encourage it as this to me portrayed a big stick approach, which I wanted firmly to leave behind.

There was further comment in the BDA *News* from Sue Greening, the chair of community and public health dentistry, who later became the third woman to hold office as BDA President. 'It is refreshing to see dentistry and oral health being included at the start of a process seeking to develop good practice. The BDA had an extremely useful meeting with Professor Philp and we are now involved in the development of the single assessment process to ensure that oral health problems are picked up at an early stage.'

This direct approach and positive outcome gave me encouragement to take instant action when it was announced that there was to be formed a National Children's Task Force. During a coffee break of the department's Top Team meetings, to which I was now invited (the chief medical and nursing officers had been included since its inception), I met the newly appointed children's Tsar, Professor Al Aynsley-Green. 'I am disappointed that you don't have a dentist on your task force,' I gently chided and suggested the name of our profession's highly regarded paediatric dentist, Professor John Murray. The Tsar agreed that he would be an excellent choice, so John was invited to participate and, as predicted, he gave his passion and commitment to the task, ensuring that the dental needs of children were not forgotten.

While my confidence in adopting the direct approach was growing, so was my realisation that dentistry had to shoulder some of the blame. 'If you don't ask, you don't get' but the request has to be directed to the individual who has the power to make a difference. With this in mind my next target for inclusion was the UK Cancer Screening Committee. Oral cancer occurs more commonly than cervical cancer but, when there is early diagnosis and treatment, the prognosis is most favourable. Shortly after my request to the Committee Secretary, Dr (now Sir) Muir Gray, I took a phone call. 'I have spoken to the chairman,' he said, 'and she has asked me to send you the agenda papers for the next meeting.' I was even more encouraged when I spotted that oral cancer screening was down as an item for discussion. The outcome was a technical workshop, which was most timely, as currently commercially available were expensive screening kits with unproven effectiveness. The findings of the workshop did not commend oral cancer screening kits: biopsy remained the most reliable diagnostic tool.

Early in the spring, the six task groups of the Dentistry Modernisation Steering Group had finalised their reports and one of the key themes from the Information Technology Task Group, ably led by Professor Chris Stephens, was the need for a communications and information technology strategy for dentistry, aimed at linking all branches together and, most importantly, to the rest of the health care services. Generally there was excitement at the developments taking place within the NHS to produce a national electronic patient record card and an electronic library storing valuable information for ready access by practitioners. Dentistry was again on the periphery of these initiatives but, undaunted, the task group in its recommendations advocated a national communication and IT forum for dentistry in order to discuss medium and long term needs and to coordinate dental communication and information technology issues.

But how was I to transmit these aspirations to the eminent scientist, Sir John Pattison, who was director of research, analysis and information at the department and in charge of the NHS IT programme? A couple of weeks later, I was mingling on the forecourt of Richmond House in Whitehall, waiting to be transported by one of the department's cars to a meeting of the Top Team at a Kensington Hotel. Two of us got into the next available car and I found myself sitting in the rear seat beside Sir John. Before he had the chance to open his bulging folder marked 'top priority', I passed him a copy of the task group report which, fortunately, I had bundled together with my papers for the meeting. Sir John said he understood my concern at the lack of engagement with dentistry and promised to see what he could do. 'Now, I must get on with my e-mails' – and I kept quiet for the remainder of the journey. Sir John was true to his word. The needs of dentistry were recognised and the profession's IT gurus, Chris Stephens, Tony Jenner, Pat Reynolds and Ken Eaton, demonstrated that dentistry had much to offer to the development of the NHS IT programme. Was the encounter leading to the successful outcome coincidence or providence? I favour the latter view.

On returning to my office one afternoon I picked up a message: 'Please phone Number Ten.' Was the Prime Minister inviting me to hear how I was doing in delivering his Pledge? This proved to be a flight of fancy when I discovered that it was the Prime Minister's special health adviser who had decided it was time to meet the new CDO. The invitation, however, provided me with a rare opportunity to get through the impressive and well-guarded iron gates that seal off Downing Street from Whitehall. I passed through the customary security checks, glanced around for a sighting of the famous cat, and then stepped up and knocked at the famous front door. This was promptly opened by a policeman and as I entered he consulted his list to ensure that I was expected and then directed me to the waiting room off the rectangular entrance hall. Number Ten is a house which is much larger than it looks from the outside because it is in fact two houses, one situated behind the other and joined by a long passageway with an extra wing linking the two buildings. I did not have long to peruse the selection of daily newspapers as I was soon collected and escorted through the narrow passageway and then up the often photographed stairs with the walls adorned with signed photographs of former Prime Ministers: John Major's was the most recent although I noted there was plenty of space to accommodate Tony Blair's in due course. I was ushered into a large airy room and encouraged to admire the impressive views over Horse Guards Parade with the vast expanse of St James's Park beyond, and to look at the priceless paintings on the walls on loan from the National Collection. Then it was down to business although, sitting on the chintz covered sofa by the fireplace, I felt it was a letdown in such grandiose surroundings to be drinking instant coffee out of disposable cups. This did not detract from a most satisfying meeting, especially when I was told on taking my leave, 'Contact me if needed. Remember I am here to help you remove any "road blocks" stopping you making progress,' an offer which I kept in mind several months later when I ran into a period of procrastination over some legislation. I also discovered that the band of Prime Minister's special advisers are not universally popular within Whitehall and the old hands in the civil service eye them with great suspicion. I like to speak as I find, and the health team at Number Ten proved helpful to me and I in turn ensured that they were kept briefed and one of their number was invited to join us when discussing our vision for the future at the June Retreat.

The annual conference of the BDA was a flagship event and it was a prime occasion for an appearance of the Minister, especially if he wanted to make an important announcement to a captive audience. Now, with the arrival of the 'New Dawn', the Association invited the department to sponsor at its May three-day conference in Harrogate a full three-hour morning session on 'Modernising Dentistry'. We could select our own speakers and the keynote address to close the session would be given by Lord Hunt. I was anxious that this unique opportunity would prove to be the showcase which the department badly needed, to explain not only the dental strategy, but also the culture change occurring in the NHS. Only the previous month the Secretary of State, Alan Milburn, had announced that the balance of power was shifting away from the centre to primary care trusts and other local health bodies in England to achieve the objective of a patient-centred service. Laudable and high ideals. The NHS Plan, and especially the role of health authorities, was not understood by dentists and I considered the best person to give a view was one of their own. Fortunately, Tom Dowell, who had been a leading light in the BDA when I was editor of the *Journal* and a much respected chairman of the Association's health and science committee, was now chairman of the large Avon health authority. When we discussed together the outline of his presentation I began to realise it was the Association's loss that Tom had forsaken BDA politics for personal reasons, but how valuable it was now to have a highly articulate and intelligent dentist occupying an influential position at a time of change. During his talk he reiterated the core observation from the NHS Executive. 'Dentistry has been isolated from the rest of the NHS and is a low priority for health authorities.' Tom concluded: 'The only long-term solution is fundamental reform of the outdated systems of providing NHS dental care.' I could not have chosen a better person, especially as I was aware that the Minister would be listening.

Lord Hunt was anxious to take a philosophical approach so he rehearsed some of the themes to be covered in his speech with John Renshaw and Tony Kravitz during our informal dinner in April. It was evident that trust was maturing when the Minister offered to share an early draft of his speech with John and Tony for comments, and in return they agreed to share their public response which would be issued after the speech was delivered. It was a packed auditorium in Harrogate's Conference Centre on 4 May when the Minister stepped up to the podium. No one wanted to miss his speech. 'What I am interested in,' he said, 'is building on the sensible, constructive and grown-up discussions that I've enjoyed having with the BDA . . . I meet John Renshaw, Tony Kravitz and Sue Greening on a regular basis and long may that continue.' It would have been unimaginable for this comment to be made twelve months previously; networking was working.

Then Lord Hunt launched into the first of his 'morning's news bulletins' – details of the Modernisation Fund, £35 million to help general dental practitioners refurbish their surgeries, buy new kit or install IT systems. Next was an announcement to make use of the order-making powers passed in 1999, during my time as president of the GDC, to pave the way for a new and smaller General Dental Council with increased representation from lay members and professionals complementary to dentistry. The Minister then returned to the findings of the Health Select Committee a few months previously. 'It gave us all a chance to stop and think about where we are going and what else we could do.' He continued: 'I'm happy to announce today that there will be a fundamental review of the workforce, the first since the 1980s, involving the whole dental team and this is to be an ongoing review.'

His final announcement was to launch the Focus Awards, a new annual joint initiative between the department and the association, open to all NHS dental practices. 'I want to recognise innovations that create outstanding patient-focused care and nomination forms are available today. I've got an open mind, no hidden agenda and I'm ready to listen . . . we'll make much better progress down those paths if we travel together.' With his parting shot, 'Thank you and enjoy the rest of your conference' the Minister was gone and the CDO was left to field the questions. During my time at the department I became accustomed to being offered up as a substitute: a non-enviable mantle. Although cynicism abounds when a Minister cries off fulfilling an engagement, it is often at short notice due to a debate in the House or summoned by his superiors, and no one is more concerned at the public perception and reaction than the Minister at a situation which is for the most part outside of his or her control.

Appearing on the horizon was the 2001 June General Election and, once Parliament was dissolved, the corridors of the House of Commons became deserted as MPs returned to canvass in their constituencies and likewise all business in the House of Lords was suspended. This period before an election is known as 'purdah' and the electoral rules ban the use of the civil service to influence the election and prohibits policy announcements. Although the possibility of a Tory victory seemed remote, we were obliged to prepare customised briefing papers for each of the major parties which might be called upon to form the next Administration.

Nevertheless, we were granted permission to continue planning for the June Retreat on the basis that whichever party was successful, the need for blue-sky thinking on the future of primary care dentistry remained. Similarly, we were given the go-ahead to draft the Minister's Speech which he was to give at the Local Dental Conference dinner on 14 June at the Café Royal in Regent Street, by which time the result of the General Election would be known. As this would be Lord Hunt's second appearance at the annual dento-political event, he was only too aware that the audience could be highly critical, if not hostile. The Minister considered that his speech at the BDA Conference in Harrogate was a sound starting point: the workforce review, tackling treadmill issues and how dentists are paid. 'So my message to you this evening is there is no hidden agenda, nothing has been decided and the future is wide open. It is for us to shape it together.' The confidence of the Minister was such that in his concluding paragraph he said, 'If you are kind enough to invite me back next year, I will look forward to coming, and I hope that we will, together, have made considerable progress.'

Labour were swept to power and Tony Blair was once again invited by the Queen to form a Government, first announcing members of his Cabinet. To my relief, Alan Milburn was reappointed Secretary of State for Health. Although the junior ministerial appointments had not been finalised it was widely anticipated especially with the same Secretary of State, that Lord Hunt would continue to be responsible for dentistry. This assumption was treated as a foregone conclusion and the Minister in the interim called a stock-take in his office. As the team made their exit down those back stairs a senior civil servant remarked to me, 'You are so lucky to have a Minister who is interested and understands dentistry.' I did not need to be reminded: I truly appreciated my good fortune to have Lord Hunt as my Minister.

The LDC dinner was on the following day. The Minister had finalised his speech and I returned to my flat to prepare for the evening. No sooner had I opened my door than the phone rang and it was a call from my private secretary. 'The Minister wants to talk to you urgently.' I straight away made the phone call and could not believe what Lord Hunt was telling me. I was stunned as he continued, 'Margaret, responsibility for dentistry and fluoridation has gone to Hazel Blears but she has allowed me to speak at the dinner tonight.' Protocol is that once an appointment is made public, the new incumbent fulfils the diary engagements, however short the notice. We discussed amendments to his speech and I was asked to organise key people to be available when he arrived at the Café Royal so that he could share this news with them ahead of his announcement to nearly 200 dentists at the end of the dinner. 'This is my last engagement in the field of dentistry. One of my new responsibilities is performance management in the NHS and IT, so I will continue to take a close interest in the progress being made in dentistry.' After this bombshell he returned to the planned key themes and ended with one final observation, 'You need to talk up the achievements of the profession.' Tony Kravitz gave a spontaneous and heartfelt vote of thanks; delegates rose to their feet and gave the Minister a standing ovation. Lord Philip Hunt, against all the odds, had achieved 'the New Dawn' for dentistry.

'The King is dead, long live the Queen' is an apt truism in politics. So who was Hazel Blears, MP? A petite, red-haired 41-year old, she had entered Parliament in 1997 as one of the famous 'Blair Babes' after contesting unsuccessfully Tatton and Bury South in two general elections. Trained as a solicitor, she had served as a Councillor on Salford City Council for eight years, was chair of Salford Community Health Council and, in 1999, had obviously caught the attention of Alan Milburn when she was his Parliamentary Private Secretary. 'Your new Minister looks great in her black leathers' was the general comment as spalshed across the evening tabloids were photos of her astride her large motorcycle, her recreational pastime as listed in *Who's Who*.

Hazel Blears's first stock-take was businesslike and, as expected from a person with legal training, she quickly mastered the brief prepared for her by the dental branch. Dentistry, for many fledgling Ministers, is viewed as a graveyard spot as they so often inherit intractable problems and contentious issues. This did not apply to Hazel because she was fortunate to have her predecessor's initiatives coming to fruition, providing a golden opportunity to score 'Brownie points' to assist her in the promotion stakes whenever a Government reshuffle took place.

Thus, the Retreat on Primary Care Dentistry proceeded as planned on 27 June for twenty-four hours, led jointly by John Renshaw and myself. It was held in the Bradlaw Suite at the General Dental Council, considered a neutral location in central London, and Professor Chris Ham of York University, who by chance had just been appointed Director of the Strategy Unit at the Department of Health, acted as facilitator and encouraged us to challenge unsubstantiated facts and professional myths which had dogged the dental debate for nearly fifty years. There was seven-a-side representation from the department and the BDA, and on the first day work was undertaken in three group sessions: firstly, 'Where are we now?', putting on the table key issues from each side, identifying the strengths and weaknesses of current arrangements from the perspectives of patients, profession, NHS and Government; secondly, exploring the main drivers for change over the next five to ten years and what the options were for the future; thirdly, to do some visioneering. What would a good NHS dental service look like for children, working age adults, older people and special needs?

Hazel Blears, without hesitation, agreed to come to the evening session held at the Durrants Hotel in George Street, particularly as it was the perfect opportunity to meet senior BDA officials. During the informal chat over dinner, key messages arising from the day-long discussions were reconveyed to her. 'There should be no "Big-Bang": change should be evolutionary. A "menu" approach should be adopted with general dental practitioners having the choice about the kind of system they work under, even if that is to stay with the system they know. Individual dentists should have the option of different ways of working, not all working on a full-time basis and not always confined to one particular branch of dentistry.' To our collective relief, Hazel Blears made it clear that she did not intend dentistry to be put on the back burner.

Following the Retreat, the Minister asked me to convene a Group to look at 'NHS Dentistry: Options for Change' and report back to her by March 2002. This time I included a wide spectrum of people in the membership, not only BDA officials, but also key stakeholders in dentistry, the wider NHS and lay organisations, especially as I was now acquainted with the 'leaders and shakers' in various spheres. Clearly the aim of the Report was to build on the work of the Dentistry Modernisation Steering Group, the Government's Dental Strategy, and the response to the Health Select Committee and the recommendations from the June Retreat. Once again, I set up task groups to focus on areas of concern, first, systems for delivery of dental care and remuneration, and I could think of no one more qualified to chair this than Dr Barry Cockcroft, vice-chairman of the General Dental Services Committee of the BDA, and I was relieved when he accepted my invitation, despite pressure from some of his colleagues to do otherwise. Again, I was delighted when Professor Andy Blinkhorn, Dean of

Manchester Dental School, agreed to lead the second task group – proposals for education, training and development needs of the dental team. Finally, the third task group was to explore a new deal for patients and I was cheered when I approached Dr Roger Matthews, chief dental officer of Denplan, that he readily agreed to undertake the chairman's role of this important group.

Such was the enthusiasm for change and the desire not to squander this golden opportunity to incorporate NHS dentistry into the new order as power shifted away from the centre to local structure, that these chairmen and members of the main working group, all invited as individuals by me, worked incredibly hard, despite their own business commitments, to complete their tasks on schedule so that the Report could be submitted to the Minister in the spring. Running parallel with this, I was busy co-chairing the dental workforce review, announced by Lord Hunt in May, looking at the whole dental team. There was not a dull or a spare moment available in my diary as this Review was also to be completed by the spring.

Fortunately, I had completed one project. 'Better opportunities for women dentists' had been submitted, almost within the year, due to the sterling efforts of the statisticians and indefatigable assistance from Laura Wiles. When welcoming the Report, Hazel Blears was quick to acknowledge that the recommendations went wider than provision of career breaks. 'Dame Margaret,' she said, 'has pointed up aspects of the current remuneration system for NHS dentists which fail to give career satisfaction.' For me, I felt all the effort was worthwhile when the Minister, in response to my recommendations, announced that 'the Government is committing £1 million annually for implementation of the proposals in the Report' and that it would also inform the Department of Health's current dental workforce review. In my foreword to the Report, I made explicit that, 'the greatest compliment will be to know that the efforts of all the people who took part will not be in vain: that the review is read with interest, that ideas for the future are suggested and, above all, that my twenty-four recommendations are acted upon, and with promptness.' I could not have wished for a swifter response from the Minister, accompanied by generous funding, for a period of three years, to implement selected recommendations in the Report. I could have plenty to keep me busy in retirement.

August is a prime month to engage Minister's interest to launch projects or to undertake visits because Parliament is in recess and, although they have to cover for each other when taking leave, there is a sporting chance of finding a space in their normally packed engagement diaries. We were looking for an opportunity to launch the £1million Department of Health's 'Brushing for Life' programme, aimed at preventing dental decay in children, under the age of five, living in the worst affected areas of the country. When I raised the possibility of a visit to Salford, the Minister's own constituency, she reacted favourably and 30 August was chosen for the launch at the local community clinic. When the Ministerial team arrived in the morning, it was evident that all was not well. Back home, the Minister's private secretary's son was suffering from severe toothache, needed a general anaesthetic to remove the offending tooth, and it was proving impossible to get treatment. Mobile phones saved the day, as I made contact with Stella Saunders, the regional dental officer in the area where the family lived. Wheels spun into action and the young lad was cured of his toothache by the afternoon. Everyone, from the Minister down, was relieved.

The Minister was comfortable in her home territory chatting with parents and health visitors and kneeling down with the children to give them their tooth-brushing kits. The press revelled in this perfect photo opportunity and the visit ended with interviews for local TV channels. Hazel Blears was an accomplished communicator and, when asked, lent her support to 'water fluoridation', although no 'line to take' had been included in her briefing notes. At the end of the day, as I boarded the train to return to London, the evening papers were running the story on the front page proclaiming that the Health Minister was going to fluoridate their water. The media had drawn its own conclusion on a controversial issue. The Whitehall press machine swung into action to dampen the speculation, but Hazel Blears remained undeterred and a staunch advocate of water fluoridation.

The end of September and of my contract was just four weeks away. Obviously, I had a surfeit of unfinished projects, but I had to decide whether or not to accept the department's invitation to stay on as Chief Dental Officer for another year. While the Branch now had a new head and additional personnel, I was determined not to run into the hostilities that greeted me on my initial appointment. I put a call through to the BDA's chief executive. 'Ian, I have been asked to stay on for another year. What does the BDA think?'

Chapter 21

Unfinished business

'The BDA warmly welcomes the extension of Dame Margaret Seward's term as Chief Dental Officer for England' was the Association's reply to the Department of Health's press announcement on Monday 3 September of my reappointment for a further year. John Renshaw continued, 'Looking to next year, however, I look forward to seeing the signs of real improvement in NHS dentistry for dentists and their patients. I would like to take this opportunity to wish Dame Margaret best wishes for the coming year.' What a change in attitude from the resentment surrounding my arrival one year earlier. I was the first to agree that there was no room for complacency because, as John rightly observed, there remained on the table business to complete in order to secure the improvement in NHS dentistry yearned by all.

Later that afternoon, I was in the lobby in Richmond House when, as Sheila Adam passed by, she observed Lord Hunt and myself in deep conversation, which prompted her to quip, 'So, what are you two plotting?' Quickly, I reassured her that there was not a sinister motive. Rather, I was sharing the full text of the complimentary BDA Press Release with the former Minister responsible for dentistry: his contribution to the success of my first year should never be underestimated. It was also encouraging to discover that the Branch welcomed my reappointment, as the team enlivened the afternoon tea break with the appearance of a sumptuous cake and signed congratulations card. I counted myself fortunate that I was embarking on my second year as CDO with the support of a great team.

Scheduled on 11 September was the quarterly meeting of the Standing Dental Advisory Committee, whose members were appointed for a four-year term by the Secretary of State for Health. Its original remit was to advise him on dental matters and when I started as a member in the 1980s it was not uncommon for the Secretary of State or the Minister to make an appearance at the start of a meeting but, sadly, this custom had long since ceased. However, the chairmanship of the Committee was still regarded as a coveted post and at that time was held by John Lowry, a highly respected member of the profession and a consultant oral and maxillofacial surgeon and Dean of the Faculty of Dental Surgery at the Royal College of Surgeons of England. My normal practice was to meet with the chairman before lunch to go through the afternoon's agenda papers and to share with him the contents of my CDO Report, which took the form of an update on the current initiatives taking place, and, importantly, to be prepared for close questioning from the 'top brass' in the profession.

John Lowry was an accomplished chairman and we finished business by 3 p.m. I caught the shuttle bus back from the meeting place, Skipton House, to catch up on my day's post and e-mails. As I emerged from the lift on the 3rd floor, I was beckoned into the correspondence offices opposite my room to look at the TV monitors. Joining other staff, I watched in horror as the slow-motion replay showed a plane flying deliberately into the middle of the mighty Twin Towers in New York, with a second plane crashing into the seven buildings of the World Trade Centre; within minutes the whole area was a burning inferno with collapsing buildings and the stark realisation that this was no accident. This was a terrorist attack of mammoth proportions.

Suddenly, panic. My son and his wife were flying out on holiday that very afternoon to New York. Where were they? Had they already taken off? And then, as we began to learn, flights were being diverted to Newfoundland. JFK in New York was closed. My CDO mantle quickly disappeared. I was a frantic mother trying all contact numbers. Eventually there was Colin's reassuring voice on the mobile. 'Mum, we arrived at Heathrow to check-in around 3 p.m. to be told that there was a problem with US air traffic control and the flight was cancelled.' So instead of returning home to Solihull, they made their way to London-based friends for an overnight stay. As the scale of the horrific events unfolded and with no prospect of convenient flights to New York, the youngsters opted for a tranquil holiday on the Ashby canal.

The extensive refurbishment programme started during my presidency of the General Dental Council was finally completed by my successor, Professor Nairn Wilson, with the enlargement and modernisation of the Council Chamber and adjoining suite of rooms in the basement area. These were used by lawyers, witnesses and dentists during conduct or health hearings. Since the establishment of the GDC in 1956, the press and public had to endure sitting, perhaps for an entire day, on uncomfortable benches, so the new upholstered seats were greatly appreciated. The modern facilities and installation of the latest technological aides deserved to be given the accolade of a grand opening by an appropriate dignitary. An admirable choice was Lord Hunt, who continued as Health Minister in the House of Lords and held within his portfolio standards and performance very much the domain of the GDC. The inscription on the plaque tells the story: 'The new Council Chamber was opened by Lord Hunt of King's Heath, Health Minister, 12 September 2001' and marked the culmination of an extensive programme of modernisation to bring the GDC's fabric into the twenty-first century.

Most weeks, the nominal three days as CDO were crammed with engagements and the second week in September was no exception. On the Thursday afternoon, I travelled, not back to Bournemouth, but to Solihull for the first meeting of the External Reference Group of the Workforce Review, which comprised some fifty people representing the wide interest groups from within the profession, and was to take the form of a two-day retreat, my favoured and well-tested model. Tim Sands, my co-chairman, got us off to a good start and, after short presentations to set the scene and provoke discussions, there was a surfeit of new ideas to talk about during dinner. In the morning we reconvened to summarise the proceedings and decided to meet again for one day in January or February to finalise the Workforce Report. As we departed everyone felt reassured with the progress, although disappointed at the absence of Chris Ham, our unanimous choice as facilitator, in order to provide continuity with the most successful June Retreat. Unfortunately at the 'eleventh hour', Chris was summoned to an urgent meeting with the Secretary of State, Alan Milburn. Although I was determined to keep moving dentistry up the agenda, I had to concede that there would always be situations where you have to bow to the inevitable: the CDO could not compete with an edict from the 'Man at the Top'.

The Prime Minister's Pledge week, the last in September, finally arrived. It was an early start on Friday 28th when I was picked up by the BBC car to be taken to its White City Studios for a live TV interview on the early morning breakfast show. A live interview remains my preference, having learnt the hard way when a pre-recorded interview was cut and pasted to suit the producers and my crunch-line was omitted, thus skewing the impact of the news story. I met up with Gary, the PR man from the Department of Health, who provided me with the latest briefing and the results of the many last-minute phone calls made to regional offices to discover the situation in their areas. Then the bonus, before 7 a.m. in the morning, of being ushered into the make-up room where, with sympathetic touching-up of my face and brushing-out of my hair, I was all set for the interview under the unforgiving studio lights. 'Would you like a chocolate? It's my birthday today' squealed one of the make-up artists, with giggles all round when I confirmed that I was a dentist. I quickly overcame my professional doubts and accepted the offer: a 'chocolate-fix' at that early hour was most welcome.

Soon I was 'live' on the couch facing my adversary, not in the flesh, but on the TV screen. 'I had to take a round trip of 120 miles to find an NHS dentist,' bitterly complained the gentleman from Devon. Sympathising with his experience, I stressed that the Government was increasing access for people by opening new surgeries, especially in rural and under-served areas and, as promised in the Prime Minister's Pledge, patients, by phoning NHS Direct, would be told the location of their nearest NHS dentist: the 120-mile round trip was a thing of the past. Gary was waiting for me when I emerged and after a debrief I was on to the next media interview. It proved a busy day putting over the message that across the country we had achieved 95 per cent success, which was a goal considered to be within the realms of fantasy twelve months previously. This was a satisfying way to celebrate the end of my first year as Chief Dental Officer.

When I was editor of the *British Dental Journal* a recurring theme in letters submitted for publication was to question the assumption that a visit to the dentist was needed every six months and Professor Aubrey Sheiham wrote convincingly that it was a tradition unsupported with scientific evidence. However, the six-monthly check-up had been adopted by patients and parents over the years and it was a convenient timescale for those involved in setting the payment of dentists. Dr Sheila Adam was well aware of the ongoing debate within dental circles and so I was very excited when she suggested to me that I should consider getting the topic aired at the Clinical Standards Priority Group and, as chairman, invited me to its next meeting. Encouragingly one member, Professor Kent Woods, agreed that there was a dearth of reliable data on the topic and enthusiastically offered to take the lead and give advice. As a result, I commissioned the West Midlands Health Technology Assessment Group based at the University of Birmingham to undertake a rapid systematic review. Its remit was to examine 'the clinical and cost-effectiveness of routine dental checks, specifically their frequency and whether the frequency could be adjusted to reflect individual patients' risk of dental disease needing treatment'. By way of explanation, a 'systematic review' is a tool commonly used by researchers and looks at all the literature on a particular topic which has been systematically identified, appraised and summarised. Even if the period under scrutiny is limited to a fixed time span, in this case 1980–2000, it can be a mammoth task despite the advent of electronic bibliographies such as MEDLINE.

By the end of July 2001, the Group presented its findings to an invited group of dental leaders, showing that there was little existing published scientific evidence to support or refute the current six-month policy of dental checks, an outcome not entirely unexpected and in tune with Professor Sheiham's seemingly controversial stance taken over the years. Now, armed with this information from the Review Group, I was keen to proceed to a further stage and interest the National Institute of Clinical Excellence (NICE) to include the topic in its forthcoming wave of research projects, in the knowledge that it would result in the issue of guidance for dentists on a controversial topic from an authoritative source. There was intense competition to get the issue accepted as there was a surfeit of pressing claims for research from the medical and pharmaceutical fields. But I had the good fortune to have an influential advocate. Lord Hunt now held the NICE portfolio among his responsibilities and he was able to ensure that the dental bid was given serious consideration. It was with great satisfaction that I was told that NICE had accepted the challenge. 'Dental recall: recall intervals between routine dental examinations' was listed in the seventh wave of review projects. It took until February 2004 before NICE published the first draft guideline for consultation with the definitive document appearing in December 2004. Its recommendations were based on its own further review of the scientific literature, collective clinical expertise and views on patients' preferences. NICE concluded that for under-18s the interval between check-ups should be between three and twelve months and for adults between three and twenty-four months. Importantly, they recommended that during check-ups, 'comprehensive histories should be taken, examinations conducted and initial preventative advice given'. Ralph Davies, then chairman of the BDA's Representative Board was receptive to the new guidelines announcing, 'Frequency of check-ups should be based on individual patients, not a "one-size-fits-all" system.'

The three-year journey had involved many hours of work, in meetings, in preparation of submissions and reports, as well as in acquiring finance for the initial study by the Technology Assessment Group. It was time and money well spent for at long last one of the 'sacred cows' of the dental profession was slain. Today, dentists are entreated to use their clinical judgement to assign recall intervals that are appropriate to the needs of individual patients.

As my tenure of office progressed, I discovered that an increasing number of issues of a scientific nature were claiming my attention: HIV, AIDS, Hepatitis B, vCDJ, tooth-whitening, cross-infection control and fluoridation, to name a few. To retain credibility in any job it is essential to hold up your hand if you have made a mistake, although in this particular instance my hand was raised to admit that I was in need of expert clinical and scientific assistance, especially when called to make pronouncements, whether to the profession or to submit information to Ministers, to answer Parliamentary questions, or to prepare briefs for Parliamentary debates. Likewise, with the exciting and challenging work commencing on the future delivery of primary dental care, through 'Options for Change', I needed advice from an independent practising general dental practitioner, colloquially referred to within the profession as a 'wet-fingered dentist'.

I was relieved that this concept of policy advisers was accepted and advertisements were placed in the dental journals for an adviser in dental science and another in the general dental services. The response exceeded all expectations, proving that there was genuine interest in this new way of working proposed by the Department of Health. Following the interviews on 21 November, Raj Rattan, an experienced practice owner and adviser to new graduates, was appointed, and brought, as a bonus, his undisputed skills as a speaker and writer in the dental press. Good fortune continued with the appointment of Professor Elizabeth Treasure, consultant in dental public health at the dental school in Cardiff, who had unique experience of fluoridation through her membership of the York Review and of workforce issues as author of a workforce review in Wales. Clearly, these appointments augmented my own Top Team of regional dental officers (RDOs); John Langford, Tony Jenner, Sue Gregory, John Beal, Nigel Thomas, John Boyles, Roger Hesterman, David Gibbons, Richard Ward and Stella Saunders. Normally we met monthly but more frequently if necessary and allocated different areas of responsibility to members of this inner circle. Without their loyalty and collective expertise my job as CDO would have been untenable.

Six months after Lord Hunt announced the first Focus Awards in England, a ceremony for the prizewinners was organised at the Royal College of Surgeons of England. The judges discovered that they had a difficult task to select five finalists because so many dentists and their teams had submitted imaginative innovations into their practices during the preceding two years. One of the judges, John Renshaw, commented in his introductory remarks that the entries had been uniformly excellent and he was not going to give any hint of the winning practice as he outlined the special qualities of each finalist. 'All had been impressive in showing what could be achieved in the NHS.'

Unfortunately, excitement about the event was overshadowed by the last-minute withdrawal of the Minister from the Presentation Ceremony. On leaving Richmond House to make my way to the Royal College of Surgeons, I met Hazel Blears on her way through the foyer en route for an Adjournment Debate in Westminster Hall. 'Margaret, please tell them I really am sorry not to be with you this afternoon, but I am being given so many debates to do at the moment: I really would prefer being with the dentists.' The Minister's apologies were grudgingly received by the assembled throng and the President of the BDA, Peter Swiss, added to his role as Master of Ceremonies and also presented the awards. Philip Ratcliffe and his team from the Woodlands dental practice in the Wirral were worthy winners, receiving the top prize of £2,000, with the runners-up awarded £500 each. Peter also noted 'that the finalist had set impressive examples of success in the delivery of NHS primary dental care, which would pose a big challenge for those entering the awards next year'.

I vowed that whatever befell next year, the Minister must be there. After all, the Awards ceremony was conceived as an original joint initiative between the Department of Health and the BDA to restore confidence in working together in the 'New Dawn'. Understandably the Association felt snubbed and I was entreated to convey this to Hazel Blears. I did, and she reiterated her disappointment at missing the Focus Awards and added, 'What about arranging for me to visit the winning practice?' This was a small step to repairing the damage but the return to the days of the Minister's informal meetings with BDA and a 'bite to eat' remained in abeyance.

However, there was a sense of relief in the profession when Hazel Blears in a press release on 12 November showed that dentistry was still very much on the agenda. 'Our dental strategy,' she said, 'emphasised that a modern health service must make the most of the talents of its entire workforce and that enabling dental therapists to work in the general dental services would be a powerful boost to team working.' She also referred to the wider range of functions which dental hygienists and therapists would be able to carry out in line with the proposals from the General Dental Council again outlined in the Dental Strategy. Hopes were raised with these positive announcements.

I continued to receive invitations to visit or lecture abroad but these I consistently declined as not only did I have more than enough assignments to keep me fully occupied, but I also strongly held the view that my role as CDO was to be in the UK, available to attend at short notice debates in the House or urgent meetings with Ministers. Nevertheless, I did break my rule in order to attend the autumn meeting of the Council of European Chief Dental Officers scheduled to be held in Riga, Latvia, as this would give me the chance to meet my opposite number in the health departments of the Countries of the European Union and share experiences and gain ideas on how to solve our mutual problems.

The temperatures in the Balkan States would be falling significantly by November and a warm coat would be essential but the only time I could see to make a purchase was to pop into John Lewis's in Oxford Street on my way back from the monthly 8 a.m. breakfast at the Ritz Hotel with some fifty women of the UK Women's Forum. Membership was through introduction and Jill McIvor, a lay member of the GDC and leading barrister, later to become Parliamentary Commissioner for Administration and Complaints in Northern Ireland, put my name forward when I was President of the Council. It proved a unique opportunity for networking with successful women holding top jobs, the chairman and chief executives ranging through industry, finance, health service and politics. However, on 15 November the major talking point was the treatment meted out to two of the members, Dame Helen Shovelton, Chair of the Audit Commission, and Dame Elizabeth Filkin, Parliamentary Commissioner for Standards. Courageously they had spoken out about areas of concern in public life and had paid the ultimate price to be silenced: removed, or not reappointed to their posts. It is worth noting that a similar fate befell the next Commissioner for Standards when he dared to criticise, yet he was a man.

It was the day of my departure for Riga when I entered the department store at around 9.30 a.m. ahead of the surge of shoppers and so quickly found my coat, a fetching Windsmoor black and white herringbone tweed, trimmed with a large collar of black nylon fur. Especially appealing was the price tag: 'reduced from £255 to £185'. I have never been able to refuse a bargain and as it fitted perfectly I made a swift purchase and carried the coat, neatly packed into a large bag, back to my flat. After dictating a couple of tapes and snatching a bite to eat I got ready to leave for Gatwick airport. As I slipped on my new coat and preened myself in front of the mirror I saw, in horror, a giant white plastic disc on the left chest attached through the material to the lining with a glass phial containing a dark black ink, with the dire warning not to break, or 'permanent staining would result'. What was I to do? This formidable security device should have been removed by the assistant when I was paying at the counter but now, with time pressing, I had no alternative but to depart for the airport with my lightweight raincoat.

The trauma was soon forgotten as we commenced our flight where, amazingly, many of my adult travelling companions were reading the same book, unaware that this was the start of a literary phenomenon: *Harry Potter and the Philosopher's Stone*. In Riga our first visit was to the stomatology clinic and we were soon sharing our experiences, which we continued to do through talks and workshops during the three-day visit. 18 November was Independence Day and the streets of Riga were filled with jubilant crowds, processions of floats depicting differing facets of life – a truly carnival atmosphere, concluding in the evening with a fantastic fireworks display which we all enjoyed from the comfort of our balcony in the De Rome Hotel. We were moved by a rousing speech from the President of the Republic of Latvia, Mrs Vaira Vike-Freiberg, the first woman to be elected to the post, and then splendidly entertained by our hosts to a display of folk dancing in the civil hall, dancing being a compulsory subject at school for every boy and girl.

The reason for such fervour in celebrating Independence Day was starkly revealed when I made a visit to the Museum of the Occupation. Latvia had been subjected to occupation since 1940, initially by the Russians who on 13 June 1941 brutally removed thousands of Latvians and deported them to Serbia. The Soviets were then forced to retreat when the Germans invaded and then systematically annihilated 90 per cent of the Jewish population. The tables were turned again in 1944 when the USSR invaded Latvia and what should have been relief at the end of the Second World War instead marked the start of another nightmare period when under Soviet rule 120,000 Latvians were imprisoned or deported to concentration camps and to Siberia. It was not until the emergence of glasnost within the communist regime in USSR that repression in Latvia ceased, resulting in the granting of independence in 1991.

My visit to Latvia was a moving experience. While relieved that no untoward incident arose during my absence, the problem with my coat remained unresolved. My initial concern was how I could enter the store with the coat, without tripping the security alarm. I chose to enter John Lewis's by the same door through which I had made my exit, and with great relief I arrived at the same counter without mishap, explaining my embarrassment and how inconvenient the error had been. More and more senior store managers were summoned, all of whom expressed profound apologies, with the final manager announcing, 'You must have a refund for the inconvenience. Is £70 acceptable?' My coat was now an even greater bargain and continues to be a trusted friend on our rare cold-weather days. It is also a salient reminder of the easily forgotten suffering and destruction which took place in Latvia long after we in the UK had celebrated the end of the Second World War.

'We don't want to carry you out in a box!' quipped David Hewlett flagging up in a light-hearted way his concern at asking me to chair yet another steering group. Dentistry had been designated as a specialist area within the National Primary Care Trust Development programme and, with representatives of the profession and a PCT chief executive, we were charged to produce guidance for primary care trusts who were taking over responsibility for delivering dental services from April 2002. This was a fantastic chance for the profession to demonstrate that it could deliver a programme when approached. It proved to be, as anticipated, hard work but it was immensely rewarding personally and professionally when our steering group was commended by Barbara Hakin and the National Team for completing our task efficiently and on time: dentistry was held up as an example of what could be achieved.

However, I remained deeply frustrated that the work on the Section 60 order, which would make mandatory lifelong learning for dentists and permit constitutional reform of the General Dental Council, was being continually postponed owing, I was told, to pressing legislation within the wider health service and to a depleted number of staff as a result of sickness within the legal department. It was now over a year since I had accepted the invitation to become CDO and was especially excited at the opportunity to deliver constitutional change at the GDC and much of the detail had already been consulted and agreed with the profession during my time as President of the GDC. The recommendations included a reduction in the size of the Council and, with the appointment of an increased number of lay members, a more balanced composition; introduction of procedures to deal with dentists whose clinical performance was not acceptable but who did not breach any disciplinary code; the establishment of a patients' complaint scheme for treatment outside the NHS and statutory registration of dental nurses and dental technicians, all seeking to improve standards and safety for patients.

'Margaret resorted to an unconventional approach to unblock the log-jam on the Section 60 order,' observed Sheila Adam in my year-end appraisal. As on a previous occasion, when I had followed the normal procedures to secure secretarial assistance and then, in desperation, made direct contact with the person-in-charge, this I decided was now the only way forward. I contacted Greer Kerrigan, head of the legislation department, and poured out my frustration, personally and professionally, regarding the situation. My nerve was rewarded with the engagement of a retired lawyer to work specifically on the Order but, to meet the tight legislative deadlines for it to be laid in the House before Christmas, it was agreed to divide the schedule of work and activate in the first package the mandatory lifelong learning and GDC constitutional reform.

At last, the work moved along at speed and the debate was scheduled for Thursday 22 November in the Lords and guided through by the Health Minister in the House of Lords, Lord Hunt. It was just like old times when called to his office for the briefing, after which we were advised that the debate was timed for between 4.30 p.m. and 6.00 p.m. This fitted in perfectly with my diary commitment in the afternoon, which was a meeting of the postgraduate dental deans and due to end at 4.00 p.m. However, on my return to the office I was not surprised to be told that the debate would be more likely to be at 7.00 p.m. Timing for Parliamentary debates is not an exact science and demands patience on the part of Ministers and all members of the team awaiting their turn. By the time the Minister rose to commence the debate there were few of their Lordships remaining in the chamber: the cynics would claim that gastronomical delights had preference at that hour. After a couple of perfunctory questions the legislation was approved and then the Minister made his way to speak with the dentists present in the public gallery, Professor Nairn Wilson, President of the GDC, and Tony Kravitz, Chairman of the General Dental Services Committee (GDSC). They had witnessed dental history in the making with the passage of the long-awaited Section 60 order permitting reform in the governance of the dental profession.

The award of civil honours to dentists and team members is always a time for celebration. In January 2002, three colleagues were honoured by the Queen in the New Year's Honours List: an OBE to Michael Watson, policy adviser to the BDA and editor of its monthly news magazine; Manny Vasant, active in the postgraduate scene and a past-president of the Anglo Asian Odontological Group of dentists, received an MBE, as did Steve Clements, whose imaginative redesign of his two practices in Sutton Coldfield and Castle Vale with the assistance of Richard Mitzin, a dentist turned architect, gained him a commendation for the best practice environment at the annual Probe Awards. There was even more delight in store for Steve when the Health Minister made a visit to the practice and was able to witness at first hand the standards of the working environment that could be achieved when delivering primary dental care within the NHS.

In recent times there has been endless reporting in the press about the 'cash for peerage' scandal and a charge of nepotism is laid at some of the recipients of honours in the New Year List or in the list published on the Queen's Official Birthday in June. As Chief Dental Officer, I can vouch that no claim of irregularity can be substantiated against the honours awarded in dentistry. It is an open and fair system, but it is very apparent that a great number of dentists and team members miss out, purely due to the intensity of competing claims for recognition and the paucity of awards available.

The days of a 'gong' with the job have long since gone. In decades past, for example, the Dean of the Dental Faculty of the Royal College of Surgeons of England would expect to receive a CBE when nearing the successful completion of his three-year term of office (so far there has not been a lady Dean!). However, this award is no longer taken for granted, especially with the proliferation of faculties and colleges throughout the UK, with the leader of each institution dedicating much time and energy in the discharge of an ever-increasing load of business. Likewise, the level of civil awards has declined to mainly OBEs and MBEs; the last dentist to be created Knight Bachelor was Sir Ian Gainsford in June 1995 'for services to medical and dental education'. All this is in sharp contrast to the early founding fathers of the dental profession almost all of whom received Knighthoods, although it should not be construed that dentistry has been devalued, rather that there is intense competition for the highest honours which are strictly limited in number in each Order of Chivalry.

The submission of names for consideration for an award can be sent in at any time throughout the year, but it has to be before the retirement of the dentists or member of the team, or the relinquishing of a prestigious post. The official nomination forms and supporting letters are sent to the Ceremonial Secretariat at the Cabinet Office, who scrutinise and check the eligibility for an award. For example, if the would-be recipient is already in possession of the award OBE, he or she cannot be considered for a promotion in the Order to a CBE until there has been a passage of five years and unless there are further achievements to be considered. A file containing all the information is sent to the office of the Chief Dental Officer who will be aware of the authenticity of the claimant and ensure that reference is clearly made to additional contributions outside dentistry, for example charity work or within the voluntary sector. As much information as possible is needed as the competition for recognition is not only within the dental world, but also with all NHS staff – doctors, nurses, pharmacists, therapists, social and care assistants. The list of those eligible is endless. 'Make sure you keep your diary clear for the Honours meeting: you have to be there' was the sound advice given to me by my predecessor, and to which I strictly adhered.

Twice a year the august body met to discuss the Health Service awards, the Permanent Secretary/Chief Executive in the chair and, around the table, the departmental chief officers and directors. On a dismal November afternoon we could be considering names for the Queen's Birthday Honours List the following June, such was the advance planning needed. Once the recommendations went from the Department of Health on their upward journey, we were, like the recipients, oblivious to whom an award had been made until publicly announced in the National Press. Undoubtedly the good advice I received from Robin Wild was passed on to my successor: the CDO's presence ensured that dental claims had a fair hearing.

At the time of my appointment I was asked 'to think ahead and find a good successor'. To assist in this process it was essential to produce a paper on the role of the future dental officer and by the time I had completed a full year in the job, I felt qualified to pursue this request. I also approached people whom I deemed to have the personality and political skills to be CDO for their insights into the role, with the possibility of incorporating them into a future job specification. Shortly after the Christmas break my paper, 'Future Dental Advice', was completed. In it I stressed that the CDO should be full-time and that the professional leader should be based in the Department of Health's main building, Richmond House, so as to be in close proximity to Ministers, senior civil servants, other chief professional officers, directors and Tsars as this is invaluable for chance meetings, briefings or attendance in the Houses of Parliament.

In my report I also enthused about the success of the two recently appointed policy advisers who were directly accountable to the Chief Dental Officer and stressed that there should be the possibility of extending their commitment from thirty days, if required, and appointing further policy advisers in different specialist areas. However, with the increasing demands on my time it was becoming clear that I needed a deputy to share my burgeoning responsibilities from committees within and outside of the department, to travelling the length and breadth of the country to encourage and inform those working in the NHS, in practice, in hospitals or dental schools. Gratifyingly, the recommendation to appoint a senior dentist to the team as Deputy Chief Dental Officer was accepted and agreement was also reached that the advertisement for this new full-time post would not be published until my successor was appointed, so that the new CDO could be involved in the selection of a deputy.

My first Christmas at the Department of Health, barely a couple of months after my arrival, was a low-key affair with the main event, a Branch lunch, at the Civil Service Club in Whitehall. By the second Christmas, I had become known and in addition to the Branch lunch, received invitations to other departmental functions and a coveted one to the Chief Medical Officer and Chief Executive joint event on Wednesday 19 December in the light and airy Cathedral Room on the first floor of Richmond House. It was a jam-packed crowd so there was plenty of opportunity to put faces to many e-mail correspondents, as well as to meet senior officers in a less formal environment. Suddenly, Alan Milburn was by my side. 'Margaret, sort out Burnley,' he chided, and no sooner had he spoken those words than my arm was jogged and I watched in horror as my wine liberally sprinkled the Secretary of State's tie. He saw my embarrassment as I began to apologise, but disarmingly he laughed, brushing off the mishap. 'You want money from me for dentistry and then throw wine over my tie!'

It will not be surprising to learn that early the next morning I was on to the case of Burnley, which had been the subject of repeated questions in the House, lobbying of MPs, and repeated letters to the Secretary of State about the difficulty in the area of obtaining the services of an NHS dentist for the patients in their constituency. Thankfully, with the assistance of Tony Jenner, the RDO in the region, I was able to provide the Secretary of State with the replies he wanted by the time he returned from the Christmas recess. However, I did not make a habit of throwing wine over the ties of dignitaries: the recipient might not be so understanding.

As the second Christmas approached, I had started to consider how I could reciprocate the hospitality to the many people who issued invitations to social events within the department, and also to the countless colleagues in the outside dental fraternity. I soon learnt that any party hosted at the department was a personal responsibility and realised that the CDO's Receptions, which I attended over the years, had been funded from their personal purse. This did not deflect me and I decided that the lull after Christmas was an ideal time. So, on Tuesday 8 January, Steve Collins managed to secure for me an excellent venue within Richmond House, the splendid oak-panelled Old Library, books long since gone. Shopping for party fare was straightforward with the use of supermarkets in Covent Garden, Wigmore Street and a local off-licence, and my willing staff offering to act as waitresses and bar stewards. When the invitations were sent out there were few 'regrets': the event had not lost any of its appeal. 'It's the dental party to be seen at,' as one guest remarked on departure. I took it as a real compliment that during the evening the Ministers, Hazel Blears and Lord Hunt, Nigel Crisp and Professor Ian Philp, to mention a few, put in an appearance. My two newly-appointed advisers were able to meet Hazel Blears who, clearly impressed after speaking with the postgraduate dental dean, Janet Heath, about her innovative residential retraining course in Ipswich for all members of the dental team, turned to ask me to prepare a submission for an official launch of the new Keeping in Touch Scheme (KITS). 'Make sure you include participants to tell us about how they have been helped by the initiative,' was her clear advice. All this was good news because when the recommendations in the *Better Opportunities for Women Dentists* report were published some six months previously, KITS and many other exciting outcomes were only conveyed to the profession through a press release. As my staff helped to clear away, all agreed that it had been a thoroughly successful evening. My colleagues were delighted to experience the unique opportunity to 'rub shoulders' with Ministers and civil servants responsible for dentistry. The party was worth every penny.

The push to gain recognition for dentistry continued to bear fruit. Professor Bill Hume, dean of the Leeds Dental School, was accepted as our representative on the newly-convened National Workforce Development Board, and David Barnard, the dean at the Faculty of Dental Surgery, was appointed to the senior house officer working party. I had been included in the initial stages by the Chief Medical Officer, Professor, later Sir, Liam Donaldson as, although it was tackling the training of doctors for senior house officer posts, it did have implications for dentists, especially those pursuing a career in oral and maxillofacial surgery. Throughout my time at the department I deeply appreciated the staunch support and wisdom of the CMO. His vision and courage in discharging his role as 'the Nation's Doctor' was without equal and an example to me in my endeavours.

I was involved in another multi-disciplinary group which was designing a much needed model for a national contract and service specifications for dental services in prisons. Aware of the disappointment of the dental profession and consumer groups at the absence of an oral health strategy, I had also invited John Beal, one of my regional dental officers and well respected in the field, to formulate a strategy with the aim of publishing in September 2002. But none of this activity deflected from the all-important work on the Options for Change. The three task groups beavered away for six months and it was commendable that by January the provisional reports were ready for submission to the main group for discussion. Already emerging were exciting ideas as to the way forward and there was an incentive to complete the final report by 25 March because the Minister, Hazel Blears, had promised to attend the Group's final meeting. Another piece of work slowly coming to fruition was the review of the Primary Dental Care workforce and it was beginning to look likely that the report would be ready in the summer, so tying in with the recommendations of Options for Change. Timing, you may recall in the civil service, for publication of reports or statements is predicated on the seasons – early spring, late summer, sometime in the autumn. The vagueness gives hope but does not tie one's hand.

During the progress on Options for Change it was becoming clear that well-honed information technology was crucial for any modernisation and delivery of primary care dentistry in the NHS. A welcome development had been the convening of the Dentistry IT Modernisation Board and the appointment of a dental project manager, all moves which enabled us to link into the mainstream NHS IT strategy and management structures. Serendipity was again to raise its head. Sharing with my son my delight that finally some progress was being made but that some expert advice could be useful at this stage, Colin came forth with a great suggestion. 'Mum, why don't you approach Cisco (a computer networking company); they will give advice, and it's free.' This was music to my ears, especially when Colin, who worked for Cisco, offered to contact his colleague Kevin Dean and see if assistance was a possibility. Then, yet another coincidence – Kevin Dean was on secondment from Cisco, working with Sir John Pattison at the Department of Health and was already aware of the operational difficulties within dentistry.

My working three days was extended yet again as the meeting was arranged for Friday 8 March in Cisco's London office housed on the third floor of Tower 42, the tallest building in the City. Our team found the meeting extremely useful and received an offer of future advice if needed. As for me, I wallowed in a maternal glow of pride to be at the same table with Colin as a member of the Cisco team.

I chose to return to London late on the Sunday evening so as to be present at a meeting convened for 10 a.m. on the Monday morning, when the final details of the restructuring of the Branch would be shared with all the members of the team. As I watched the various power-point presentations I became aware that all was not well with my vision. The vertical sides of the slides were bent and the bottom of the picture was moving in and out like waves on the seashore. Once the meeting was finished, I skipped the sandwiches for lunch and retired to my office to phone my ophthalmologist, Alan Mushin, a friend since our student days at The London who has cared for my eyes for ever. With relief, I was able to speak with him in his consulting rooms in Harley Street and described my symptoms. 'Where are you, Margaret?' he asked, thinking I was probably at home in Bournemouth. 'In London,' I replied.

'Get yourself over here and I will see you as soon as you arrive.' This he did and confirmed my suspicion; I was in the process of detaching my retina in a spectacular fashion and speed was of the essence. Alan made a phone call to his colleague at the world-famous Moorfields Eye Hospital in the City. Luckily he was not only operating that very afternoon, but had a space for me at the end of his theatre list due to a cancellation. Collecting a few overnight necessities from my nearby flat, I was soon on my way to the hospital, thankful that I had forgone any lunch so I was ready for a general anaesthetic. Once admitted, I phoned Sonia who was taken completely by surprise when I asked her to cancel my appointments for the afternoon and those for the next week or so. 'Where are you?' she enquired, and, once I had explained, she, ever thoughtful, offered to bring anything I might need. I did not worry Gordon until the operation was over when I could reassure him that all was well and that I would be home the next day. How people can manage without friends in these emergencies I cannot contemplate, for mine turned up trumps, from offering to collect me from hospital and drive me back to Bournemouth, to doing my ironing. They also during the following week came up with ingenious ways to help. Alan Lawrence swung his video into action, recording my message to the 50th Anniversary Spring Meeting of the Christian Dental Fellowship which I was due to attend, so saving me the journey to Solihull. The same method was used by the organisers of the glittering Probe Awards Dinner at the Royal Lancaster Hotel, so that while I continued my recuperation at home, my thank-you message could be beamed to the diners when the life-achievement award to me for 2002 was announced.

My retinal tear was not straightforward to repair, so my skilful surgeon, Eric Ezra, had inserted a gas bubble into my eye with strict instructions. 'Lie on your back and do not move.' I was also banned from flying, being warned that any increased pressure could result in blindness, a warning not to be ignored. The problem was that I was due to be in Belfast at the end of April for the BDA Conference and, as I was chairing a session, I again did not want to let people down. Once more a friend came to the rescue. 'Get yourself to Cockermouth and I will drive you and Gordon to the ferry and cross over to Belfast.' This was an offer from Meredyth Bell, which was gratefully received, and a fun time with generous hospitality in their delightful home was an additional bonus. I was greatly cheered by an avalanche of get-well cards and splendid bouquets from well-wishers. Most memorable was a shrewd observation from Alison Lockyer, 'I would like a video of you keeping still,' fully sympathetic that for a person who is in perpetual motion this would be the worst aspect of my recovery.

Sometimes enforced rest can be good for the soul. Unexpectedly, I had now plenty of time to think and to plan for there is a limit to how much one can listen to Radio 4 and the Talking Books. With the bubble virtually obliterating my vision in one eye and the other eye ready for a cataract operation, I began to contemplate what a world of impaired vision could mean. The gift of sight can be too easily taken for granted.

It is also salutary to discover that despite an enforced absence, life does continue and certainly the dental branch did not close down. The final meeting of the main steering group for Options for Change went ahead on 25 March and the Minister attended as planned and welcomed the recommendations in the final report. We were well on course for early completion because, after attending to amendments flagged up at the meeting, the next stage was to make a formal submission to the Minister for approval to publish.

However, it was wonderful to get back into harness within three weeks and my first venture was to the British Association for the Study of Community Dentistry (BASCD) Spring Meeting in Winchester which was a most convenient train journey from Bournemouth. I had been invited by the President, Stella Saunders, to chair the closing session when the newly-appointed chief executive of the NHS University would speak about this initiative. The concept was a Labour Party manifesto commitment in 2001, with the goal of providing a new kind of learning organisation aimed at all staff working in health and social care. The chief executive and vice-chancellor designate of this new university was Professor Bob Fryer who had held top jobs in various educational institutions, the most recent as assistant vice-chancellor at the University of Southampton. We established immediate rapport: his enthusiasm for this ambitious project was infectious and he was quick to grasp the desire for dentistry to be included in the pilot phase. We could all see the immense opportunity for members of the dental team, particularly dental nurses and technicians for whom statutory registration was firmly on the horizon.

This move also neatly tied in with our announcement of a further 150 training places for dental therapists in England and, to the profession's surprise, giving the green light to establishing the first school for professionals complementary to dentistry within a university without a dental school. Many dentists in the south-east of England and, notably, Alan Jones, had been badgering me to increase the availability of hygienists and therapists in the area and there was no doubt that an impetus to this would be to provide training facilities in the region. The idea came to fruition through the vision of the vice-chancellor of Portsmouth University, Professor John Craven, who earmarked a building within the campus, later in 2003 to be opened and named by the Minister, Rosie Winterton, the William Beatty Building, after the senior surgeon on board HMS *Victory* at the Battle of Trafalgar, who attended Nelson after he received his fatal wound. The three-year course leading to a B.Sc. in Dental Hygiene and Dental Therapy was heavily oversubscribed, which proved the popularity of the initiative, one which would bring enormous benefits to patients in the longer term.

Then, with great relief, we were given the date of Thursday 25 April by Hazel Blears's private office for the launch of the new Keeping-in-Touch Scheme, which fitted in snugly with a sixth-month review of the progress achieved in activating the recommendations welcomed by the Minister, when the report *Better Opportunities for Women Dentists: A review of the contribution of women dentists to the workforce* was published the previous August. The venue chosen was the lecture theatre at the BDA which was crammed to capacity as it was known that the

Minister would undoubtedly use the occasion to make some important announcements. It was also fortunate that the postgraduate dental deans and directors could also attend before their scheduled meeting at the GDC that very afternoon. Their support was crucial because one of the initiatives, the appointment of the new breed of Retaining and Retraining Advisers, would ensure the success of the Keeping-in-Touch Scheme (KITS).

The ebullient Minister, as anticipated, got the symposium off to a good start. 'Today, I launch the modernised KITS and increase the payments to dentists in the scheme from £85 to £350, providing realistic funding to dentists who wish to stay in touch and take part in continuing professional development.' In a profession already experiencing a shortfall in the number of dental practitioners, any move to keep people within the workforce was welcomed, especially as it made economic sense when the cost of training a dentist in 2002 was £150,000.

Hazel Blears's next announcement demonstrated her commitment to team-working. 'I am making available a second wholly-funded course to professionals complementary to dentistry and resources will be made available to all twelve deaneries to improve or establish hands-on facilities.' Often, owing to too many applications from dentists for practical courses, the dental therapists and dental hygienists missed out from getting a place: now they would be assured of participation.

The Minister then returned to the issue at the forefront of the profession's concern, the modernisation of primary care dentistry. 'I attended the last meeting for the Options for Change steering group and believe the programme has potential to achieve the Government's priorities for patients. Today, I announce the Government's intention to set up demonstration sites working with the NHS Modernisation Agency. Their aim will be to minimise the risk posed by far-reaching change through providing a testing area for innovative ideas, which if successful can be adopted nationally. The sites will also model menus, allowing dentists to choose to work in different ways at different times in their careers which should be especially relevant to women dentists.'

In a nutshell, the Minister was reassuring a nervous profession that changes would be tested before introduction: there would not be a 'Big Bang' as the great majority feared.

When the arrangements for the symposium were being made, the Minister asked that she should share the platform with three of the women who had participated in the various schemes, telling their story of how the initiatives had helped them to regain confidence and return to work as dentists and therapists. The Minister had also agreed to launch an innovative and much needed hands-on facility for postgraduate training, dubbed as a 'Skills Centre on Wheels' which was the brainchild of the London Deanery where the facility was taken to the dentist and the team. Unfortunately, the ingenuity of the Mobile Dental Training Unit did not endear itself to the Westminster City Council who would not grant parking permission for the large van outside the British Dental Association headquarters in Wimpole Street. However, Raj Rayan engineered a way to open it through a sophisticated interactive computer link. 'This is the first time I have ever opened anything by power-point,' Hazel confessed with great aplomb and to enthusiastic applause from the audience as she pressed the appropriate key.

The afternoon session in comparison was low-key because once the Minister and guests had departed, the training session for the Retraining and Returning Advisers got underway with valuable information given to them about how to register important data. Evaluation of this initiative was unique and we were fortunate to commission an expert team from Birmingham University to undertake this research. All in all, the progress made in the first six months of publication of the Women's report was most satisfying. Disappointingly, this could not be said about progress on the Options for Change report. I was desperate to get it released, with approval, from the clutches of the Minister's office so that I could get it published and recommendations activated.

Ever since the Minister's welcome given to the report at the final meeting in March of the Options for Change steering group, followed by her ringing endorsement in her speech at the April symposium, I had been prodding, cajoling and pleading for its release, interspersed with visits and phone calls to the Minister's private office. Then, on 24 May, travelling on the train to Manchester for the retirement dinner for Geoff Taylor, one of the postgraduate deans who had worked wonders with his innovative training courses for refugee dentists wishing to work in the UK, I put another call through to the Minister's Private Secretary. 'Please,' I begged, 'get Hazel to sign off the report. I won't be able to retain the goodwill of the profession much longer.' Then, music to my ears: 'Margaret, I will make sure it's in the Minister's weekend box.' I was elated because from past experience I could expect the written reply needed from the Minister by the middle of the next week. On the Wednesday afternoon, I was at the regular Top Team meeting when Nigel Crisp was unexpectedly called away for a meeting with the Secretary of State. This was intriguing because we had just heard about the sudden resignation of Stephen Byers, the Transport Secretary, from the Cabinet. However, I was completely unprepared for the news that he brought on his return. Hazel Blears was to be moved within the department, taking on the Public Health portfolio. I was devastated. Having spent eleven months getting Hazel up to speed on dentistry and, more importantly, gaining the confidence of the profession, I would be back to square one. Then the full consequences of the move gripped me. The Options for Change report was still nestling in her Red Box and would become her successor's responsibility.

I had to wait until the next day to learn that David Lammy had been given the post. The bright young black barrister, elected in 2000 for Tottenham following the death of Bernie Grant, had been taken under Tony Blair's wing and within two years had made a stellar rise to be the youngest member of the Government at 29 years of age. Explaining to Colin that my new Minister was younger than him, he wisely cautioned: 'Mum, don't treat him like your son!'

For me it was a return to the starting blocks. His Private Office was incredibly cautious and protective of their new and inexperienced Minister and they were in no rush to allocate an appointment to me to meet with him for an actual briefing. A couple of weeks later we were given a time with the Minister's request that we should give a power-point presentation, a truly modern touch. David Lammy was absolutely charming, sharp and articulate. It was easy to see why he had come so far in his political career in a short time. It was also interesting to discover that he understood the regulatory side of the dental profession through, during his earlier career, attending a disciplinary hearing at the General Dental Council, coinciding with my term as President. The Minister quickly grasped our impatience regarding the non-appearance of Options for Change and insistence that this could be an early win for him with the profession if he gave the go-ahead for publication. Less than a week later I received a call to go to the Minister's office. Expecting to be given the long-awaited good news, I was told instead that the Minister was having trouble with his wisdom tooth and could I help. The phone lines were soon busy and Professor Crispian Scully, my friendly dean at the Eastman Dental Institute, had soon worked wonders with an appointment for the Minister to be seen by an oral surgeon, and the whole matter was swiftly resolved to everyone's satisfaction. Surely one favour deserved another, and the report should be given the green light. During my time at the department I became accustomed to the phone calls from Top Team members, 'Can I have a word?' only to discover it related to a dental problem. 'It's not what you know, but who you know' is a sound maxim and definitely my dental colleagues always turned up trumps when I made an approach for assistance.

However, I began to question the credibility of a system of Government which permits three Ministers in a period of sixteen months to be responsible for dentistry. Inevitably, if Ministers serving in Government for the first time make an impact, they will be candidates for promotion when vacancies arise. One cannot deny them the opportunity to widen their CVs but to my mind stability for dentistry would be best served by giving the dental portfolio in the first place to a more experienced Minister. This is where the quiet efficiency and performance of the Civil Service is crucial: the mandarins of Whitehall deserve every plaudit going.

So how was I to rescue my 'Options for Change'? I was within three months of leaving the Department of Health and doom and despondency descended on me as I faced the reality that I could finish my time as CDO with mission unaccomplished, a situation for which I would never forgive myself. To whom could I turn to kickstart the process again within the higher echelons of the department without undermining David Lammy in his first job in Government?

The report espoused philosophies. Funding and costs would be worked through in detail in the implementation stage. I could see no threat or reason for the delay.

18 July had been earmarked as the day for a London Underground Tube Strike and commuters in their thousands took to the streets in their trainers and armed with London Street Maps. I joined the city walkers as I trudged my way from my flat to the Top Team meeting in Holborn and was more than ready for the welcome cup of coffee on arrival at the meeting venue. I fell into conversation with the Head of Communications and vented my frustration over the non-appearance of Options for Change. 'Why haven't you spoken to Nigel Crisp?' she ventured. 'I am sure he could help.' The meeting was soon underway and at the mid-morning coffee break I acted on the advice and spoke with Nigel. It was akin to releasing a cork out of a bottle as all my pent-up frustrations tumbled out. 'I am meeting with the Secretary of State this afternoon and will see what I can do,' responded Nigel. My relief was instantaneous, especially as I was reassured that I should dismiss any thought that I was going behind David Lammy's back in making this approach. For the remainder of the meeting I struggled to concentrate on the business under discussion but just as we approached the tea break, Nigel reappeared and came straight over to me. 'You can go ahead and release the report: it has been approved.' The tedious walk home was forgotten; instead I was walking on air as I made my way to Whitehall in order to lose no time in putting into action the procedures necessary for publication.

An appropriate date for the report's release had to be explored with the Press department so that its appearance did not clash with an already scheduled announcement. On the day after my birthday, I was able to write to colleagues: 'It gives me great pleasure to enclose a copy of *NHS Dentistry: Options for Change*, which has been given a warm welcome by David Lammy, the Under Secretary of State for Health when published today.' (6 August)

What a fabulous birthday present, especially when accompanied by relief and jubilation all round – at the department, the BDA, the colleges and consumer groups. It was not a consultation document but, as chairman of the Implementation Steering Group, I called for comments to assist us as we took forward the report's proposals and suggestions. At the time when Hazel Blears was Minister, she wrote to the BDA Chairman, John Renshaw: 'The Government has paid attention to the British Dental Association's position that an incremental approach to change is needed. New ideas should be tested out on a small scale before applying them to the majority.'

The responsibility to test the ideas through demonstration sites was devolved to the newly established NHS Modernisation Agency. Under its wing was the Modernising Dentistry Programme, which was supported with funds allocated by us. Darrin Robinson had been appointed the National Programme director in March and brought experience gained in senior roles in hospital management at the Addenbrooke's Trust in Cambridge, and as a bonus was a qualified dentist.

While he awaited the official release of Options for Change, he ran a series of challenging workshops, providing useful insights for practitioners into different approaches to achieve successful change and the kind of leadership that change requires. He also invited Jack Silversin and Mary Jane Kornacki, healthcare consultants from Massachusetts, to conduct an interactive session for senior team members to discuss how to engage clinicians in the changes likely to be associated with the modernisation of the NHS dental services. We did not underestimate the impact on the profession of the proposed changes and we needed to be well prepared to deal with the inevitable negative responses.

A joint letter from David Fillingham, Director of the NHS Modernisation Agency, and myself was sent out on 15 August, inviting expressions of interest for field site status within the Modernisation Agency's 'Modernising Dentistry' Programme. Dentists were encouraged to volunteer and become involved in the process as it was a unique opportunity to take control of their future practising lives. It was envisaged that through field sites, in partnership with PCT's strategic health authorities and other agencies, dentists would be able to assess new ways of working, from creative ways of developing skill-mix and new forms of commissioning and remunerating primary care dentistry to use of information technology to improve services to patients and new models to improve access, booking appointments, or communication with patients. In the final paragraph of our letter we reiterated that, 'The Modernising Dentistry Programme is a major initiative that in taking forward Options for Change will help to shape the future of NHS dentistry in this country. We would encourage you to be part of the process.' Gratifyingly, the BDA endorsed this call as John Renshaw wrote in the *BDA News*: 'The challenge is to create a future attractive enough to persuade dentists to engage in NHS dentistry.'

But the plaudits were not universal. The radical proposals in Options for Change received mixed reaction, especially a key recommendation that a patient's gateway to NHS dentistry should be through an oral health assessment. This was signalled to replace the routine dental check-up through widening its focus on prevention of disease, providing lifestyle advice, discussion of any necessary treatment options and the date of the next assessment, which would be informed by the already commissioned NICE guidance on recall intervals. This was to encourage a partnership between dentist and patient for oral health care.

Further scepticism was levelled at the proposal that a clinical pathway approach should be developed based on best practice and the available evidence base. This was seen by the enlightened, and by the chairman of the Clinical Pathways Group, Ruby Austin, as a fundamental step forward for dental care, and entirely consistent with developments in other areas of the National Health Service. But the preparation of these protocols in dentistry demanded a high level of expertise, so on 19 August I invited Professor Nigel Pitts to work through the mechanics of pursuing this ideal. Nigel enjoyed a well deserved research reputation and was director of the Dental Health Services Research Unit at the University of Dundee, and I was delighted that he not only confirmed that he believed that Options for Change was 'clearly a landmark document in terms of breadth and scope of the agenda set out in its 62 pages' but that he was also agreeable to undertake groundbreaking work establishing clinical care pathways. At last, after all the delays and disappointments, the report *NHS Dentistry: Options for Change* was having an impact on the future thinking of the profession. We were back on course.

Nevertheless during the agonising wait for the report to be published, life could not stand still. There were many issues on the agenda and none more important than infection control in dentistry. Health and Safety legislation for dental practitioners brings responsibilities and each dental practice has to have a written infection control policy which should be on display. Emerging infections bring challenges and I recall when President of the GDC attending with David Barnard, then Dean at the Faculty of Dental Surgery, the symposium at the Royal College of Physicians to launch the publication of the Chief Medical Officer's annual report. We heard about the devastating consequences of methicillin-resistant staphylococcus aureus (MRSA) found in patients who are hospitalised. David and I looked blankly at each other. Today, through media bombardment, there cannot be a professional, patient, or member of the public who has not heard about the bacterium resistant to antibiotics.

But there is no room for complacency in relation to conditions which we are lulled into thinking only affected earlier generations. Sadly, the incidence of all forms of tuberculosis (TB) is rising and it is salutary to be aware that now approximately one-third of the world's population is infected. Now, as Chief Dental Officer, I had a new threat to face: a variant of the Creutzfeldt-Jakob disease (vCJD). The dental involvement was centred on the potential risk of its transmission, and other related conditions, from human to human, particularly during root-canal treatment of teeth. My scientific adviser Elizabeth Treasure and I were involved in discussions with top level scientists within the Department of Health, as well as with Tony Kravitz, representing general dental practitioners, and Tony Reed, the chief executive of the British Dental Trade Association, exploring the feasibility of disposing after one treatment of certain root-canal instruments, files and reamers, instead of reusing the instruments after sterilisation. The financial and supply implications of change in procedures were considerable, but rest assured, patient safety and protection remained paramount.

There was also time for pleasurable escapes from the Department and notably a most enjoyable one was on 26 April when I was invited to open the new offices of the British Orthodontic Society in London's Gray's Inn Road, the first specialist society to make a leap to purchase their own premises. Another organisation, the British Dental Health Foundation, also took an imaginative step under its energetic Chief Executive, Nigel Carter, with the development in Rugby of a new headquarters, aptly designated as Smile House, which I proudly opened on

28 May in the sure knowledge that it would continue, as it had for the past thirty years, to help people to improve their health and dental understanding.

You may recall that my first appearance at a national conference in my new role as CDO was when Lord Hunt announced the Government's response to the York Review on water fluoridation and asked the Medical Research Council (MRC) to set up a working group to advise on any additional research needed to strengthen the evidence base. Learning that the MRC report was soon to be published, the Public Health Minister, Hazel Blears, asked for a briefing which I attended on 22 July with my scientific adviser Elizabeth Treasure, who had been a member of both the York and MRC reviews and the head of the dental branch. We were asked if we had any objections to a video being taken of the meeting, which would be used for training purposes. We readily agreed and on entering the room we noticed that all of us present for the meeting were women. The sole man was behind the video camera. There was a wry grin when the news came through that the recording had been unsuccessful. Surely we had not distracted him!

Throughout my time at the Department, I had also kept in contact with Pamela Taylor, the Chief Executive of Water UK, and now with publication of the MRC report imminent, her support was crucial to assist in breaking the impasse on setting up new schemes when the local population wanted fluoridation of their water supplies but the water companies would not cooperate.

Friday, 6 September 2002, can be considered a red-letter day for the future health of our children's teeth. On this, the day of the publication of the MRC report, Hazel Blears in welcoming the findings said, 'This report demonstrates once again that water fluoridation is an important and effective method of preventing the population from tooth decay and reduces inequalities in dental health . . . I have today, therefore, asked the Chief Medical Officer, Sir Liam Donaldson, and the Chief Dental Officer, Dame Margaret Seward, to advise on the implications of the report for Government policy on fluoridation.'

My initial desire, when appointed, to move the debate along to a positive conclusion, could not have been more amply satisfied. However, previous legislation did not place the water industry under a statutory obligation to fluoridate, even when asked to do so by Strategic Health Authorities after thorough consultation with communities, which sadly had the consequences that no new schemes had been introduced since 1985. It was to be my successor who was able to see this anomaly corrected when, in 2003, a new Water Industry Act was voted for by a considerable margin in both Houses of Parliament.

I greeted the arrival of September with mixed emotions as this would be my last month as CDO. It had been an extraordinary experience and a privilege to work alongside so many talented people within the civil service during my two rollercoaster years in Whitehall. I have always enjoyed my jobs and believed in turn that each one presented unique opportunities to influence change within the profession, for example, through writing leader columns when editor of the *British Dental Journal*, and in my role as President of the General Dental Council, ensuring the highest standards of education and quality of care, and developing new ideas to embrace the skills of the dental team. But nothing had prepared me for the status of the Chief Dental Officer post. It is the most influential dental post in England, providing the opportunity to brief Government about successes and difficulties in the profession and to suggest solutions, so conveying enormous responsibility and power in equal measure. If at any time a profession feels so aggrieved with Government that its negotiators suspend dialogue, it has to be understood that while Ministers will be disappointed, they too will have pressure to deliver changes and will turn to others for advice. Government Ministers hold the ace card.

'You could have stayed on,' David Hewlett reminded me when one morning I was articulating about my withdrawal symptoms. However stimulating and enjoyable, the job was physically demanding and now, as the next stage was the implementation of the Reforms, which could last for some years, it seemed to me an appropriate juncture to hand over to a full-time and younger CDO who could see the changes through.

This time, after a thorough selection procedure conducted by the Civil Service Commission, Professor Raman Bedi, the 48-year old head of the National Centre for Transcultural Oral Health at University College London and specialist in paediatric and dental public health at the Eastman Dental Institute and Hospital, was selected from an impressive list of candidates. I was delighted that he made himself available to 'shadow' me during my last month at the Department and accompanied me to various meetings, especially as he would be assuming the chair on my departure. I also took Raman as my guest to the dinner of the Strategic Review Group held at the Le Meridian Hotel in Piccadilly. During the day I had shared with the chief executives of Strategic Health Authorities and the Tsars the news of the imminent release of the MRC report on fluoridation so that their media departments could be well primed. I was thrilled at Raman's immediate rapport with colleagues. All augured well for a smooth transition.

'Come fly with me,' I requested present and past members of my team during my penultimate week. I reserved a capsule on the London Eye and, after an exhilarating ride, they joined me for supper in nearby All-Bar-One. I was touched that so many came, several travelling considerable distances, as by this time many had received well deserved promotions to other parts of the civil service. I realised I had worked with a lovely group of people and I was going to miss them.

At last, the final week arrived and the diary confirmed it was going to be a busy one. Monday would be my last public appearance with the Minister as he was due to present the 2002 Focus Awards to the five finalists at a ceremony held in the Royal College of Surgeons. Again this was an opportunity for the Minister to make announcements to the profession, so the finalists had to contain their curiosity and excitement as to the overall winner until David Lammy had given his speech. 'I am able to announce,' he began, 'that the National Workforce Development Board have agreed that up to 150 new training places for dental therapists should be commissioned during the academic year 2003.' Even more good news followed. 'Work is underway on the second Section 60 Order, which will extend the powers of the GDC to register professionals complementary to dentistry (PCDs). In addition to dental hygienists and therapists, dental nurses and dental technicians will be required to register with the Council. Also new classes of PCDs will be created, including orthodontic therapists and clinical dental technicians, and for all these groups who will register with the GDC there will be mandatory continuing professional development.' My dreams, nurtured over three decades, were coming to fruition. Patience in dental politics is an essential virtue.

The Minister continued with other news flashes. 'I am delighted today to launch the sixth volume of "Teamwork: Changing Roles in the Dental Team" providing information on CPD for all professionals complementary to dentistry as well as guidance on extended duties for dental hygienists and details on the NVQ Level 3 for dental nurses.' This launch also marked the important transfer of Teamwork publications to its new home, the Faculty of General Dental Practitioners (UK), who had produced this latest volume with funding from the Department of Health.

The Minister concluded his speech: 'John Renshaw expressed in response to the Audit Commission Report published last week, "the BDA's view is that Government should get on with the job of reform." I am happy to accept this challenge and look forward to working on it with the profession.' It was reassuring to hear such positive comments. I was leaving with relations between the Department and the BDA on a high note.

Finally, it was the turn of the staff of the Zetland House Clinic in Northallerton to experience elation as their practice was declared the overall winner of the Focus Award and collected the trophy, certificate and cheque for £2,000, recognising their great efforts to improve the dental practice by listening to the views of patients and then implementing their suggestions. Then David Lammy called me to the podium. 'I have a special Focus Award here for the CDO, given jointly by the Department of Health and the BDA.' It had been a well-kept secret. The surprise and trophy I continue to cherish.

Tuesday promised to be a more normal day, with a meeting of the Standing Dental Advisory Committee in the afternoon. Within a couple of hours the business was completed and I was quickly engaged in conversation by several members, until Almas, the Branch Head, suggested that we should make our exit through the Old Library in Richmond House, not unusual if you wanted to avoid being waylaid. On entering, I found a throng of people and as a glass was pressed into my hand I was told that this was a retirement party organised by the Dental

Policy Branch and it was for me. Invitations had been sent to colleagues and friends – 'Remember, this is a Surprise Party . . . so don't tell Margaret!' – and no one did. All my dental friends from through the years until the present day seemed to be there and just kept on coming. I suspect Steve had raided my Christmas card and party lists for names. Then I was amazed to see David Lammy enter the room. He too had kept the secret when I had said goodbye to him the previous day after the Focus Awards Ceremony. 'You're too young to retire,' he exclaimed. 'I know I have missed out by not having more time to work alongside you,' a sentiment I shared. With the shock of two surprises in as many days I began to doubt if I would reach retirement unscathed.

Then the Permanent Secretary, Nigel Crisp, said it was one of the privileges of his job to speak at retirement parties. I was still in shock. Just how did they manage to tie down these busy people to come along? My team possessed hidden talents. Nigel recounted in his speech, 'that Margaret who retired from the GDC in 1999 and began a career, as she will tell anyone who asks, selling ice-creams on Bournemouth beach and executing excellent Mr Whippys plus a flake, that she was approached by the Department of Health to be more gainfully employed.' This was my often repeated story when under interrogation about the circumstances of my appointment as CDO.

What an evening. Nothing had been left to chance. I was presented with a soft black leather-clad book with personal and penned messages, ranging from the 'Top of the Office', Secretary of State, Ministers, senior Department colleagues, to friends at the BDA and the wider professional family, cards in profusion and gifts. Then the chatter and excitement was suddenly brought to an abrupt halt as the persistent and strident rings of the fire alarm bell demanded our immediate evacuation. It did turn out to be a false alarm and eventually some of us were able to enjoy a quieter meal nearby and a time of reflection.

Wednesday was destined to be a less busy day, with an afternoon meeting of the Modernisation Board chaired by the Secretary of State. By now everyone seemed to know I was departing and at the conclusion of the meeting Alan Milburn, in wishing me well in retirement, commented that he would not forget my repeated interventions, 'and what about dentistry?' If so, then thankfully we had moved dentistry up the NHS agenda.

What a week it had been and now my final day had arrived. It began with a most welcome press release 'Two new dental appointments to drive forward the dental reforms' – Barry Cockcroft appointed to the new post of Deputy Chief Dental Officer and Tony Jenner appointed as NHS Dentistry Change Project Leader. Both would bring valuable experience and expertise to the task. The modernisation agenda for dentistry was secure.

Around lunch-time in my office, Sonia, who was diligently dealing with my last-minute requests, e-mails and phone calls, casually commented that I was needed in the outer office area. I popped out and found trays of 'charged' glasses and substantial nibbles. The team had successfully executed another surprise – a gigantic card over-brimming with kind messages and 'advice', a generous cheque from the office 'whip-round', and an intriguingly large and attractively wrapped box. I was soon ripping off the paper to reveal 'Dr Drill and Fill Play-doh Kit' with a working drill and silver play-doh to fill the holes in the white plastic teeth neatly secured in pink plastic jaws. My resourceful team were providing me with hands-on experience to return to clinical dentistry. However tempting, I was anticipating that retirement this time would be 'third time lucky'.

Chapter 22

Retirement for real

'Do you want to be called Grandma or Granny?' was the subtle way Colin and Claire chose to let us know that we were to become grandparents. A little bundle of joy the following spring would fit in perfectly with my new-found freedom from the Department of Health and it was an easy decision to settle for Grandma and for Gordon to opt for Grandad. This news provided the passport to enter an exclusive club and with adequate warning we had plenty of time to brush up on nursery rhymes and consult the latest books on child rearing: our guru, Dr Benjamin Spock, was old hat. I was also secretly relieved that the endless and irksome enquiries from well-meaning relations and friends would cease. 'Aren't you grandparents yet?' seemed to suggest we had failed to produce productive offspring, although I am sure it was uttered with kindly intent.

On my appointment as chief dental officer, Gordon had cheerfully predicted, 'Make it a success and they will send you to the House of Lords.' However, in January 1999, the Government published a White Paper: 'Modernising Parliament – Reforming the House of Lords'. In addition to removing the automatic right of hereditary peers to sit in the House of Lords there was the promise to establish an Appointments Commission. The Prime Minister, Tony Blair, hailed this move, as 'an important step in the modernisation of the House of Lords. It removes an important source of patronage from the hands of the PM of the day. In the future, independent peers will be recommended by an independent commission.'

The House of Lords continues to play an important part in reviewing and discussing legislation as well as permitting members to bring forward Bills. The independent peers, referred to as 'cross-benchers' because they sit on the red upholstered seats at right angles to the main rows occupied by the peers of the Government and Opposition parties, are unpaid, although they receive expenses and daily allowances. I had been handed the nomination papers to complete for non-party political membership of the House of Lords during my last couple of months at the department (contrary to a commonly held belief, a Dame does not automatically have a seat in the Lords). I was greatly buoyed to have as my referees the Permanent Secretary and Minister of Health, as well as supporting letters from the British Dental Association, General Dental Council, Faculty of Dental Surgery, and the British Dental Health Foundation.

Some eighteen months passed from submission of the forms before I received a letter from the Commission Chairman, Lord Stevenson, asking permission to keep my nomination on file as they wanted to revisit my papers as the

Commission 'wished to draw up a pool of high quality nominees that it might recommend over time'. I had all but dismissed the notion of entry into the House of Lords so I approached Lord Hunt, one of my referees, as to how to respond. 'Disappointing, but don't give up – ask them to keep your name on file.' Nevertheless, it was not totally unexpected when I received the letter of 3 December 2004 informing me that 'after careful consideration the Commission has decided not to recommend you for appointment.' Strangely, I was not unduly perturbed by this courteous letter of rejection as life had moved on in the intervening two years. My greatest disappointment was that I would not be able to entertain family and friends to the legendary tea and toasted teacakes in the ornate Peers Dining Room in the Palace of Westminster.

Within a month of leaving the department I was on my way to the USA at the invitation of my opposite number, Dr Dushanka Kleinman, whose office was located in Bethesda. The visit had been postponed a couple of times due to pressures at my end but now I was well placed to share the exciting ideas published in *NHS Dentistry: Options for Change*. Gordon came with me and as we joined the line for cabs at Washington airport on 16 October we agreed not to mention the 'sniper fever' which was gripping Washington and which had been extensively covered on our TV. We need not have concerned ourselves as no sooner had the luggage been stowed and the hotel destination given than the cab driver launched into the topic with fervour. 'Don't worry about the low-flying helicopters; they are hunting for the sniper.' During the preceding fortnight the gunman had attacked in broad daylight in parking lots of shopping malls or gas stations killing nine people and seriously wounding two others. The local community was so fearful of the sniper that we were forbidden to walk the very short distance from the hotel to the restaurant for a welcome dinner with colleagues. But the hunt was not limited to helicopters: the Military's sophisticated surveillance planes had been approved by the Pentagon to join in the search, which, from eye-witnesses accounts, was for a white van with a roof rack, not an uncommon vehicle on the roads of the Capitol.

My first meeting was to attend a quarterly gathering of the oral health coordinating committee chaired by Dushanka at the impressive offices of the National Institute of Dental and Craniofacial Research (NIDCR) in Bethesda. Here I learnt about the US initiatives: a National Call to Action to Enhance Oral Health, the Oral Health Data Surveillance Program and the Surgeon-General's Healthy People 2010. It was clear when I followed with my presentation on 'Perspectives on Dental Public Health in the UK' that we were exploring issues which we held in common. International dialogue within dentistry has too often been neglected and, in this twenty-first century, with improved global communication networks, it needs to become the norm so that we can share our knowledge of the diverse and challenging issues affecting health care for our respective populations.

The following day, on Thursday afternoon, I was driven by Dushanka in company with Dr Larry Tabak, the director of NIDCR, to visit the impressive National Health and Nutrition Examination Surveys (NHANES) Mobile Examination Center located in Baltimore County in Maryland. Unusually, the roads were jammed with cars fleeing from Washington to the safe haven of Baltimore in order to replenish their tanks. In addition, such was the frenzy incurred by the sniper that the sacrosanct baseball matches and other outside activities had been suspended. On my final morning, I had to get myself to the National Press Building in the centre of Washington for an interview with Dushanka commissioned by the International College of Dentists as part of its videotape series of 'Leaders in Dentistry' which aimed to form a historical record of the profession, the series housed at the Samuel D. Harris National Museum of Dentistry in Baltimore. The cab driver completed the trip in half the normal time as the streets, normally crammed with tourists, were deserted. Even the cab driver when drawing up at the kerbside for me to alight just a few metres across the pavement to the main entrance of the Press Building urged me to 'bend down and run for it'.

Despite all the kindness shown to me during the trip and the dental intelligence received, I was not unhappy to leave the sniper excitement behind and head off for the American Dental Association annual conference in New Orleans where I was scheduled to give a 'lunch and learn' seminar on leadership. During the conference I met up again with Dushanka who reported that life in Washington was back to normal: the sniper had been caught. It transpired that he was a loner, a young man who had set up a firing range in the back of his black estate car. So much for the publicised description of a white van which had probably contributed confusion and delay in catching the culprit.

When we moved to Bournemouth, Gordon and I decided not to rush to join a church fellowship but to take the opportunity to dip in and out of different churches and denominations akin to preparing our own Good Church Guide. This proved to be spiritually refreshing, as well as an illuminating experience sampling a variety of congregations and preachers. After a few months we found ourselves returning more often to worship at the United Reformed Church, which sat comfortably with our initial upbringing, Gordon in the Congregational and myself in the Presbyterian traditions. We were inspired and challenged by the well-researched and commendably short sermons given by the newly arrived minister, Revd Dr Donald Norwood, coupled with the warmth of welcome from members of the congregation, and so it was not long before we joined the Richmond Hill United Reformed Church in the centre of Bournemouth.

One of the many social activities offering 'Fresh Air and Fellowship' was the Richmond Ramblers, when about twenty people would assemble in the church car park on the second Saturday each month and then be taken by car or the church minibus to a starting point from which to explore for some six or seven miles the hidden secrets of the delightful countryside, with nuggets of local history supplied by John Jones, the church treasurer, who had lived in the county for a good part of his life. It always proved to be a most convivial day out, chatting and making new friends, and, at the end, replenishing our spent energy at a local hostelry before returning home.

It was on one of these jaunts that Donald asked me if I would consider taking on the editorship of the monthly church magazine, as its most capable editor, Roy Davis, was retiring at the end of 1997 after producing it for fourteen years. Due to my continuing commitments at the GDC during the week, I was unable to get involved in weekday activities at the church but felt content to brush up my skills learnt on the *BDJ* and make some contribution to church life. But there was an unresolved problem. The former editor had also been responsible for printing the magazine. Fortunately, help was at hand from a fellow rambler, Jean Ness, who not only typed copy but also was master of a fearsome photocopying machine so that we were able to claim for the first time on the magazine: 'Printed in the church office'. The task as editor was not onerous and we always managed to publish on time, through the support of a grand team of volunteers – from writers to collators and staplers, thus forging lasting friendships with congenial folk, a true bonus from any corporate activity.

A couple of days after returning from New Orleans, Donald Norwood was knocking at our door. 'Margaret, I have come on behalf of the elders to ask if you would consider becoming church secretary.' I was taken aback and certainly had not been contemplating acquiring an additional church commitment, akin to a church warden in the Anglican church, especially as I was beginning to savour the freedom of real retirement and preparations for Christmas were fast approaching. I was also reminded of the wise counsel given by a great friend of ours, Jean Fellows, to Gordon on his retirement: 'You will get inundated with requests to do this or that once they hear you are retired. Don't accept anything for six months. If they are serious they will return and by then you will have a clearer idea of what you really want to do.' This advice I have passed on to new retirees on countless occasions.

In the New Year the minister did return and the situation was indeed becoming clearer. The greatly loved and outstandingly efficient church secretary, Hugh Harding, had retired in 2000 after ten years' dedicated service and, despite repeated pleas, no successor had been forthcoming. I was only too aware of my lack of knowledge of church affairs and was daunted by Hugh's perfect discharge of a myriad of responsibilities and his depth of Christian beliefs which he conveyed month by month through his column in the church magazine. However, as I considered the way forward I believed it was time to put something back into the life of the church family who, throughout our membership of various fellowships, had provided us so generously with Christian love and support. What better way to use my knowledge and expertise accumulated during a professional lifetime than by becoming church secretary.

I was also acutely aware that volunteer jobs can grow and become all time-consuming and never ending. So, before accepting the invitation, I gave two provisos: firstly, I would serve one four-year term; secondly, that I wanted to be called Church Secretary/Coordinator, to reflect what I considered was my role ahead, to be the link person for many of the exciting initiatives proposed by several organisations within the church, to coordinate the many responsibilities shouldered by the elders, as well as to provide crucial support for the Minister. The provisos were accepted and so at a moving and inspirational morning service on 6 April 2003, I was ordained an elder and inducted as church secretary/coordinator. 'I seem to have been given this large folder by Margaret, containing the draft of April's magazine,' Colin Trounce announced to his wife on returning home from helping to print the March magazine in the church office. With relief I had found, to take over from me, someone who possessed experience of producing a magazine at his previous church in Camberley.

As church secretary I was on a steep learning curve and, as old habits die hard, I asked if I could facilitate an evening retreat for the elders at a local hotel, with the aim of exploring issues facing the church and of getting to know one another. 'Few burdens are heavy when everyone helps,' I was reminded by one of the elders, quoting his favourite Confucius saying. There was also a need to embark on some strategic thinking as to the way ahead for Richmond Hill; short term, three years, and ten years. The list compiled for action now was daunting and a subsequent inventory of the buildings confirmed we were outwith the current requirements of the Disability Discrimination Act and Health and Safety Regulations, but of top priority was the need to upgrade the electrical and fire alarm systems. As a consequence it did not take long for my diary to fill up with meetings with contractors, in addition to now being on the town centre churches council and Wessex Synod, some of the commitments which came automatically with the office of church secretary.

But there could be unexpected disruption to work schedules, as occurred during the mammoth repairs to the weather-beaten and disintegrating stonework of the church tower and spire. 'There is a falcon and its family nesting at the top of the tower,' announced the indefatigable church keeper, Bob Bembridge, to me one morning. (Throughout my time as church secretary he was my eyes and ears. 'Dame Margaret, you mean I am your spy?' translated Bob.) However, the noble Peregrine, whose eyries have a fascination for collectors because of their rich red-coloured eggs, is a protected species and we were aware that the repairs would have to be suspended until the chicks were hatched. Thankfully, despite a goodly supply of their favourite nourishment, pigeons from the nearby town square, the falcon family abruptly abandoned their nest and work on the tower continued apace. As time progressed I was fortunate to have the support of an excellent buildings committee, led by an energetic elder, Paddy Pollock, who had a wealth of knowledge and practical know-how, all imparted with good humour, of the maintenance and improvement of church premises. Upkeep and modernisation of many churches throughout the UK are financial challenges, especially when of Listed status. Richmond Hill, a beautiful and substantial church of Gothic design was built in 1891 with a high vaulted roof, large windows, including a magnificent stained-glass west window with panels depicting the Knights of the Round Table and Bunyan's Pilgrim's Progress, a part Willis organ of three manuals, extensive seating in balconies, and wooden pews for nearly one thousand people, so there was always something needing maintenance.

Materialistic considerations, while essential, must not be allowed to distract members from the mission of the church: to grow in faith, in love and closer to God; to serve one another, and to embrace the wider community. The fellowship also needs periods for quiet reflection and reaffirmation of the vision for the church. One such occasion arose due to the impending retirement of Donald Norwood in May 2005. From previous experience it was expected that this would be followed by an interregnum, which could last many months due to the practice that a vacancy was not advertised until the incumbent had physically departed. This procedure, widespread amongst churches and not confined to the non-conformist denomination, is one which I still fail to understand as to me it runs contrary to normal business practice.

As Donald's ministry was drawing to a close there was a desire for the successful conclusion to the long-standing talks aimed to unite Richmond Hill with St Andrew's Presbyterian Church, which had been established when one-third of Richmond Hill congregation departed with the first pastor in the mid 1880s due to disagreements over the form of service. So, on 25 April 2004, it was a tearful yet joyful occasion when the Revd Brian Rawling preached the last service at St Andrew's Church prior to its closure and sale, eventually becoming a venue for the popular Land Marc Restaurant. This fate or similar is not unknown for vacated church buildings but in its wake it brings heartache to loyal members who have worshipped there for a lifetime and who have happy memories of notable events like weddings and baptisms, as well as recalling the sombre funerals of loved ones. However, despite the distress, many members continued to worship together for the remainder of the year and were then able to realise a long-held dream, the establishment of a new and vibrant church, Richmond Hill St Andrew's. The preacher and celebrant at the first service on Sunday 2 January 2005 was the Revd Brian Rawling whose contribution, with his wife Shirley, to the fruitful union must never be underestimated. Celebrations continued at the Inauguration of the new church on the next Sunday with Dr Donald Norwood conducting the service as the first minister of the united church, a post he held until his retirement a few months later in May. We did not have to endure a lengthy interregnum as Revd Martin Ambler became our minister, in October 2005, an inspirational preacher and teacher with a calm leadership style and outstanding pastoral gifts, the latter shared by his delightful wife Doreen. How blessed we all were.

As many foretold, becoming church secretary/coordinator would become a full-time job so I was thankful that at the outset I had stipulated a finite term. On Sunday 10 June 2007 at the AGM following the morning service, the minister, on behalf of the elders and congregation, bade me farewell and to my surprise gave me a gift voucher so that Gordon and I could go to the Chichester Festival Theatre with an overnight stay in Bosham. A print of the delightful harbour and village now hangs in our living room as a tangible reminder of their imaginative generosity. With confidence I was able to pass on my assembled compendium to my successor, Shirley Rawling, who possessed the organisational talent and sensitivity to be a great church secretary. I was further reassured that she would receive the incredible support that I had enjoyed throughout from Eric Freeman, the minutes secretary, whose eye to detail was second to none and who had shouldered the many additional responsibilities when we organised in 2006 special events to celebrate the 150th anniversary of the founding of the church.

My time as church secretary was for me a privilege and a period of spiritual growth as it enabled me to meet and work with folk who personally knew and loved their Lord. Such encounters make one truly humble: titles, degrees, trappings of power or wealth count for nothing against this Christian yardstick.

Becoming church secretary was not the only excitement in 2003. Jake Robert Stanley Seward decided not only to make us proud grandparents, but also to make his entry a month early, on 11 February, just as his mother embarked on maternity leave from work. Soon Grandma was at work washing the baby trousseau and shopping, with guidance, for bottles, milk and nappies, while Grandad helped Colin to assemble the furniture kit for his home office, all tasks expected to be completed well in advance of Jake's arrival. Zoë Elizabeth Seward repeated the premature trick two years later, on 1 April 2005, but this time all was prepared and we were up to speed with babies' demands, nursery rhymes and foods, and had discovered children's soft-play areas and playgrounds within the proximity of our flat. However, top of the popularity stakes was a day on the beach, reliving the magic of childhood pursuits, digging in the sand, building castles and dams, hunting for shells, paddling and swimming in the sea, with a brisk game of beach cricket to warm up before a picnic lunch or tea in the cosy comfort of our beach hut. To be with grandchildren is a tonic, especially sharing the wonder of a new experience, the excitements or disappointments. 'Oh Daddy,' said Jake forlornly when, after a day on the beach, he was asked to pack up to go home. 'Do we really have to go? I do so love the seaside,' intoned with the solemnity and wisdom of a five-year old. Now, as Jake gains independence we have been allowed to have him to stay on his own and, hopefully, Zoë will in due course. Times together with grandchildren are very precious. The innocence of youth passes all too quickly.

'Sail your way to Sea-P-D' was the arresting headline in the *Probe* magazine, announcing a weeklong Eastern Mediterranean cruise that it was organising in June 2003. This innovative idea provided fifteen hours of continuing professional development, the verifiable quota needed by a dentist each year to keep his or her name on the Dentists Register. The *Costa Classica* cruise ship boasted all the usual facilities and married dentists with young families who experienced difficulty in attending courses together or in the evening could make use of the excellent crèche or junior club available on the ship.

I was thrilled to be invited to join the cruise as course facilitator and to host the opening evening. A well-equipped seminar room on board was allocated for our use and, as lectures were given while at sea, there was no absenteeism. In fact everyone was anxious to make the most of the excellent speakers on board, Phillip Dowell, Graham Barnby, Gary Unterbrink, and Paul Willmer, exploring a wide range of clinical and management topics. Inevitably I was drawn into discussions about the *Options for Change* Report and the wider modernising dentistry agenda and was able to dispel fears engendered due to the circulating misinformation. We all joined the ship in Venice and then called in at captivating destinations in Italy, Croatia and Greece – Bari, Olympia, Santorini, Rhodes and Dubrovnik – before returning to Venice all basking in glorious sunshine.

This proved to be a highly successful initiative and, before disembarking, participants were anxious for another cruise the following year, and so 22–29 May was pencilled in the diaries. Much to my delight I was asked again to host this trip, starting from the beautiful city of Marseille, and give talks on leadership with clinical talks by renowned international speakers, Andras Volom and Piet Haers. As I was putting the finishing touches to my presentations at the beginning of May the phone rang. 'Margaret, the cruise is off. The ship has been impounded as the company owes landing fees.' It proved impossible to re-book thirty-five people on a vessel similar to the luxurious *European Festival Stars* cruise ship at short notice so the decision was taken to postpone the venture until the autumn. Unfortunately, this proved inconvenient for many dentists who had already booked out time from their practices and had to make their own hurried alternative holiday plans for May. The momentum was lost and, coupled with staff changes amongst the organisers, June 2003 sadly proved to be my first and last lifelong learning cruise as facilitator, which I had discovered was a most agreeable way to stay in touch with the dental world in retirement.

One event which, unlike the cruise, did not end with its inaugural meeting in June 1998 was the highly successful International Women's Leadership Conference organised by the American Dental Education Association, later to be renamed the American Association of Dental Schools. The meeting was the brainchild of Dr Jeanne Sinkford, its dynamic associate executive director, who had gained international recognition and respect when she became the first black woman dean of a dental school. I was pleased to receive an invitation to give a paper at the first conference in the glamorous location of Cannes Mandelieu, which was to coincide with the annual International Association of Dental Research (IADR) meeting in nearby Nice, thus encouraging attendance at both events.

The conference focused on three themes, education, research, and women's health. Nearly 200 women came from eighteen countries and six continents to exchange, collaborate, network, and to take home strategies for developing leadership skills. My talk explored the needs of women during different stages of life which I had divided arbitrarily into 'the age of teenage dreams', 'fair, fat and forty' and 'getting past it'. The latter is sometimes referred to as the invisible stage and is an increasing challenge in the UK where, as the population continues to grow older, we now have 16,000 centenarians in our midst.

The three-day conference was hailed an unqualified success and the papers, abstract and posters were published in a special issue of the *Journal of Dental Education*. Above all, delegates forged new friendships across different countries and cultures, resulting in a deeper understanding and desire to enhance the potential of women in the dental profession. Earmarked for the second conference was 4 October 2001 and Vancouver was chosen as the venue. I found myself again on the planning committee with the conference title 'Global health through women's leadership'. Registrations were up, hotel reservations confirmed, flights booked, and final touches were being made to presentations when the news of the fateful attack of 11 September on New York came through. Air travel within North America was disrupted or cancelled for several weeks and delegates were fearful of international travel, which left the organisers with no alternative but to cancel the conference.

But the preparations for 2001 were not in vain as the meeting was rescheduled to be held in August 2003 alongside the IADR, this time in Göteborg, Sweden. The programme followed the popular format of a mixture of papers and workshops with evenings filled with social events. The organisers had decided that the highlight of the conference would be to hold a closing celebrity dinner at the elegant and historic Börsen, the city hall built in 1844 as a commodity exchange place for merchants as well as a banqueting hall for the town authorities. Learning that the Lord Mayor of Göteborg had offered to host the reception, it sounded an excellent idea to hold a celebrity dinner, until I found myself billed as the celebrity. Naturally, I kept my speech light-hearted but was surprised that one of my comments was widely reported in the press. 'Beware of some women who break the glass ceiling and then pour concrete down behind them – to have women in leadership positions does not necessarily solve all the problems.' Sadly, this comment remains true today.

Enthusiasm continued for a further conference and in 2005, Montreal was chosen when the World Dental Federation (FDI) Congress was in progress in August. Once more, inspiring papers and workshops were given by women in top jobs in universities, politics and health sciences. There was also a fascinating, if sometimes heated, discussion about the evolution of women's leadership styles, which seemingly reflected the very different ways that men and women view the world. Men, it was claimed, generally follow a command and control leadership style, while women are more likely to use an interactive style. It remains to be seen what issues will be debated as the organisation gets under way for the 2010 Conference in Salvador, Brazil. As I have been roped on to the planning committee again, I hope to find out.

Over the years I have been told by countless colleagues that the Greater New York Dental Meeting held each year in November was the one to attend as it was the largest dental conference and exhibition in the United States. However, with my GDC and Department of Health commitments, I was unable to be free at that time so when an invitation to speak at its 79th annual session in 2003 arrived, I accepted at once. It proved to be a unique occasion because a remarkable and gifted dental practitioner, Donna Rumberger, who lived and worked in New York, had as a member of the organising committee persuaded her colleagues to let her arrange a whole day programme covering women's issues. It was also a bonus to be in New York on Thanksgiving Day and Donna took Gordon and me into the hospitality suite on the top floor of the Marquis Marriott Hotel from where we watched the famous Macy's Christmas Parade make its way down Broadway from Central Park where the assembling of marching bands, floats, jugglers, clowns and life-sized helium balloons, and, as the climax, the all-important Father Christmas on his sleigh, took place from early dawn. Once the two-hour long procession had passed, Gordon and I wrapped up against the biting wind and joined the jostling and good natured throng in Times Square, many of whom would meet up later with family and friends to feast on the traditional Thanksgiving fare of turkey and trimmings followed by pumpkin pie.

Donna graciously asked us to join her for dinner so we would not be alone and during our conversation around the table that evening we realised that Donna was a very special person. 'If you have free time, do something good,' she said. 'I view dentistry as a conduit for helping other people.' In New York City a programme 'Suited for Success' existed to assist low-income women find employment by providing them with clothing, accessories and shoes to wear for job interviews. Donna, with optimism and perseverance, embellished the programme with her own project 'Smiles for Success' where she restored pretty smiles and dental health, which gave back women's self-esteem and increased their suitability for more sophisticated jobs. All the dental treatment was given free by volunteers. Donna's vision has since been replicated by the American Association of Women Dentists in fourteen other cities in the country. 'It is one of the most gratifying experiences of my life,' she confided. Her creative talent remains undiminished as she launched further programmes – 'Skate safe', providing mouthguards for inner-city children in Harlem and a dentistry merit badge for the Boy Scouts of

America Jamborees. Along the road in life's journey we will meet exceptional people: for me one is Donna Rumberger.

Like all New Yorkers, Donna was still deeply affected by the events of 11 September. 'I lost nine very special people that day, including one fire-fighter patient.' Gordon and I took the subway from Times Square to Courtland Street Station to visit Ground Zero but we were completely unprepared for the vast 20-acre crater site before us where, since 1973, the iconic Twin Towers had soared, representing the business heart of New York. The crowd was quiet and sombre as we joined them to read the placards attached to chain-link fencing sealing off the area and which, through photographs and text, gave the stark grim details of the carnage on 11 September 2001. Two commercial airlines, American Airlines and United, had been hijacked on a scheduled early morning flight from Boston to Los Angeles and at around 9 a.m. had been flown like guided missiles, one into the South Tower and the second into the North Tower, both of which collapsed within a couple of hours with seven of the surrounding buildings of the World Trade Centre. Often forgotten were the simultaneous attacks by other hijacked planes; one was steered into the Pentagon and the fourth, destined for the Capitol in Washington, was crashed into a field near Pittsburgh, the crew and passengers giving their lives to avert further carnage. The total loss of life of more than 3,000 people, countless injured and maimed for life, children orphaned, moved the writer of the leading article in the *New York Times* to claim 'It was the day that changed the modern world.'

A visit to New York is never long enough to see all the tourist attractions – the Statue of Liberty, Radio City, the Rockefeller Center and the great shopping stores of Bloomingdales, Lords and Taylor and Saks on Fifth Avenue. But, however pressed, time must be found to visit Ground Zero, a shrine to honour the memory of those who perished and the army of workers and volunteers who toiled to bring comfort and medical help to the victims. The freedom we cherish today can never be taken for granted.

Although I had retired as chief dental officer, I continued as director of the project 'Better Opportunities for Women Dentists' and was in the enviable position of still having money to spend. We had already introduced a new cadre of Retaining and Returning Advisors (RRHs), one in each postgraduate region in England, funded for one day per week. They provided mentoring and educational support and organised keeping in touch and getting back to practice or refresher courses. It was particularly gratifying that the twelve RRAs established their own networks, holding regular meetings together to share information and support each other through a time of changing policies and priorities in the NHS. 'I don't have to tell anybody locally that I am the RRA . . . If they have got anything at all that they don't know what to do with they send it to me' was how one experienced RRA viewed her role. To me it demonstrated how these men and women were carving out an indispensable niche for themselves within the postgraduate deaneries, and seven years on they continue to do so.

It was also pleasing that with my extra funding I was able to provide much needed hands-on facilities and courses where places were to be made available in the first instance to women who wished to return to dentistry or to refresh their clinical skills in certain procedures. I was soon on my travels opening new facilities in postgraduate centres from Carlisle to Plymouth and from Salisbury to King's Hospital Dental School in London. As mentioned earlier a tour to view the plaques I have unveiled could occupy me in retirement. Included would be a visit to the superb headquarters of the British Orthodontic Society in Bridewell Place in the City of London, the only dental specialist society to own its premises and house its museum, library and meeting rooms which I was delighted to open in June 2006. I have been indulged by the orthodontists over the years and was particularly thrilled when they made me an honorary member of the Society, although this, of course, did not permit me to practise orthodontics!

But one recommendation of the Report remained undelivered – 'Encourage women to participate fully in professional activities, including seeking leadership roles and membership of negotiating teams'. Leadership positions ideally should reflect the social composition of society but I have always been strongly opposed to representation on committees being secured through reverse discrimination. It is essential that women put themselves forward and prove themselves through election in open competition. However, it remained clear that some women dentists required enhancement of their self-esteem and confidence in their abilities so as to offer themselves for election. I needed help in solving this challenge and so decided to host a Women's Leadership Forum. I invited eight top female dentists to join me for dinner at the Lansdowne Club and, bearing in mind there is no such thing as a free dinner, we ended the evening with a full and frank discussion of the challenges. What were the major obstacles to women's leadership in dentistry, bearing in mind that these were top leaders who had broken through real or perceived barriers. Was there a need for structured mentoring? Would a Buddy Scheme help? Many exciting ideas were generated that November evening in 2003 and one which gained universal support was the suggestion that we should hold a second Women's Leadership Forum when each of us would bring along a 'buddy', a protégée who we believed could be a future leader in the profession. One of the diners was Mary Wylie, chairman of the dental practice board, and she invited me to travel with her at the beginning of January to Cranfield University in Bedford and meet the Director of the Centre for Developing Women Business Leaders, Professor Susan Vinnicombe, and Dr Val Singh, one of the UK's foremost researchers in the field of women's leadership research activities. They provided us with abundant and relevant information and clearly we needed Cranfield to deliver our Buddy Day Workshop. However, with my limited Department of Health funds I could not compete with the vast sums which Cranfield University commanded for running a course in the private sector or for training modules at their site. At the end of our discussions we had convinced them that the leadership challenges in dentistry could provide valuable research material and so a more reasonable fee was agreed, which secured the services of Cranfield for the second Women's Leadership Forum in March.

Following a review of the research comparing how men and women manage their careers, Val Singh pointed out that young women needed to manage more effectively and promote the image they portray at work in order to make the most of their skills and talents. My 'buddy', Andrea Ubhi, a very successful practice owner focusing on cosmetic dentistry and experienced in juggling an impressive career with active family life, summed up the overwhelming message of the day. 'If you want to develop in your career, show what you can do and what you will be able to do to those who matter in the decision-making.' During the afternoon workshop, strong evidence emerged of the struggle experienced by women in juggling family responsibilities with the demands of postgraduate training, as well as the problem of social barriers. 'If a man is moving round the country for his career, the woman has to take a back seat' was a comment which rang true with many present. The fascinating day left the participants with personal challenges. It had been money well spent to deliver the remaining recommendation of the Report.

I was soon to become a septuagenarian and was of the view that, with a life blessed with good health and happiness in full measure, it should be appropriately celebrated. A couple of years previously we had marked our ruby wedding anniversary with a 'Gang' reunion in Bournemouth, involving a special group of people whose company we had enjoyed since our carefree days as members of St Paul's Church Badminton Club in Enfield. Our friendships were enriched over the passing years as we attended each other's landmark events: 21st birthdays, weddings, offspring's christenings, and then in time weddings of the next generation. It is so easy to neglect friends with the pressure of modern living but there is no excuse to forget; rather we should nurture past friendships – 'a friend in need is a friend indeed' and we never know what trials await around the corner when true friendship will be tested and must not be found wanting.

However, in 2005, we opted for a family-centred 70th birthday celebration from the youngest of three months, our granddaughter Zoë, to my eldest brother and sister-in-law over 80. Center Parcs at Longleat in Wiltshire was selected as the venue, which offered something for everyone, and so for three days of brilliant sunshine, forty-five of us swam, played badminton and table-tennis and partied the evenings away with an extra special supper to mark my big day, when the family surprised me with the gift of a trip to Sicily. My birthday was a unique occasion as usually one or two family members were missing from various gatherings. This time, amazingly, the dates fitted snugly with school holidays and work commitments so that my niece in New Zealand and nephew in USA travelled with their families to join in the celebrations. It was a full house and although demanding a high degree of organisation, a group photo was secured for the family albums.

The occasion was even sweeter as our daughter was with us. Following a severe bout of flu during the winter of 1989, she had been dogged by ME/CFS, which goes under the grand name of myalgic encephalopathy/chronic fatigue syndrome, and as a consequence she had missed many family gatherings since that time. No one has yet established the cause of this debilitating illness affecting some 250,000 people in the UK and many different treatments are tried and discarded and opinions are divided on its management. Pamela has learnt to live with ME for nearly two decades, and has borne her illness with great fortitude. There have been periods of relapse and remission when she was able to work using her mathematical prowess exemplified by her degrees: BA Cambridge; D.Phil. Oxford. Although the illness is frustrating for Pamela, it is also testing for friends and family. Parents inevitably find it tough to see their offspring repeatedly unwell: in this I am no exception.

It was at the time of my birthday party that Pamela, a devout Christian who used her prolonged periods of solitude especially when bed-bound to develop her prayer life, was of the conviction that she had been 'miraculously healed'. 'Don't give up on God' was her message. Not only did she come to my party, but also recommenced work at Surrey University, was awarded the prestigious Daphne Jackson Fellowship for research, and, to make up for the 'lost' fifteen years, lived life to the full, visiting friends at home and abroad. It was on a trip to Germany that she caught another viral infection and suffered a severe relapse, needing carers once more. Her climb up the mountain began again using her well practised pacing regimes so as to build up her general energy levels in order to again enjoy independent living.

Literature on the topic of ME/CFS is extensive: books, magazines of support associations, and reports from distinguished sources including the Royal College of Physicians, the Chief Medical Officer of Health, the National Institute for Health and Clinical Excellence (NICE), and the papers of discussions held by the All Party Parliamentary Group with the call for an adjournment debate in the House of Commons. Now, the Medical Research Council is collaborating on the search for the cause and cure for ME/CFS. Let us fervently hope the breakthrough comes soon.

My spectacular birthday party, with my brothers, nephews and nieces and their families, would not have been possible if my brother Derek all those years before had not knocked at the door of 85 Uvedale Road in Enfield to announce that my mother had died. But Number 85 was destined to give up another secret. In 1988, I received a letter at my home in Hadley Wood addressed to 'the occupier' and the opening paragraph read 'I am attempting the very difficult task of tracing somebody from about 1935. She is or was at that time called Christina Brown

Cleland and I believe at the time concerned she was either living or staying at 85 Uvedale Road in Enfield.' Contact numbers were given and the letter was signed Stuart Wheeler, which meant nothing to me. But the lady he mentioned meant a great deal to me.

Aunt Chryssie, as I called her, was a childhood friend of my Mum, Mrs Mitchell, as they were pupils together at Kilmarnock Academy and both trained to be teachers. We often spent holidays in Cliftonville at the home of Chryssie, which she shared with her sisters, Mary and Jessie, and, in common with many young women who lost loved ones during the First World War, they all remained unmarried.

After receiving the letter I arranged to meet Stuart Wheeler for lunch and he showed me a copy of his birth certificate revealing that Chryssie was his mother. I was stunned to think that this sweet maiden aunt had a son and had the sad task of breaking the news to him that his mother had died in 1969 and that I did not have details of any other living relatives. However, I was able to provide him with the first photos he had seen of his mother from our family album.

We did not arrange to meet again but the entrepreneur Stuart Wheeler, founder of the IG Group, the spread betting firm, was a multi-millionaire and a generous donor to the Tory party. From time to time he would appear on TV and his likeness to Aunt Chryssie was uncanny. For me there was no doubt that Stuart was Aunt Chryssie's son who had been given up for adoption at birth, which was the expected course for an unmarried mother to take in the 'Thirties'.

'Mum, I have googled you today,' e-mailed Colin, 'and you are mentioned in *The Mail on Sunday*,' and I was given a link to the four-page article in the 2 November 2008 issue. The newspaper had researched Wheeler's genealogy and, in so doing, further fascinating details emerged. He learnt that Chryssie was 42 years old when he was born, no youngster who could claim an innocent indiscretion, and that he had a cousin, Mabel, aged 87, living in Edinburgh. Soon, Stuart was meeting his new-found relatives, watching videos of his mother, visiting his grandparents' graves, and the school house where his mother grew up, her father being a headmaster, and he arranged a get together at his home, Chilham Castle in Kent, for his new Scottish family.

At the beginning of December, Stuart invited me to join him for lunch at Odin's in Devonshire Street in London and shared with me that he had one remaining mystery to solve: who was his father? In the newspaper article it suggested my dad, Mr Mitchell, or a teacher at the school where Chryssie taught in Cliftonville, could be the father. After attending a special Burns Supper at the Royal College of Surgeons in Edinburgh to mark the 250th anniversary of the Bard's birth, I made my way on the Sunday morning to Mabel MacDonald's flat for coffee. We spent a precious hour together leafing through photograph albums and recalling happy memories of Aunt Chryssie. 'She was such a dear soul,' opined Mabel, 'I can't imagine her having an affair, and surely not with the husband of her best friend.' Certainly the courage and loyalty of the Mitchells to offer their home as a safe haven to a friend in need should be respected. Suggestions have been made that DNA tests could shed light on the identity of the father. Mabel and I are uncomfortable with this thought. Rather, the grave should remain the custodian of this extraordinary secret.

There remained one incomplete item of business from 1999 when the Garter King of Arms informed me that, as a Dame, I was entitled to petition for a Grant of Armorial Bearings. I was oblivious to what this entailed so I took myself to The College of Arms in Queen Victoria Street in the City of London, which is one of the few remaining heraldic courts in Western Europe and is now the oldest existing college in the world. The building alone is worth a visit as the fabric is largely original and it is one of the few Listed buildings remaining from the seventeenth century in this part of London. I soon learnt that, during the Middle Ages, armour became increasingly sophisticated and the medieval soldier became encased in iron from head to toe with a closed helmet to ensure anonymity. However, it made it impossible for friends to recognise each other in battle and the flat and broad surface of the shield seemed to be the ideal surface on which to put a symbol or pattern which could be identified, and this was referred to as a charge. Then the identifying symbol was used on the surcoat which was a garment covering the armour to give protection from the sun and rain, and so gave rise to the term 'coat of arms'.

My first act was to sign a petition or a Memorial addressed to the Duke of Norfolk, the Hereditary Marshal of England, in which I requested the granting and assigning of Arms, 'as they deem suitable to be borne and used by her and her descendants'. I was then allocated one of the six Heralds, the Richmond Herald, who is a member of the Royal Household and participates in the great ceremonies of state wearing his traditional scarlet uniform and tabards of the Royal arms embroidered with gold. It was to be his job to put together a design of arms and badge that was in keeping with current heraldic convention and was distinctive when compared to any coat of arms recorded in the College over the centuries. This is contrary to the rules governing the motto which can be adopted or adapted from one in use by a family or institution and the words can be in any language, preferably comprising not more than six or seven words.

The Herald, Patric Dickinson, asked me to give thought to the aspects of my professional life and family which I would like symbolised in the coat of arms and for any firm views regarding colour and heraldic charges. A sketch of the design would be sent to me with the opportunity to comment before seeking formal approval from the Garter King of Arms. After six months, Patric sent me a sketch showing his ideas for my shield and explained the elements in the design. 'The indented line is often used in heraldry as a reference to your profession and appears in the arms of the General Dental Council.' This ornamental indented line bisected the shield and the upper half was coloured red, again as appears in the GDC arms, while the lower half was coloured blue, and five white seagulls were also painted onto the shield. They had appeared on my logo for the 1993 BDA Conference in Bournemouth and symbolised the dental team: dentist, dental nurse, hygienist, therapist, and technician. For the badge, the Herald took the cross crosslet from the arms of the Latymer Foundation which also provided Christian symbolism to represent my involvement in church affairs. The cross crosslet was superimposed on the crossed gold quills, which when I was editor of the *British Dental Journal* we had chosen as the distinctive design to appear on the tie or headscarf presented to the Scientific Advisers or referees of articles.

'Am I right in thinking your husband is still alive?' enquired Patric. 'This affects the way the arms are painted on the Letters Patent.' The Herald was making reference to a tiny heart positioned on the top half of the shield which was painted in with gold leaf if the husband was alive, but filled in black if deceased. When the final sketches arrived for my approval I was asked to make my decision about the motto. Without hesitation I chose my school motto: 'He who endures conquers' but replacing 'he' with 'she'.

I was told it would be some nine months before the Letters Patent, a legal document hand-painted on vellum, would be completed, signed and sealed by the Garter Principal King of Arms, P. Ll. Gwynn-Jones, and the Provincial King, Hubert Chesshyre, Clarenceux King of Arms responsible for those living in the south. When the time came, I returned to the College of Arms to collect the illuminated document and was excited to see waiting for me on the Richmond Herald's desk a scarlet red-leather rectangular case, 32 inches long, 3½ inches wide and 4 inches deep, adorned on the top surface with three motifs in gold, E11R surmounted by a crown. I had seen these before but only in Stately Homes: now I was to possess one. Inside was the rolled vellum of my Letters Patent and as it was removed and unrolled I was overcome with the intensity of colours and its sheer beauty.

Above the text which begins traditionally 'To all and singular' were three Coats of Arms: in centre position the Royal Arms of Her Majesty Queen Elizabeth II, on the left the arms of the Duke of Norfolk, and on the right the arms of Her Majesty's College of Arms. The Seward Coat of Arms was displayed prominently on the left of the text and at the foot of the vellum were the seals of the two signators, enclosed in gold cases and suspended on blue ribbon.

Everyone wanted to see my new prized possession and hear the story about its compilation, but as it was rolled and unrolled so regularly it was suggested that I should frame it so all could enjoy its splendour without its being damaged. Nearly ten years previously when Colin married, I had promised him cufflinks inscribed with the Seward Coat of Arms. At last, I could fulfil my promise and give Gordon a pair too and I hung the Coat of Arms on the lounge wall.

Life continues to be full of thrills and surprises and none more so than when I receive a letter intimating that I am to be nominated for a coveted award or invited to a prestigious event. Sometimes this entails a trip overseas and to an exciting destination, as was the case when I was invited by great friend Dr Marcia Boyd, the first woman to be president of the American College of Dentists, to deliver the Convocation Address at its annual meeting in Las Vegas. Stockholm was another intriguing city to visit when hosting the World Dental Congress in 2008 and during the Opening Ceremony I was admitted to the List of Honour, limited to thirty dentists worldwide. 'I thought you had already got the badge,' remarked a senior member of the FDI. The reason for the delay was now history, but I could at last draw a line under my turbulent departure from the editorship of the *International Dental Journal.*

There were other occasions nearer home, including London in 2008 to the BDA Honours and Awards ceremony to accept the Fellowship of the Dental Technologists Association. Here I met again the dental technicians who, against all odds, possessed the vision and courage to metamorphose their craft into a profession and now reap the reward as valued members of the dental team.

'Your name was recommended to receive an Honorary degree in recognition of your former role as CDO and the development of programmes for students in professions complementary to dentistry.' This statement filled me with amazement as I read the opening paragraph of the letter from the Vice-Chancellor of the University of Portsmouth, Professor John Craven. I attended the Congregation for the Conferment of Academic Awards and was admitted as an honorary graduate and with the degree of Doctor of Science. It was also a privilege to be asked to respond at the end of the ceremony on behalf of the graduates receiving their degrees the hard way. Now, as a member of the university community, it is a delight to return to the school to present named student awards and to celebrate with the graduates receiving their Bachelor of Science degree in Dental Hygiene and Dental Therapy. It is for me a dream that has become reality, and, gratifyingly, most dentists now recognise their unique contribution to patient care.

In the twilight of my career I admit it gives me a 'buzz' to be remembered. Dentistry has been exceptionally kind to me, repaid me in abundance, and provided me with wonderful colleagues, challenges and memories. Retirement continues to be fun, with more time to be involved locally in volunteer organisations, amongst these the National Trust and Dorset Victim Support. Here and in other charitable endeavours I meet dedicated people, the true unsung heroes and heroines, who strive to improve the quality of life and surroundings for countless people.

Retirement is also punctuated by phone calls. 'Please can I give your name for a reference?' 'Would you write an obituary?' 'Can I ask a favour? Will you propose the toast at the dinner?' These are opportunities to exercise my mind and keep me feeling involved. 'Margaret, you will never retire!' – perhaps these pundits were right after all.

Index